# WARSHIPS
## FOR THE WORLD

# WARSHIPS
## FOR THE WORLD

BARRY STOBART-HOOK

PUBLISHED BY CROSS PUBLISHING
NEWPORT, ISLE OF WIGHT

# ACKNOWLEDGEMENTS

I would like to thank all those members of VT, past and present, who contributed a great deal to this book.

Firstly, to those, including Sir John Rix, who patiently read the various drafts and offered their comments and suggestions.

Secondly, to several people who also contributed large sections of text, in particular, Tony Dorey and Peter Usher.

Thirdly, to the hundreds of people who worked for the Company during the times in question, each of whom made their unique contribution to the events described here. It has been impossible to mention more than a small and random selection of these people by name; I hope that all the many others, whose contributions were in no way less significant, will understand.

B.S-H.

© Vosper Thornycroft Holdings PLC 1994.
Produced & Published by Cross Publishing, Newport, Isle of Wight.

ISBN 1 873295 50 2

# CONTENTS

# BY THE CHAIRMAN

For 125 years or so the Companies which have now become Vosper Thornycroft were building naval, usually fast, and quite small ships for the Royal Navy. They went on to build ships for the navies of the world.

Large naval ships are now the exception, so the change in the market both at home and abroad has benefited the only shipbuilder on the south coast of England. Vosper Thornycroft has today a larger order book than at any time in its long history.

This book tells the story of the period from 1966 to 1993. It does so through the eyes of Barry Stobart-Hook who joined as an electronics engineer soon after the merger of Vosper and Thornycroft, and it is in many ways a personal reminiscence giving life and a human face to an otherwise dry and fact-filled record.

For those of us in the business there can be no other career which has the same charisma as the designing and building of fast complex ships. Add to this the other technologies brought in to broaden the base of the company, and the unprecedented upheaval in ownership and management structure caused by Nationalisation, and you have a period of intense activity to report. From those of us fortunate enough to see it through, the greatest possible pleasure comes from being competitive once more after the dark days of demarcation disputes and restrictive practices, which we struggled through for much of this century but which were at their height in the 1970's. Those foolish days have gone. Today after substantial investment, the environment in the VT facilities is good. Accuracy of manufacture exceeds anything that our forefathers could have dreamed of, and the interest and enthusiasm shown by everyone has never been higher.

This book spans a time when the peaks and troughs of industrial life were at their most extreme. I look forward to reading the next instalment in about 20 years time.

Peter Usher
June 1993

Peter Usher.

HMS *Gurkha*. A typical Thornycroft product.

*Brave* class MTBs. Typical Vosper products.

# INTRODUCTION

This is a brief history of the Vosper Thornycroft warship building Company (VT) in its various forms since Vosper Ltd and John I. Thornycroft & Company Ltd merged in 1966.

Histories of the separate companies prior to that date are covered in two earlier books: "100 Years of Specialized Shipbuilding and Engineering", by K. C. Barnaby, was published by Hutchinson in 1964 to mark the Thornycroft centenary, and "A Quest for Speed at Sea" by Christopher Dawson (also published by Hutchinson) marked a similar anniversary for Vosper in 1972.

Because the merger is the obvious starting point for a history of Vosper Thornycroft, the period covered by the main narrative of this book slightly overlaps that of the latter volume. Also, for the sake of completeness, and because the earlier books are now out of print, a very brief survey of Thornycroft and Vosper is included.

Few modern companies are fortunate enough to make such a complex and interesting product, and to be responsible for marketing, sales, design, construction, trials, and after sales support. In the period in question, no other shipbuilder in the world built such a wide range of warships: five classes of frigates, three of mine countermeasures vessels, two of corvettes, several novel hovercraft, and many different types of patrol craft of all sizes. VT not only achieved all this, but was responsible for the design, from scratch, of almost all of them.

In that same period, the Company suffered dramatic organisational upheavals, arising successively from the merger, the winning of huge export orders, nationalisation, recession, privatisation, diversification, and flotation as a new company on the London Stock Exchange.

The shape of the organisation has obviously been affected by these upheavals, which also gave rise to some independent offshoots. Most of these have now, sadly, gone into liquidation, but their similar names sometimes continue to cause confusion which it is hoped this book will help to resolve. The "only true and original Vosper Thornycroft" has remained active in the two largest of the original shipyards, at Woolston, near Southampton and Portchester, on the upper reaches of Portsmouth Harbour, and is alive and well, and now expanding into different, but related, lines of business and other locations.

This book is not, however, a political history of the shipbuilding industry, nor, (although it includes some details of the various warships) is it a text book on naval architecture. It is the history of an unusual company during a particularly eventful period. It is hoped that it will be of interest to the layman, to our customers and to all those interested in warships and shipbuilding as well as to those past and present employees of the Company who have personal experience of the times to which it relates, and to whom, ultimately, all the great successes of VT are due.

## Chapter One

# BIRTH OF A COMPANY

Mr. Herbert Vosper began his shipbuilding and engineering business at the Camber docks, Portsmouth in the early 1870s. At first, the business dealt mainly with refitting and repair of coastal craft, but Vosper also manufactured marine engines and small working boats and tugs.

It was not until Commander Peter Du Cane became Managing Director in 1931 that the Company began to concentrate on high speed craft, starting with a number of yachts, tenders and racing boats. The most notable of the latter was Sir Malcolm Campbell's *Bluebird* (the second boat of that name) with which he took the world water speed record of 141.7 mph (123 knots) just before the Second World War broke out in 1939.

Commander Du Cane had always set his sights on military orders, and in 1937 Vosper built as a private venture a 68 ft motor torpedo boat prototype which achieved 48 knots in trials. This boat was bought by the Royal Navy, and became MTB 102. She survives to this day, belonging now to the Norwich Area Scout Council, who preserve and maintain her in working order (although not with the original engines!), allowing young people a unique way of going to sea.

MTB 102 was the prototype of a large number of similar vessels built during the war, during which Vosper gained a great deal of experience of fast craft, and became firmly established as a naval shipbuilder.

In the immediate post war period when orders were very scarce, various fast motor boats, tenders, yachts and air sea rescue boats were produced. All sorts of miscellaneous jobs were taken on to keep the Vosper works in business, an oft-quoted example being the manufacture of fairground equipment at one time! Design and production of wooden high speed planing boats also continued after the end of the war, eventually leading to the Royal Navy's *Brave* class of gas turbine powered boats which achieved well over 50 knots in the early 1960s. Vosper designed and built a private venture boat, *Ferocity*, which led to a line of similar,

high speed gas turbine powered export boats. However, this line was not enough to keep the Company fully employed.

Strenuous efforts were made to establish sounder long term business more in keeping with the Company's expertise and facilities. Unlike many of their UK competitors, who (if they tried to export at all), were offering ships originally designed for the RN, Vosper realised that even its relatively inexpensive MTBs were too sophisticated and operationally unsuitable for many of the potential customers. By visiting many of the small navies around the world, some of which were ex-colonial forces adjusting themselves to independence, Vosper began to understand the needs of this market, and set about designing ships to meet them.

Although some success came from exporting the *Brave* or *Ferocity* fast MTB derivatives, Vosper had a much steadier demand for somewhat slower, steel hulled vessels about 100 foot (30 m) long, with a more sea kindly performance and a greater weapon carrying capability. By the early 1960s these had become Vosper's main product. Simpler and less spectacular, these 103 foot and 110 foot steel hulled, diesel propelled patrol boats were specifically designed to the needs of third world navies. Many of these ships are still in service today. Indeed a modernised version of the design was even purchased in 1984 by the United States Coastguard and 49 vessels have been built in the USA.

The birth of Vosper Thornycroft, (VT) and its subsequent prosperity, came about largely as a result of the success of Vosper Ltd in the export market, which in turn could be attributed to this policy of "bespoke" warship construction, made possible by the technical expertise and persistence of Peter Du Cane and his team. The Company had many ups and downs through some financially precarious days, but in the mid 1960s had achieved stability under the control of the David Brown Corporation. Sir David Brown, who had bought a

*Ferocity*. Vosper private venture MTB.

96 foot fast patrol boat firing SS 11/12 missile.

Commander Du Cane.

Sir David Brown.

Sir John Rix.

Alan Griffith.

Model of high speed corvette.

Mk.1 Corvette.

controlling interest from Peter Du Cane and Lord Hardwicke, was Chairman; John Rix, a long time Vosper man and former Thornycroft apprentice, was Managing Director. Du Cane himself was still very active as Deputy Chairman.

Even in the early 1960s, Vosper was not content with designing and building patrol boats. In those same markets, a need was identified for larger vessels, and orders were obtained from Ghana and Libya for Mark 1 Corvettes.

The building of these 177 foot corvettes was the first step towards larger ships. They were simple, diesel-propelled vessels with modest top speeds, and were logical developments of the 103 foot and 110 foot patrol boats. However, there was every intention of capitalising on Vosper's hard won experience with gas turbines and super cavitating propellers. Powered by Olympus gas turbines, the high speed corvette was designed as a 50 knot anti-submarine escort vessel, and was armed with anti-submarine rockets, an automatic, remote controlled gun and Seacat guided missiles. Although never built, the "split-arse corvette" as it was less formally known, caused a stir in the technical press, and an attractive model of it stood in the board room for many years afterwards. It was a stepping stone to the fast frigate designs.

Still with an eye on the export market, the designers, headed by Peter Du Cane, John Rix, and the Technical Director, Alan Griffith, newly appointed and ex RCNC, had begun work on a larger and much more sophisticated design which was referred to as a light frigate, although of only 1400 tonnes displacement.

Not only was this ship intended to carry a much larger and more complex weapon outfit than the earlier designs, but it was also to have a much higher top speed, made possible by the application of Vosper experience in marine gas turbine propulsion and by the development of the marine Olympus turbine for the RN.

Vosper was gaining confidence in the export market. What it lacked was a yard big enough to build a frigate. The Company's original Camber shipyard in Old Portsmouth had some deep water, but not nearly enough space, nor even a long enough slipway. The newer Portchester yard (to which the Company had moved early in the war),

in the upper reaches of Portsmouth Harbour, had more space, but insufficient water to float a frigate. Some consideration was apparently given to building a ship in two halves and floating them out of Portchester or the Camber to be joined elsewhere, but this idea was not really a serious contender. Moreover, the detailed design of such ships would greatly overstretch the resources of the existing Drawing Office. Vosper began to look around for a more viable alternative.

From the purely financial viewpoint, taking on the design and build of a ship as large and sophisticated as a frigate would represent a substantial risk, and it was only prudent to lay off some of this. A precedent existed, since the Company had shared the Mark 1 Corvette order with Vickers, who had built one of the two ships for Ghana. Whilst a similar arrangement for a frigate order would make commercial sense, Vosper had to be able to build at least one ship in a yard of its own, close to the design offices.

In the early 1960s most shipyards in Britain were in decline. Vosper was one exception. Another shipbuilder in the South of England which had been determined to survive was John I. Thornycroft and Company Ltd, whose main Yard was at Woolston, across the Itchen river from Southampton, and only some fifteen miles from Vosper at Portchester.

Thornycroft had a long and distinguished history of designing and building warships, particularly high speed vessels. The founder, Sir John I. Thornycroft was a pioneer, at Chiswick on the Thames, of the development of fast steam powered torpedo boats and destroyers at the end of the nineteenth century, achieving speeds which had previously been considered impossible by leading naval architects.

During the first world war Thornycroft produced a large number of destroyers and designed and built coastal motor boats; small, fast launches propelled by petrol engines and designed to carry one or two torpedoes. A number of such boats were successfully exported between the Wars, and Thornycroft also continued to build larger warships for the Royal Navy as well as for foreign governments. During the second World War, the Woolston yard turned out a vast number of types,

HMS *Juno*. A *Leander* class frigate. MOD design.

HMS *Abdiel*. Exercise minelayer. Designed and built by Thornycroft.

from target towing and RAF rescue launches, to landing craft, corvettes and destroyers.

After the war, Admiralty work began to give way again to tugs, ferries, launches and even barges. In the 1950s, Woolston built three frigates, and a dozen TON class coastal minesweepers. One of the former was HMNZS *Otago*, a Type 12 frigate delivered to New Zealand in 1960, and one of the latter was for South Africa. These vessels were to Admiralty designs although attempts were made to design, as well as build, warships for export. Many of these were based on the very successful Thornycroft *Hunt* class destroyers, HMS *Brecon* and HMS *Brissenden*, designed and built for the RN in the late 1930s when the Admiralty designed *Hunts* were suffering from stability problems. However, no weapon expertise existed in the company and all quotes were based on weapons supplied by Vickers. As the latter company was also competing, it was obviously very difficult to get any priority for this, let alone a competitive price. There is also no doubt that Thornycroft did not develop the commercial and sales flair which Vosper had acquired.

In the 1960s naval orders were scarce. By 1963, HMS *Gurkha*, a *Tribal* class destroyer, was the sole naval order of any significance since *Otago*. Thornycroft's Hampton yard, on the Thames, was losing money and Thornycroft's Brazil subsidiary was having problems. Wages and salaries in shipbuilding were not particularly attractive; a result of falling sales. The work force was ageing; in June 1962 the board discussed laying off several employees who were more than 75 years of age! At about the same time, one of the directors celebrated his 70th birthday and completed 50 years service with the Company. When HMS *Gurkha* was completed and handed over in February 1963, there was negotiation with the Admiralty on the final price; Cost Plus contracts were the norm - one of the many reasons why the British shipbuilding industry was becoming less competitive.

Nevertheless the cash situation at Thornycroft was generally healthy and the shares were being traded slightly above the par value of four shillings (20p) each. The directors, headed by John W. Thornycroft, grandson of the founder, were ploughing capital back into the Woolston Yard, for example by building the new Centenary Quay, although with an eye to future merchant navy business rather than warship building.

The Company declared a bonus of 12% on ordinary shares for the accounting year ending 31st July 1963, plus a further 2.5% Centenary Bonus, and a 1 for 5 bonus issue. 1964 began on an optimistic note, with a new *Leander* frigate (HMS *Juno*) for the RN being laid down at Woolston, and the new Centenary quay being opened. Phase two of a feasibility study on Glass Reinforced Plastic (GRP) hull construction, later to be of great significance, was commenced. A new subsidiary, Thornycroft Malaysia, began trading in June, and Thornycroft Brazil showed a modest profit for the first quarter, although the long-dormant Thornycroft Egypt was liquidated.

However, by October the Company announced a "substantial" trading loss for the year and the dividend on ordinary shares was reduced to 6%. Shares fell to below par value.

In 1965 the Company continued to survive on a mixture of commercial shipbuilding, ship repairing, and warships. An order for an Exercise Minelayer, HMS *Abdiel*, was received from the RN in June and the following month Kuwait ordered two 78 foot patrol boats. Another Isle of Wight car ferry was launched in October, but the Company announced only a small trading profit and the dividend remained at 6%. J. I. Thornycroft was trying, with little success, to win other warship export orders; Argentina was showing possible interest in the *Ton* class minesweepers: The Company submitted a tender in November for two more RN *Leander* frigates, and, in conjunction with Bristol Aeroplane Plastics, asked the Admiralty to fund a study on building a Leander in GRP.

None of these bids bore fruit. Thornycroft at the end of 1965 was ripe for takeover. Down on its luck, perhaps, with some ageing workers and struggling to survive, but with good facilities in which a board determined to survive was investing money. There was also a hard core of experienced people, particularly technical staff who had wide experience in the design and building of many different ship types, and in marine engineering on

ocean liners and other large merchant ships. There was a capability to manufacture engineering products of no small order: Thornycroft had itself built the G6 gas turbine for HMS *Gurkha*.

All this was exactly what Vosper was looking for, and almost on their doorstep. Nevertheless, the decision to go ahead by the Vosper directors must have taken considerable nerve.

The Thornycroft share price apparently continued to drop, because on 13th January 1966, Vosper made an offer to purchase all the 4/- (20p) Ordinary shares for 2/- (10p) each, or to exchange nine Thornycroft shares for one Vosper. The Thornycroft board was advised that a hostile takeover bid was likely to succeed as Vosper already held 26% of the shares. Nevertheless, they haggled successfully, obtaining improved terms of 2/6 (12.5p) per share, or eight for one, and decided to recommend acceptance to their shareholders.

On 22nd February 1966 Sir David Brown, John Rix and Peter Du Cane were appointed directors of John I. Thornycroft & Company Ltd, and at a board meeting on 2nd March received a briefing on the state of the Company. In addition to *Juno* and *Abdiel*, still in hand for the RN, and the two Kuwaiti patrol craft, two more were on order from Libya, plus two small ferries for Portsmouth Harbour, and a couple of barges. More significantly, for the future, there was a contract from the RN to build a test section in GRP to allow evaluation trials on this material. On a different note, the furnishing department was said to be diversifying into banks and pubs!

John Rix stated that for the time being each Company would remain as a separate entity, although sales and representation abroad would be amalgamated.

There was an obvious need for rationalisation at board level, and on 7th April Jack W. Thornycroft resigned and retired to become Honorary President of the Company, a post which he held until it was abolished as a result of reorganisation in 1971. Mr. R. F. Newman, also past normal retirement age, resigned his directorship. The Chairmanship was taken over by Sir David Brown, with John Rix as Managing Director.

On retiring, John W. Thornycroft was happy to be able to record that the company was on the whole in good shape, and not in debt, having liquid assets of around £1.5 million. Moreover, following the board's determination to survive the shipbuilding recession, almost £1 million had been ploughed into the shipbuilding facilities in recent years. Vosper had acquired a bargain.

Bargain it may have been, but in addition to changes arising from the merger of the two companies, there was room for improvement and cost-saving surgery. One of the first victims was Thornycroft's London office, a prestigious building in Smith Square, and the Hampton yard began to come under close scrutiny. In due course, it was closed and the yard sold off, as the market in bespoke one-off small craft had died. It had tried to move into GRP boat building, but not on a big enough scale to be successful. The Thornycroft (Hampton) company became dormant for a while. However, in 1966 this was as yet unresolved, the main line policy being expressed purely as a firm intent to "Stay in warship building". The pace of revolution within Thornycroft was relatively slow but sure. By the end of 1968, the last of the original Thornycroft directors had resigned; "Vosper Thornycroft" was a going concern, but in fact the formalities in some respects had to wait until June 1970, when there was an organisational shake up for technical reasons: John I. Thornycroft & Co. Ltd became "Vosper Thornycroft Ltd", and effectively the only shipbuilding operating company of the group; responsible for all three yards. "Vosper Ltd" became simply a holding Company. Vosper Thornycroft was born.

## Chapter Two

# WARSHIP EXPORTING

As well as the work in hand at Woolston at the time of the Vosper/Thornycroft merger, the company was quite busy at the Portchester and Old Portsmouth yards. The Mark 1 corvette *Tobruk*, for the Kingdom of Libya, and three 103 foot patrol craft for the Kenya Navy, were all nearing completion, and two large orders for Malaysia were under way. One of these was for four 96 foot Gas Turbine powered fast patrol craft, and the other for no fewer than fourteen 103 foot PCs. During 1966 orders came in for Portchester to build four more 96 footers armed with SS12 missiles, (three for Libya, and one for Brunei). There were also follow-on builds of two more "Thornycroft type" 78 foot PCs for Kuwait, and four more 100 footers for Libya. These were all built at Portchester or Portsmouth, together with a new floating bridge for the Itchen River crossing. Woolston also soon received new orders for a yacht, *Romantica,* then the largest aluminium yacht in the world and, again for Libya, *Zeltin*, an unusual vessel incorporating a floating dock, specially designed as a support ship for the 96 foot missile armed boats.

All this was good news for the new company, and due largely to the vigorous and continuous efforts of the Vosper salesmen. In the late 1960s and early 1970s, this team was, oddly, it seems in retrospect, almost unique in the British shipbuilding industry who in general seemed content to let the customers come to them of their own accord.

With the acquisition of Thornycroft the way was now open to pursue the market for larger warships, especially frigates. To Vosper's experience of selling, designing and building ships for export was added the much larger Thornycroft yard, together with a staff with knowledge of larger vessel practices and the necessary capacity to handle them. The embryo designs which had already been worked out by the Vosper designers were a step nearer reality.

To appreciate the magnitude of the task faced by the new Vosper Thornycroft company, it is

necessary to understand the general state of British warship design and building in the late 1960s.

With a few notable exceptions, the British Admiralty, now the Ministry of Defence (Navy), or MOD(N), had always designed its own ships and weapon systems, but even in the 1960s, the Royal Dockyards were largely occupied with repairing and refitting RN ships, and most of the actual building of new warships and equipment was undertaken by civilian companies to MOD(N) designs. In more recent years much of the design responsibility has also been contracted out to industry, but in the 1960s there was still a large number of civil servants responsible for designing all types of warships and much of their equipment.

Therefore, although there were several commercial yards capable of building warships, and of producing the working drawings, few had the ability to design them from scratch, and even fewer had exercised this ability.

Similar problems affected the equipment, such as weapons, which these ships carried. MOD(N) was, and still is, responsible for the design and development of systems to meet future requirements specified by the Naval Staff. The latter have the unenviable responsibility of predicting future threats in time to permit suitable equipment to be produced to counter them. As the gestation period of a new weapon system can be quite lengthy, it is not surprising to find that the required performances can change quite dramatically, before the new equipment enters service. Similarly, during their service lives, and even whilst still under construction, the requirements which the ships are called upon to fulfil can change considerably. Such changes can further delay completion of both ships and equipment, and make the fixing of prices and delivery dates virtually impossible, particularly if, as was often the case, MOD(N) personnel responsible for the design are remote from the manufacturing establishment.

Although in the early 1960's most warship

103 foot patrol craft.

96 foot gas turbine fast patrol craft.

Woolston floating bridge.

Motor yacht, *Romantica*. Built for Mr. J. C. Bamford.

Maintenance and Repair ship, *Zeltin*, for Libya.

contracts moved to fixed price, the British naval equipment industry had in general become used to "cost plus" contracts as the only viable way of handling such open ended situations. Human nature being what it is, costs soared, and delivery programmes were constantly "revised".

Thus, although there were many British companies making equipment for the Royal Navy, few were in a position to supply VT with suitable items for export contracts. Foreign navies, and therefore VT, quite naturally required a fixed price and delivery date for their ships and the equipment fitted in them, and also expected to know in advance exactly what performance would be achieved.

MOD(N) were far too busy to get involved in exporting equipment which they themselves did not make. The manufacturers were in no position to quote firm prices, performances or deliveries for products for which they had no design responsibility, and which, in some cases, might not work anyway.

Even equipment already at sea was likely to be modified by MOD(N) without warning, and who was to pay for such modifications to export equipment? Certainly not the customer if, as was often the case, such modifications were necessary to achieve the specified performance.

The changing nature of weapon systems in the 1960s also created another problem. Up to about that time, guns, torpedoes, radars, radios, and all the other paraphernalia installed in a warship were, broadly speaking, operated independently of each other. Interconnections between them on board were usually simple, or nonexistent. There were therefore few problems of compatibility to be solved and equipment could be standardised throughout the fleet, an important factor when spares and maintenance were considered.

The MOD(N) organisation was geared to this state of affairs. Different departments responsible for different equipments operated independently, and sometimes jealously, of each other and were a law unto themselves. In a few cases where complex interfaces were required, the whole subsystem would become self-contained, complete with all its own supporting equipment, which would not normally be shared with any other users. For example, a gun fire control system would have its own radar, vertical reference gyro, power supplies, displays, and so on.

This organisation may have had its advantages, but it was not conducive to producing equipment for the export market. In any case, the requirement for the latter was generally for smaller vessels than the RN needed for its ocean going role, and each piece of equipment had to earn its keep. Resiting it in a different type of ship might necessitate all sorts of modifications for different reasons. Whereas many of these might appear simple to achieve, there could be unexpected complications in departing from a "standard" item, and for reasons just explained, both the MOD(N) designers and the industrial manufacturers were reluctant to get involved in such "unauthorised" modifications to suit export customers.

As warship systems grew more sophisticated, the degree of integration, or interconnection and interdependency between different equipments increased. The organisation within MOD(N) and equipment manufacturers in industry was not well suited to deal with such problems.

VT was fortunately free to organise their design department accordingly, and combining all the different ship, propulsion, electronics and weapon designers under the same management became one of the company's greatest strengths. Conversely, these designers were to find that the MOD(N) organisation, whose support in dealing with foreign Navies was invaluable, was in those days often frustratingly cumbersome, despite the enthusiastic support of many individuals. Most of the engineers one met in MOD(N) were well qualified, bright and enthusiastic, but quite unable to realise more than a fraction of their potential, due to the restraints of the organisation. It was not until several years afterwards that somebody in the MOD(N) began to try to create the type of organisation which a systems engineering approach required. This must have been quite a struggle against the huge inertia of the status quo, but slowly, converts began to emerge.

It would however be unfair to give the impression that in the 1960s and 1970s there was no British naval equipment suitable for export. Fortunately, there were several far sighted British companies who had themselves developed some

(1) Anti Submarine Mortar Mk.10.

(2) Twin 4" Mk.19 Gun Mounting.

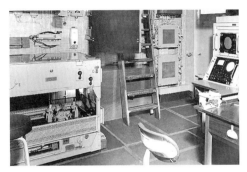

(3) Plot (left) and Decca RDL1 (right).

(4) Plessey AWS1 air surveillance radar.

(5) Short Seacat lightweight AA launcher.

(6) Sistel Sea Killer missile (Italy).

(7) Sea Hunter fire control (Switzerland).

(8) HSA WM 22 Fire Control system (Holland).

In the 60's, most exportable British Naval Weapons were obsolescent RN equipments, (1, 2 and the electro-mechanical plotting table on the left of 3). A few enterprising UK manufacturers produced good export equipment (Decca Electronic Warfare equipment on the right of 3, also 4 and 5). A much more comprehensive selection was available abroad (6, 7, 8).

excellent pieces of equipment. They were generally both willing and able to adapt such equipment in order to meet the demands of various different markets; in some cases, of even the Royal Navy! There were also many European and American manufacturers whose products were suitable and available for use in VT export warships. Vosper was already accustomed to doing business with foreign subcontractors: As long ago as the early days of the second world war, when Italy was still neutral, Cdr Du Cane was buying Isotta Fraschini engines to fit in RN torpedo boats. Moreover, Isotta themselves were procuring certain parts of the same engines from German suppliers!

At the time of the merger, Vosper had embarked on a weapons development programme with a French company, with the aim of reviving the flagging fortunes of the fast torpedo boat.

The torpedo had always, at least supposedly, conferred upon the patrol boat the ability to pack a punch out of all proportion to its size and cost. Torpedoes could be devised to run accurately on a preset course for a considerable distance. To hit a moving target necessitates predicting its future position. Measuring course and speed with sufficient accuracy to do this is by no means easy but the biggest problem is the need to assume that the target will obligingly continue in the same direction without altering speed; an unlikely eventuality save when in blissful ignorance of attack. Hence the requirement for the attacking craft either to fire its torpedo undetected, or to do so from as close as possible, leaving insufficient time for evasion.

With the advent of seaborne radars, clandestine approaches under cover of darkness or bad visibility became a less feasible proposition. Improved accuracy of fire control for naval guns made sheer speed less effective as a means of evasion. The days of the traditional motor torpedo boat were numbered.

In any case, RN interest in small warships was waning, for different reasons, but Vosper made a novel effort to revitalise the fast planing boat, which had for some time been a company speciality.

The solution was clearly some weapon whose course could be corrected after launch. Moreover, a reduced time of flight would be an advantage.

This was long before the days of the now well known Exocet surface to surface missile. Because of cost, and the difficulty of persuading foreign Navies to accept prototype weapons, there could be no question of developing a new system from scratch. Vosper had to take what was available and adapt as little as possible.

A number of likely weapon systems then available were considered. The most promising was the French SS11/12, a small guided missile developed for use by helicopters against ground targets. The missile remained attached to the launching vehicle by a fine wire, the purpose of which was not, as some wag suggested, to enable the crew to pull it back for another shot if it missed, but to pass steering signals to the missile in flight. An operator "flew" it to the target using a small joystick control and an optical sight. The normal procedure was to aim the helicopter (and thus the missile launcher) at the target, acquire the target in the field of view of the optical sight, and fire. The missile should thus quickly enter the aimer's field of view. Using his joystick, he would then steer it to the centre of his field of view (known as "gathering" the missile), and keep it there, at the same time keeping the sight pointed at the target. His ability to maintain this state of affairs until the missile hit the target depended upon his skill and the degree to which both target and helicopter manoeuvred in the meantime. On the whole, it was a simple and effective system. However, when transplanted into a fast patrol boat, there were several problems to solve apart from simply making the equipment impervious to salt water.

Firstly, when guided from the bridge of an FPB along the line of sight to another ship, the trajectory of the missile was very low, and it was all too easy to hit the water. Recommended procedure was therefore to keep the missile somewhat above the sight line until the last phase of the approach. This required the aimer to estimate the distance between the target and the missile, which was not easy. Secondly, as anyone who has tried to use binoculars from a moving vehicle will understand, it was extremely difficult simultaneously to track the target and control the missile whilst sitting on a boat travelling at high speed, even in relatively calm conditions. A lot of effort went into solving these problems by using a stabilised sight, a specially sprung seat, padded eyepieces and so on, to give the operator a steady image, and enable him to perform the task without severely injuring himself by violent contact with the equipment.

In conjunction with the French company Nord Aviation, which produced the SS11/12 missile system, Vosper carried out some trials on its own demonstrator FPB *Ferocity*, and managed to achieve reasonably satisfactory results. At any rate, as we have seen, several export orders for Vosper gas turbine powered FPBs fitted with the system were obtained. This was however the swan song of the fast hard chine patrol boats and with the exception of three unarmed training boats for the RN, the *Scimitar* class, no more were built.

This exercise showed that weapons engineering could make an important contribution to exporting warships. It had long been clear to Vosper that successful exporting meant tailoring the product to the customer's requirements. In general, foreign Navies had a clear idea of what they wanted, and since their roles were different their requirements seldom coincided with those of the RN. Most Navies were anxious to acquire modern equipment, but without being used as guinea pigs for high risk new developments. As ever, prices, delivery dates, and performance had to be guaranteed in advance.

As designers and builders, VT was no more anxious than the customers to take high risks, but the dividing line between these and the innovation essential to produce a better warship than their competitors was a fine one, and the judgement could not be delegated. The only way of achieving this was to build a team in house capable of taking design responsibility for the entire ship and its equipment.

Just as Vosper had done with SS11/12, it was going to be necessary to take existing equipment, British, foreign, or probably a mixture of both, and knit them all together to form a satisfactory ensemble. In this way modest development steps could be taken within the limitations imposed by predetermined prices, deliveries and performances. In fact, as experience grew, the departures from proven designs of both ships and equipment became quite considerable. Nevertheless, despite inevitable and sometimes quite dramatic teething troubles,

standards were achieved and VT never had to pay compensation for failure to achieve standards. When delivered, the performances of the ships and weapon systems were as good as or better than most of their contemporaries.

But in 1967 most of this was in the future, and the immediate need was to set up a design department capable of performing all these tasks. It was a relatively small but versatile team, since no attempt was made to duplicate the role of the actual equipment designers. VT's role was to co-ordinate them, and to monitor them closely enough to detect potential problems before they became disasters.

The new company already had many of the necessary ingredients for a design team with knowledge of MOD(N) requirements and practices, as well as a strong innovative ability. As Alan Griffith was now heavily occupied supervising the Woolston shipyard, a new Technical Director was recruited from the Royal Corps of Naval Constructors. Peter Usher had spent much of his previous career working on submarines, about the only type of combat warship which VT did not propose to construct, but this did not prevent him from successfully pulling together the new design department.

By about two years after the merger this design group under Peter Usher consisted of a happy mixture of Vosper and Thornycroft members who were subsequently joined by several new faces from outside. The Technical General Manager, Tony Dorey, was responsible to Peter for naval architecture, marine, electrical and structural engineering. Tony was a naval architect by profession; a Thornycroft technical apprentice who had spent all of his subsequent career with the company.

As already explained, a vital, and unique, feature of the new department was the combination of all the disciplines necessary to design a warship under the same roof: Peter Usher also had the small but growing weapons department, and the vital hydrodynamics team, which designed hull shapes and propellers and ran the cavitation tunnel, reporting direct to him.

It is impracticable to list all members of that remarkable team, but certainly some characters

Tony Dorey, Technical General
Manager. Later Director.

Len Pierce, Chief Ship
Designer.

Ron Crook, Chief Electrical
Designer.

George Cameron, Electrical
Designer. Later Director.

Geoff Kingslake, Chief Structural
Designer.

Klaus Suhrbier, Chief
Hydrodynamicist.

Dave Cole, Chief Engineering
Designer.

Terry Grisley, Chief Weapon
Systems Engineer. Later Director.

## SOME OF
## THE VT
## DESIGNERS

must be mentioned. The Chief Ship Designer, Len Pierce, and Chief Electrical Designer, Ron Crook, were both long term Vosper employees who had begun their careers with the company in the late 1930s and early 1940s respectively. Neither had many letters after their names, but each had a unique wealth of practical experience. Both had learned the hard way, Len starting in the Mould Loft and Ron in the Electrical Maintenance shop. Both could occasionally be persuaded to reminisce about the old days, and both at least pretended to be sceptical of Thornycroft men and their apparently old-fashioned shipyard. Ron had a disarmingly blunt way of demolishing bright young engineers - for example, salesmen from other companies - if he thought they were talking what he referred to as "a load of bullshit". He also delighted in referring to the occasional internal "cock-ups" which inevitably occurred in the small, eager and over-busy design group as a "bit of a Harry Worth situation". Harry Worth was a TV comedian who specialised in complex situation comedies based on a chain of misunderstandings.

Ron's assistant at the time was a young ex-Vosper apprentice called George Cameron, later to become the director in charge of all the non-shipbuilding part of the company.

Marine engineering - the art of shoe-horning powerful and complicated machinery into small engine rooms and then persuading it to work - was the province of a small team under Stewart Adamson. This team had acquired considerable experience in marinised gas turbine systems as well as diesels in the various patrol boat designs, and was well placed to tackle the COmbined Diesel Or Gas turbine (CODOG) systems planned for the new frigates.

Other members of the team included Geoff Kingslake, a structural engineer and sometime member of the team which had designed the De Havilland Mosquito aircraft; Klaus Suhrbier, the hydrodynamicist who ran the cavitation tunnel and was becoming a world authority on high speed propellers and associated topics; Dave Cole, who had been Chief Engineering Designer under Vosper, now ran the Portchester Drawing Office and was responsible for the engineering layout of the Mark 5s; Ken McColl, his opposite number at

Woolston, and a host of others.

In February 1967 the Sales department achieved a huge success when four very fast and heavily armed frigates were ordered, "off the drawing board", by the Imperial Iranian Navy. The design and build of these ships would exercise all the skill of the existing members of the Design department, and as the ships possessed a substantially bigger and more complex weapon system than anything which either Vosper or Thornycroft had previously tackled, some further reinforcements were required.

The management of the technical problems arising from the SS11/12 missile system project had been successfully undertaken by John Fricker, then Vosper's sole full-time weapons expert, aided and abetted as required by Ron Crook, Len Pierce, and their departments. Although the selection and initial design of the weapon systems for the new frigate designs was handled by these people, additional help was needed to manage the very complicated new weapon systems through to completion. The Thornycroft organisation included a number of ex-RN weapons personnel, but their experience was mainly practical and concerned with installation and setting to work of RN equipment. Design and commissioning of RN weapon systems was normally undertaken exclusively by RN specialist teams.

To solve this problem, Peter Usher recruited a British electronics engineer who had gone down the "brain drain" to the USA. After some time in America, Terry Grisley and his wife decided that they would prefer to raise their young family in England, and Terry joined the company in 1968, with a view to building up a small team of Weapons engineers within the Design department. Their first major project was to be the Weapon Systems management of the Iranian project. The new warships became known as the Mark 5 fast destroyers.

Vosper patrol boats had come to be referred to by their lengths; the 103 foot and 110 foot steel hulled patrol craft have already been mentioned. This system has continued almost to the present day, although metrication caused a certain amount of confusion, and the number of different lengths, and different designs of the same length, have now made the system almost unworkable.

To identify different designs of corvette and larger vessels, Vosper instituted Mark numbers, with the Mk.1 corvettes built for Ghana and Libya. This practice also continued until recent years, when the number reached 20, giving rise to possible confusion with contemporary RN ships such as the Type 21 and Type 23.

Not all of these were built, but whenever a sales campaign demanded a radically new hull design to be worked out, the next available number was allocated. Of course, some Marks appeared in several different variants, with different weapon systems or different propulsion, and sometimes changes to the superstructure too.

Thus the Mk.2, Mk.4 and Mk.6 were designs which never got beyond the proposal stage. Two Mk.3 corvettes were later sold to the Nigerian Navy, but the first significant project for the new company was the Mk.5. The IIN referred to these ships as destroyers, although despite their formidable offensive capability some would have even questioned classifying a 1400 tonne ship as a frigate.

Questions are often asked regarding the difference between these various types of ship. In modern terminology it is usually accepted that a destroyer is larger than a frigate, and the former word now usually describes a very major warship. A century ago, torpedo boat destroyers were amongst the smallest seagoing members of the fleet. VT also uses the word corvette, meaning a ship smaller than either of the former, but larger than a patrol boat. There is however no hard and fast rule except that whoever foots the bill is entitled to call the ship whatever he likes! Later, despite being twice the displacement of the Iranian destroyers, the Brazilian Mk.10 was to be called a frigate. *"Our Treasury will not give us enough money to buy destroyers"*, explained a Brazilian officer, with a smile.

Nevertheless, whatever it was called, the Mk.5 was a very major project. To design and build from scratch a vessel as complex as this, even with the available combined skills and experience of Vosper and Thornycroft, was a formidable undertaking. Moreover, the Mk.5 was and, as far as is known, remains the fastest major warship in the world, the speed eventually achieved during trials only being exceeded by much smaller boats. The 40 knots equalled the world record established by an earlier Thornycroft destroyer, HMS *Teazer*, built at Woolston in 1917. The Mk.5 weapon outfit was also revolutionary.

*Chapter Three*

# THE FAST FRIGATES

As a curtain raiser to the Mk.5 project, and to provide some of the crews with some practice and experience before the new ships came along, the IIN acquired an ex-RN *Battle* class destroyer, HMS *Sluys,* renamed *Artemiz,* to be refitted by VT and equipped with some of the new systems destined for the Mk.5.

The *Artemiz* refit provided a valuable training ground for many of the VT engineers. Not only were many of the technical problems solved in readiness for the Mk.5s, but personnel from the various equipment suppliers and VT had a chance to get to know each other and form relationships, which in some cases stood them in good stead for many years.

The *Artemiz* contract also arguably spawned what was eventually to become the Support Projects Division. It was clear that in view of the extensive changes proposed to the equipment fit of the old ship, the original RN documentation would not be entirely relevant. Obviously someone would have to do something about this, and all eyes turned to VT. Dick Rycraft was detailed to tackle the problem, but it seems that at the time the matter was not considered to be of sufficient moment to give him an office or any staff. The ancestor of SPD therefore came into being in an old Skoda car, parked alongside the Southampton dry dock where *Artemiz* was being refitted. Unabashed by this lack of recognition, the one-man Division set about producing a Ship Equipment List and a very basic Maintenance System. Later, a desk and chair were allocated in the Repairs Division Estimating office; Support Projects was under way!

The Mk.5 design originated before the Vosper/ Thornycroft merger under the leadership of Peter Du Cane and John Rix. Alan Griffith was responsible for carrying it forward, and the detailed design was later worked out after the merger with the help of the Thornycroft design team, and Vickers Shipbuilders, with whom the Iranian order was shared.

The Mk.5 was not only a big step into territory hitherto unexplored by Vosper, but a radically innovative one in the field of frigate design. In order to "lay off" the risk, and speed up the delivery time, the Board arranged for Vickers to assist with detail design, and to build two of the four ships, in a similar way to that in which the Ghanaian Mk.1 corvettes had been handled.

Great emphasis was placed on the requirement for speed, and therefore on weight saving and simplicity. The hull was of all-welded steel, with transverse frames and longitudinal stiffening in order to achieve adequate strength. It has been said of offshore racing powerboats that "*If they don't bend a bit, they're too heavy!*" In the case of the Mk.5, which was intended to have a rather longer life than a race boat, the requirement was to remain unbent, but only just. This implied careful structural calculations, rather than "belt and braces" methods.

The superstructure - all of the ship above the highest continuous deck - was constructed in aluminium. An aluminium structure is approximately half the weight of a steel structure designed to perform the same task, and requires much less maintenance. Steel, especially when exposed to salt water, requires frequent repainting to keep corrosion at bay; an expensive and time-consuming task. However, care is required in the use of aluminium. Narrow gaps or crevices in the structure can cause rampant corrosion and it is vital to insulate joints between aluminium and steel components to avoid electrolytic action between the different metals. Vosper had long since met and solved such problems in the construction of patrol boats.

The snag with aluminium of course is that it melts at around 650 degrees centigrade, a temperature which can be exceeded in major fires. Serious structural damage can therefore be expected in such circumstances. This fact was well known, understood and accepted long before damage was inflicted on RN Type 21 frigates in the Falklands war, when the popular press suddenly "discovered" it and screamed that "*aluminium burns*" (untrue)

Mk.5 fast 'frigate' for Iran.

A Mk.5 in dry dock. Note roll damping fins, a long standing VT product.

A roll damping fin.

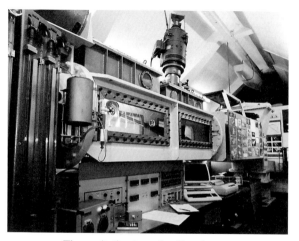

The cavitation tunnel at Portchester.

and that "*the RN should have known better*" (unreasonable). The RN knew very well the advantages and disadvantages of aluminium structure, and accepted both, although there has been a change of policy since.

In 1966 there were no universally accepted standards for warship stability; those defined by Sarchin and Goldberg and now widely accepted were first published in 1962, but not used by the world's navies until later. Before that, the RN and shipbuilders used their own judgement.

Like the later VT corvettes and frigates, the Mk.5 had a relatively high freeboard and superstructure, which gave good stability at high angles of heel, without excessive stiffness when upright. In other words, a lively but safe design.

The ship - like most VT warships - was fitted with roll damping fins, also of VT design and manufacture. These fins protrude sideways from the hull below the waterline, and are controlled by gyroscopes in such a way as to reduce the rolling motion of the ship when under way in rough weather. They are widely fitted to modern passenger ships to make life more comfortable for the passengers; on a warship they are a considerable help in reducing crew fatigue, improving the accuracy and efficiency of weapon systems, and, most importantly in ships equipped with a helicopter, enabling flying operations to be carried out in rougher weather than would otherwise be safe.

Roll damping fins are sometimes referred to as "stabilizers", implying, wrongly, that the ship might capsize if they ceased to operate.

The Mk.5 propulsion system was novel, comprising a twin CODOG system whereby the main propulsion was provided by two Rolls Royce Olympus gas turbines; a marinised version of those used to power the Concorde supersonic airliner. Each of the two controllable pitch propellers was driven either by its Olympus, or, for slow speed cruising, by a diesel engine. The heart of each system was the CODOG gearbox, capable of accepting either the very high speed, high power input from an Olympus power turbine, or the more modest input from the diesel, and driving the propeller at the required speed.

Although the MOD(N) had selected the marinised Olympus for the Royal Navy, thereby imparting a vital cachet of respectability and ensuring that spares and backup would be available for years to come, their implementation of this followed the usual procedures which were logical but slow. They meant that a prototype installation had to be tried out at sea before the main RN programme proceeded too far. Thus before the RN trials ship, HMS *Exmouth*, had yielded any useful information on its single screw installation, VT were contractually committed to the Government of Iran to supply a satisfactory twin screw outfit, and although the RN's first twin Olympus powered ship, HMS *Bristol*, was designed before the Mk.5, the latter completed her sea trials over two years before the RN ship first went to sea. However, during the RN trials a problem was discovered which was avoided on the Mk.5s by redesign of the air intake.

In the interest of saving gearbox weight and complication, relatively small, and thus fast turning, controllable pitch propellers were selected for the Mk.5. The design of these presented a difficult task, even to Vosper who had many years of experience in designing high speed, super cavitating propellers for patrol boats. The problems fall roughly into two areas; cavitation and vibration.

When the motion of a propeller blade through the water causes the pressure to fall below the local vapour pressure, the water is effectively "torn apart", or boils, creating a bubble filled with water vapour. This bubble eventually collapses violently, and if this occurs repeatedly on the surface of the propeller, it can do a surprising amount of damage in a very short time. Within a few hours of running, large areas of the propeller can be eroded away. Thus cavitation erosion can be a serious problem, and since cavitation itself cannot be avoided in high speed propellers, it is necessary to design the blade shapes so that the cavity collapses away from the surface. This necessitates careful experiments with model propellers, and minute adjustments to blade shape to achieve the desired results.

VT is one of the few shipbuilders in the world with its own cavitation tunnel. This is similar to the wind tunnels used by aircraft designers, but with water circulating instead of air. This facility

Brian Greenaway.

Mike Cory.

The Vickers 4.5 inch Mk.8 gun. Developed for the RN, and exported successfully to Iran and Brazil.

was acquired in the 1950s by the far-sighted Peter Du Cane and has played a major part in the development of high speed propellers over the years.

The propellers for the Mk.5 were developed in conjunction with KaMeWa, the Swedish propeller experts, and proved very successful in service.

Another design problem, that of vibration, is equally difficult. Each time the blade of a high speed propeller passes close beneath the hull, the skin plating receives a "kick" from the pressure pulse. A three bladed propeller rotating at 300 rpm therefore shakes the ship at a frequency of 15 Hz. It so happens that many typical bits of ship structure can have resonant frequencies somewhere between about 10 and 20 Hz and to avoid this is almost impossible. In practice therefore, as the ship accelerates through its speed range, various bits and pieces tend to get soundly shaken. Part of the solution is to design equipment, such as radar antennae, with this in mind, and to try to avoid troublesome resonances at often used power settings, such as maximum continuous speed. This is much easier to say than to achieve, since calculation of the many different modes of resonance of such complex structures in advance is not an exact science. Increasing the number of propeller blades can help by tending to shift the input vibration above the troublesome structural resonances, but at the time of the Mk.5 only three bladed controllable pitch propellers were in common use.

However, despite the innovative nature of the ship, the policy of taking only controlled development risks in order to stay within the commercial constraints of cost and time paid off, and the first Mk.5, IIS *Saam,* kept to programme and achieved her contractual performance, even exceeding the magic figure of 40 knots - just!

For First of Class speed trials, the measured mile at Arran in Scotland is favoured by naval architects to obtain accurate power/speed data for the class. This is because the water is deep and sheltered from the prevailing south westerly winds. After three runs on the mile, a speed of 39.6 knots was obtained; quite sufficient to satisfy the contract. The project manager, Brian Greenaway telephoned Alan Griffith at Woolston to give him the good news. The response from Alan was "*Don't bother to come home until you have done 40 knots!*"

Fortunately VT had a good shore party on hand led by Mike Cory, who arranged for *Saam* to berth at Ardrossan where 40 tons of fuel and all the fresh water on board was unloaded.

Back at Arran the following morning, after a five mile run up to the measured distance, a speed of 40.34 knots was recorded. The "*Yippee!*" from the bridge was said to have been heard 20 miles away in Troon. Even the MOD overseers smiled.

The weapon system was in many ways as innovative as the ship herself. For the reasons already discussed, there was no clear choice available from the RN inventory, and a somewhat cosmopolitan outfit was selected. The centrepiece was the gun and missile fire control system, manufactured by the Swiss company, Contraves, in Zurich.

Contraves, (the name is a contraction of the nearest Latin equivalent to "Anti-aircraft"), a sister company of the well known gun manufacturer Oerlikon, had sold a large number of land-based anti-aircraft gun systems called Super Fledermaus to Iran. Super Fledermaus used a Contraves-built radar and analogue computer to control an Oerlikon twin 35 mm Anti-Aircraft (AA) gun. A naval version of this system, christened Sea Hunter, was selected for the Mk.5s.

The main anti-ship weapon was the Sea Killer missile system, manufactured by an Italian company called Sistel, with whom Contraves had a close association. Sea Hunter was also to control a British Short Seacat anti aircraft missile system and a 4. 5 inch general purpose gun. The new Vickers Mk.8 automatic gun mounting was selected, but as this was still under development for the Royal Navy (another ponderous exercise constantly delayed by dozens of modifications), the first two ships were fitted with second hand Mk.5 (no relation) mountings.

The anti-submarine system consisted of the RN type Mortar Mk.10, directed by two searchlight sonars, types 170 and 172. The whole outfit was obsolescent, even at that time, but little else was available and it had the advantage of being a well-proven working system, and similar to that already fitted to *Artemiz,* the ex-RN *Battle* class destroyer refitting in Southampton Docks also for Iran. *Artemiz* was also fitted with a slightly simpler version of Sea Hunter, her original fire control equipment having reached the end of its useful life. With Seacat and a twin 35 mm gun, she was a useful test bed for the more complex Mk.5 systems. Computerised Action Information Organisation (AIO) was still in its infancy in the 1960s, and although the radars were quite modern, the display and action information systems fitted to the Mk.5 were of a similar vintage to the anti-submarine equipment, consisting mostly of vacuum tube or electro-mechanical technology and relying heavily on manual intervention. Although crude and unreliable, this equipment was at least relatively simple to maintain and plenty of spares were available from RN stocks, provided one could speak the language! Most equipment was designated by a series of apparently arbitrary letters, and new recruits to the VT Weapons Group would spend hours puzzling over, for example, what the letters JUA stood for in relation to a particularly troublesome type of radar display. Frustratingly, there was no answer to this question, and although there was some well-concealed logic to the system, it became necessary to learn a whole new jargon as well as to persuade the archaic equipment to work.

Nevertheless, as a whole the Mk.5 was a formidable fighting machine, and more than a match for many larger warships. The main reason for this was her Sea Killer missile system which, before the days of the now well known Exocet missile, posed an exceptional threat to enemy ships. Unlike Exocet, Sea Killer worked on the beam rider principle. The target was tracked by a pencil beam radar which locked on and followed it continuously. The missile was fired into the beam and, using a special receiver which looked backwards, steered itself down the middle of the beam. Thus, provided the latter stayed on target, the missile would eventually and inevitably score a direct hit.

This system had its disadvantages. An alert target would detect the guidance beam and do its best to evade or jam it. To achieve maximum range, the pencil beam radar had to be sited high on the ship, which was difficult to achieve with sufficient rigidity, and it could only follow one target at a time. As it was also required for anti-aircraft (AA) defence, a second such radar was also carried.

The AA system was centred on the Sea Hunter fire control system which could simultaneously control the 4.5 inch gun and the twin 35 mm Oerlikon. There was also a novel and much improved mode of controlling the Seacat AA missile.

Seacat, like SS11/12, was a command-to-line-of-sight missile but with a higher performance, and with a radio command link instead of a trailing wire, which gave it an AA capability. It was normally controlled by the aimer, who followed the target with a binocular sight and guided the missile onto the sight line using a small joystick. In its basic form, this system was simple and reliable, but required considerable skill to visually track the target and guide the missile at the same time. It also required the target to be visible and thus could not work in darkness or bad visibility.

The Sea Hunter tracking radars were equipped with television cameras mounted upon and aligned with the antenna dish. Visibility permitting, the radar operator sitting inside the Operations Room of the ship, could see what he was tracking; a considerable advantage. Moreover, because the radar could automatically track the target, the Seacat aimer could be relieved of this chore and thus concentrate on guiding his missile to the centre of the TV screen. More importantly, provided that he could see the missile - which was equipped with suitable flares - he did not actually have to be able to see the target since he could assume that the radar was aiming the TV in the correct direction. This system could therefore work equally well in the dark, although not in fog. It was therefore designated the Seacat Dark Fire System.

The reader now perhaps has some grasp of the complexity and novelty of the Mk.5s weapon system. The cosmopolitan nature may also be apparent. As well as Contraves, Oerlikon and Sistel, in Switzerland and Italy, there were Short Brothers and Harland (makers of Seacat) in Northern Ireland, Vickers, (the manufacturers of one of the 4.5 inch guns), Plessey and Decca in the UK, (supplying radars and associated bits and pieces) and many other different suppliers scattered

Iranian Navy Ship, *Artemiz*. Ex HMS *Sluys*.

Mk.7 for Libya. *Dat Assawari*.

far and wide. A lot of the equipment was supplied by the MOD who, understandably perhaps, took a very much "take it or leave it" attitude and supplied their second-hand equipment very much "as seen". Most of the equipments needed inputs from the ship's compass and log, not necessarily in the same - or even in a conventional - form.

Sorting out this lot and ensuring that it would all work when it eventually came together on the ship was an excellent grounding for the newly-formed VT weapons group. Inevitably there were problems, and inevitably all the equipment suppliers were quick to protest their innocence: seldom was it as simple as proving that Company X had supplied a round pinned plug to fit in a socket clearly specified as square. Indeed, the VT engineers often had to roll up their sleeves and spend long hours delving into the details of electronic systems some of which, it transpired, had never worked satisfactorily anyway, let alone with each other!

Of course, the ships themselves as well as all this equipment would eventually have to be operated and maintained by the Imperial Iranian Navy, and it was clear that this totally new design would require a totally new set of documentation. This support task was obviously an order greater than that which had been undertaken for *Artemiz,* and a Support Services Manager, Charles Hill, was appointed and given a staff of seven (including a typist) and some offices in Silvermere House, behind the Woolston Canteen. Support Projects had taken another step forward.

In almost every case of VT's building or repairing warships for foreign navies, the Ministry of Defence acted as an independent inspecting authority to ensure that the terms of the contract were carried out, and to act as adjudicator in cases of dispute. Since it is almost impossible to specify every detail of a complex warship in advance, this was an essential function, and although there were times when VT considered that the MOD(N) Overseers demanded more than the customers had paid for, this was on the whole a good arrangement for both the company and the customers, and one which VT invariably recommended when making a new sale. Despite being hard and sometimes pedantic taskmasters, the MOD(N) were, and remain, a great asset to warship exports and

themselves sometimes gained a valuable insight into the foreign weapon systems which VT sometimes procured for its customers.

Another important function undertaken by the MOD(N) was the training of foreign naval personnel. Whilst VT themselves gradually began to undertake more and more training, particularly in the maintenance and repair of non-RN equipment, operator training, including the "work-up" and "shake-down" of new crews on taking over a new ship from the builders, could only be properly carried out by the RN, with their extensive facilities and personnel with up-to-the-minute operational experience. Indeed, the availability of such training was itself a powerful incentive for foreign navies to buy British, and earned significant amounts of foreign currency over the years, although on some occasions the MOD(N) felt obliged to remind VT that the training facilities were basically intended to fulfil the RN's own needs and that the inclusion of foreign trainees sometimes threatened to stretch the system beyond its capacity.

*Artemiz* successfully went through her HATs and SATs (Harbour and Sea Acceptance Trials) in the autumn of 1969. She was duly handed over to the Imperial Iranian Navy just before Christmas, and commissioned early in the New Year of 1970.

VT and the other engineering teams could then concentrate on setting to work the first of the Mk.5s, IIS *Saam,* the equipment for which having by then gone through Works Acceptance Trials (WATs). This meant that before each piece of equipment left the factory, it was subjected to a comprehensive series of tests designed to prove, as far as was possible in the works environment, that it met the requirements of its specification. This was not always just a formality; it was surprising how often problems were detected unexpectedly at this stage, leading to frantic repairs or modifications, and sometimes necessitating last minute rearrangement to the already tight sea trials programmes.

A delay was caused to the second VT built Mk.5, IIS *Faramarz,* by a fire which started whilst coming out of No.5 dry dock in Southampton, just across the river from Woolston. Much of the superstructure was damaged and the delivery delayed by several weeks, but fortunately very little equipment had been installed at this stage.

Sea trials with the Mk.5s were even more interesting than those of *Artemiz,* for several reasons. Apart from the excitement of running the world's fastest frigate at over 40 knots, the VT team as such had their first taste of commissioning a completely new ship. *Artemiz* had provided an introduction, but there were many new problems to be solved, and although some of the old Thornycroft hands were used to RN-style trials procedures, much of the equipment was totally new to them. On the other hand, some of the young engineering graduates whom Terry Grisley had recruited had virtually no seagoing experience but had had a chance to study some of the theory, and were soon delving into the electronic equipment, and arguing with the Contraves engineers about obscure points such as whether the earth rate correction term had been correctly applied in the fire control computer.

The latter machine was arguably the most modern and sophisticated analogue computer ever to go to sea; it must have been almost the last of its kind to do so before digital computers took over virtually every function of naval weapon systems. It relied on an enormous number of precision-built electromechanical servo multipliers and resolvers and gave rise to many jokes about the resulting scarcity of skilled workers in the Swiss watch industry when Contraves' Zurich factory started building the equipment. The proof of the pudding, however, was eventually amply demonstrated by the successful trial gun firing against targets, an exciting climax to the programme.

Such trials were always a source of worry as well as excitement. A successful shoot was usually accepted by all as a conclusive demonstration that the ship was complete and in full working order, no matter what other outstanding problems remained, but a less successful one could be disastrous since there were many possible reasons, such as the weather, the unrepresentative behaviour of the target, or the state of the ammunition, all of which were beyond control of VT but which might contribute to an unconvincing demonstration even if nothing was wrong with the new equipment. In such cases a repeat performance could be very

expensive indeed; a short sortie by a target-towing aircraft and a supply of ammunition for the shoot each costing about as much as an up-market saloon car. By the time the running costs of the ship and a large team of specialist engineers from half a dozen or so different suppliers had been added, the bill was considerable.

Another interesting factor was always the customers themselves. Invariably, foreign navies would send one or more officers to stand by their new vessels during construction and to be responsible (usually advised by the RN Overseers) for seeing that the requirements of the contract and specification were met. This was, as can be imagined, a fairly onerous task and although some excellent relationships were struck up with many different officers of all sorts of nationalities, they usually managed to be hard task masters.

Some of the Iranian officers were remembered with respect for a long time afterwards. Part of the reason was explained by a friend in another company who had previous experience of supplying hovercraft to the Iranians. Loading a hovercraft had to be performed correctly if dire effects upon the handling were to be avoided; normally this involved a very simple calculation to establish the position of the centre of gravity. "*The problem is,*" he maintained "*that there are only two types of Iranian; I will refer to them as the Aristocrats and the Peasants. The Peasants, never having been taught, are quite incapable of reading or writing the load sheets, let alone doing the calculation. The Aristocrats, on the other hand, mostly have masters degrees in science or mathematics and could run rings around most of us. However, performing such a menial task is, for them, quite out of the question. Therefore, the job does not get done.*"

It was certainly true that, like most navies, the IIN had some difficulty in recruiting and retaining men of a suitable calibre to maintain modern equipment. It was also true that some of the Officers standing by at Woolston were very bright indeed, and often demanded to be briefed in considerable technical detail if they were not satisfied with explanations of problems. It would be interesting to know how many of them, if any, survived the regime of the Ayatollah Khomeni and

the war with Iraq. Properly maintained and handled, even a fifteen year old Mk.5 could have provided anyone with a formidable threat.

In early 1968, VT also obtained an order from the (then) Royal Libyan Navy for a slightly larger version of the Mk.5, known as the Mk.7 frigate. Only one ship was sold and, although larger than the Mk.5s, it was slightly less heavily armed. The differences were sufficient to provide another significant task for Support Projects, who were continuing to grow in size and experience.

The propulsion and weapon systems were very similar to those of the Iranian frigates, but Sea Killer was omitted and it was originally intended to fit an anti-submarine torpedo and an SS11/12 missile launcher, similar to those already in service on the VT built Libyan patrol boats. In the event, the torpedo, under development for another customer who cancelled it, never materialised and, following the revolution in Libya which took place whilst the ship was under construction, the SS11/12 was cancelled as well. The same anti-submarine system as that in the Mk.5 was eventually fitted.

After dealing with two Mk.5s, the VT team found the Mk.7 relatively smooth going; the Libyan Officers standing by the ship were also less exacting than their Iranian counterparts. However, there were other problems to preoccupy the engineers; having a slightly larger hull of a different shape to the Mk.5 made a significant difference to the mechanical characteristics of the ship, and there was a troublesome structural resonance which happened to be excited at an often-used shaft speed. Such problems are as difficult to cure as to predict, and there is always considerable scope for argument over what constitutes an acceptable level of vibration, it being manifestly impossible to eliminate such effects entirely. Engines running at more than 25,000 horsepower in a lightweight structure are bound to draw some attention to themselves! Despite modifications which did improve matters, some grumbling continued intermittently for some time after the conclusion of trials and the acceptance of the ship.

Although VT was always responsible for the acceptance trials, the MOD Overseers who were there to see fair play, also provided many other invaluable facilities, without which the trials would not have been possible. For VT, another vital factor in attracting foreign customers was that the RN should be seen to buy VT products. The company therefore was anxious to sell some of its newer products to the RN, especially as there seemed little likelihood of the latter taking much further interest in patrol boats. The company had therefore been following the RN's requirements for frigates with very keen interest.

## Chapter Four

# THE TYPE 21

By 1967 it had become clear that a replacement programme for the RN's very successful *Leander* Class frigates was becoming urgent. The MOD(N) themselves were fully occupied with HMS *Bristol*, the Type 42 and *Polaris* submarine programmes, and thus the resources required to undertake the design programme for a new frigate in their accustomed manner were not available in house. In December 1967 the MOD(N) invited builders to submit designs for a Royal Navy frigate. VT had by then just entered the frigate market, having laid the keels of two Mk.5s that summer, and a joint bid was prepared in conjunction with Yarrow Shipbuilders of Scotstoun, on the Clyde.

This ship, which became known as the Type 21 frigate, was to be an interim design, so that the MOD(N) could, when their own resources became available, get on with the "real" *Leander* replacement (which was to become the Type 22) in the normal way. The whole objective was to get the interim design to sea as soon as possible, and the Vosper/Yarrow proposal was accepted in February 1968, when the design phase began. MOD(N) kept up the pressure, and the Staff Requirement was completed and approved to enable the preliminary design to be finalised by September. This was a remarkable achievement. It was necessary to cut short the decision making procedures and select predominantly proven and available equipment. In some areas this was perhaps observed a little too literally, but the ship still incorporated some important new developments.

Of course, it was clear that when the detailed design began one of the two shipbuilding companies would have to take the lead, and it had been tacitly assumed in some quarters that this would be Yarrow. However, John Rix had other ideas and made sure that the senior MOD officials were aware of the merits of the new VT organisation, particularly the Design department. Soon after laying the keel of the Libyan Mk.7 frigate, VT was awarded the Type 21 Lead Yard Contract. This meant that it became responsible for the detailed design of the ship, building the first of class, and supplying all the necessary drawings and information to other builders; in this case to Yarrow. Such a design and build contract for an RN front-line warship was not an innovation, but it was the first to be placed outside the MOD(N) for some thirty years, the previous occasion being the Thornycroft designed *Hunt* class destroyers.

The first Type 21, later named HMS *Amazon*, was ordered in the spring of 1969. The keel was laid in May 1971, following the detailed design process, and production of a large proportion of the working drawings.

Although this design process was short by MOD(N) standards, it did nevertheless go through the full Ministry procedure; starting with a design concept; proceeding through outline phases to fully detailed design, with VT acting as Design Authority in place of Director General Ships (DGS). Each phase was subject to scrutiny by DGS. In particular the design standards for matters such as strength and stability were discussed and agreed, and there was never any question of the Type 21 being "substandard".

It is interesting to recall that, as already mentioned in the last chapter, no formal standards for stability and strength existed at this time within MOD(N). This made it more difficult for the designers, situated unusually far away from the influence of the senior constructors at Bath, to anticipate in detail what the latter would ultimately accept in the completed design. After some discussion, MOD(N) and VT agreed on a modified and extended version of the standards published in 1962 by Sarchin and Goldberg, and these were not only applied to the design of the Type 21, but also form the basis of the comprehensive standards for both intact and damaged stability which are in use today.

In the case of strength, the required standard was defined in terms of the stresses imposed in conjunction with a defined wave, calculated statically. The succeeding twenty years have seen

HMS *Amazon*. Lead ship of the Type 21 class.

Type 21 controllable pitch propellers.

Exocet. The French "fire and forget" surface to surface
missile was fired from a box launcher.

enormous progress, due almost entirely to the development of computers and their application to the incorporation of dynamic effects as well as to more detailed assessment of local stresses.

The Type 21 project therefore provided some of the incentive for the MOD(N) to produce today's very comprehensive range of Naval Engineering Standards which provide designers with clear and unambiguous guidelines along which to work.

However, the design was still to an extent handicapped by the requirement to adhere to many of the then existing MOD(N) specifications and procedures, not all of which were entirely relevant to modern warships, and, also for good reasons of commonality with the rest of the fleet, by the necessity of fitting certain equipments which were neither the best nor the cheapest available. Not all the requirements of RN schools and centres of expertise reached VT, and this led to some difficulty and rework in the detailed design phase when such experts necessarily became involved.

An important factor in the design and development of this new frigate was the requirement that it should have the same machinery package as the Type 42 destroyer, the development of which was intended to be completed by MOD(N) well ahead of the Type 21 programme.

During the processes of design and building the two firsts of class changed places. HMS *Amazon* and the first Type 42, HMS *Sheffield*, actually met and exchanged signals of good wishes off the Arran Mile in Scotland, when *Amazon* had been handed over and was wearing the White Ensign whereas *Sheffield* was still in Vickers' hands. This change over had a considerable effect on the marine engineering, as *Amazon* found herself leading the way during setting to work the first Olympus/Tyne controllable pitch propeller package.

This main machinery package was an all-gas turbine system. Turbines were selected for ease of maintenance (usually by replacement of the gas generator), flexibility of performance, and light weight. The smaller Tynes were used for cruising, at which speed the Olympus would be inefficient. As with the CODOG arrangement of the Mk.5s, the heart of the system was the gearbox, which had to cope with widely differing inputs and allow for smooth transition from cruise to boost engines,

whilst under way. This was achieved by Synchro Self Shifting (SSS) clutches, which automatically engage, or disengage, when the input and output shaft speeds coincide.

As with the Mk.5s, reversing was achieved by controllable pitch propellers, but those for the Type 21 were fitted with five blades. The main machinery package was later also fitted to the Type 22, as well as to ships of the Royal Netherlands Navy and other foreign warships, albeit in somewhat modified form.

The Type 21 design incorporated a number of features which were novel or controversial and, looking back, the perspective is naturally clearer as to which were successful and which were not. Hindsight is a marvellous thing!

The very wide transom stern, adopted to improve top speed performance, differed from the then current warship practice (such as the Type 42) and has since been shown to enhance sea keeping, but to incur a penalty (which was recognised at the time) on fuel consumption at low speeds.

The bow knuckle, which is a most distinctive feature of the ships, is liked by the ships' companies but argued over by experts as to whether wetness is improved or not.

The reduction in weight achieved by using aluminium alloy for the superstructure improved speed by about one knot throughout the operating range. Put another way, this equates to a considerable saving of fuel throughout the life of the ship. The true military value of this can never be calculated although the lively performance has always been appreciated. There have been cracking problems in service which could be avoided in future ships, and of course the material has a lower melting point. This latter feature, although provoking much comment as a result of the loss of two Type 21s during the Falklands conflict, did not contribute to these losses. As has already been mentioned, and contrary to what was stated in some sections of the press, aluminium does not burn under such conditions.

The Type 21 was designed from the start to be an anti-submarine (AS) ship, and therefore to carry a helicopter capable of dropping A/S torpedoes. This aircraft could also carry the air to surface missile Sea Skua for the anti fast strike craft role.

Later Type 21s were fitted with French Exocet surface-to-surface missiles. This was also a considerable enhancement, but represented an admission that Britain was unable to provide a suitable home-built SSM, despite investment in various projects in the past. The position regarding the surface-to-air missile was not much better; it was originally hoped that the Type 21s would, at some future date, be fitted with Seawolf, but to make adequate provision for a system which was then still in the early stages of a very lengthy development programme was impossible. When Seawolf eventually emerged from development, after several updates to the staff requirement, and several years too late for the Type 21s, weights and power requirements had grown substantially from those originally envisaged. Fitted to a Type 22 frigate, Seawolf ultimately performed in a most spectacularly successful manner in the Falklands war, and contributed significantly to the defeat of the Argentinean Air Force. It was of course designed to combat far more sophisticated targets than the ageing Skyhawks.

Some new weapon systems were however ready in time for the Type 21. Two Ferranti FM1600B digital computers were at the heart of the Computer Aided Action Information System (CAAIS) and Weapon System Automation (WSA4) fire control. Lightweight, solid state digital computers were past their infancy, and rapidly replacing analogue machines in most such applications on account of their higher speed, greater versatility, and better reliability.

The FM1600B computer was, for its day, fast, and very powerful. Compared to the enormous volumes of thermionic electronic equipment, much of which was still in service, it was unbelievably small, incredibly reliable, and required very little power. Such is the pace of development that much the same could now be said of a modern microprocessor when compared to the FM1600B!

However, microprocessors are now almost literally two for a penny, whereas the FM1600B was an expensive machine. This meant that only one or two could be employed even in a major warship, to perform many functions, whereas today microprocessors are used in increasing numbers to perform the simplest of tasks in every household.

CAAIS was not the RN's first digital Action Information System, but it was smaller and less costly than previous systems. It was an enormous advance on the crude systems fitted to the Mk.5s and Mk.7, which consisted of various radar displays and semi-manual plotting devices.

The Captain of a modern warship has to cope with a vast amount of information. Before the days of radar, his knowledge of the outside world was confined to the visible horizon and what he could glean from radio transmissions.

As radars became more capable, the horizon soon became limited only by the height of the ship's mast rather than visibility, and high flying aeroplanes could be "seen" at much greater distances. Information could be also obtained by intercepting other people's radar signals. Radio communications and sonar improved. Not only was there much more information to be assimilated, but everything began to happen much faster.

In TV dramas, a radar display is often portrayed as a blank screen, with a single brightly flashing blob representing the enemy battleship, missile, or submarine. In real life the screen is covered in random dots and dashes, most of which are "noise", but one of which may be an aircraft or a ship. It takes considerable experience to detect real targets, and then to follow or "track" them. This used to be done by the operator manually moving a pointer across his screen and whereas this worked well some 30 or 40 years ago, it cannot cope with the volume of information from modern sensors. The function of CAAIS was to assist in the performance of this task. The skilled jobs, such as deciding whether a particular echo was a real target, whether to track it, and what to do about it, were left to the operators. CAAIS performed the menial tasks, tracking defined targets, calculating their course and speed, and displaying information on demand.

CAAIS' partner, another FM1600B computer, had the task of controlling the 4.5 inch gun and the Seacat missile.

The two radars fitted for the purpose of tracking targets for the gun and Seacat were made by Selenia in Italy. Huge sums of money had been spent in the UK in developing very sophisticated tracker radars for the Sea Dart and Sea Wolf missile systems, but these were large, expensive,

The Ferranti WSA4 Fire Control Console.

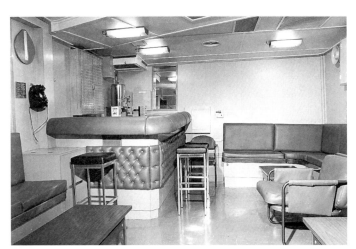

Senior rates recreation space, Type 21.

Brian Spilman, Weapons System Engineer.

Tom Orr, first head of Support Services.

Dennis Kemp, Commercial & later, Ship Building General Manager.

and unsuitable for gun and Seacat control. Not until the Marconi Radar Company (encouraged by VT) developed the 800 series of radars using its own funding was there a British tracker radar suitable for any light frigate or smaller vessel.

Liaison with Selenia meant frequent visits to Rome and to undertake this task, VT Weapons Group recruited Brian Spilman, a cheerful young engineer who was bored with sitting behind a desk at the Admiralty Surface Weapons Establishment on top of Portsdown Hill. Brian was seldom seen without a broad smile on his face and continually struggled to keep his weight below 20 stone. Neither of these conditions were noticeably affected by long hours in Selenia's factory and the pasta houses of Rome!

Brian's negotiations with the Italians were, by and large, successful. He claimed that although he spoke little or no Italian, he could always tell when they were being "economical with the truth" in order, for example, to bring a trial to a satisfactory conclusion!

Some of the "standard" pieces of RN equipment were supplied "free issue" to VT in the traditional manner, but the nature of the Type 21 design and build contract placed responsibilities on the shipbuilder which could only be properly discharged by giving him control over equipment suppliers. Much of the equipment was therefore purchased by VT and supplied to the RN as part of the ship. This was of course the way in which VT was obliged, for similar reasons, to operate when exporting warships. As ships became more and more closely integrated with their on-board systems, this type of organisation became more normal for RN contracts. For similar reasons, VT engineers were heavily involved in the first-of-class weapon system trials which, up to that time, had been the exclusive responsibility of MOD(N) teams.

Co-location of the design and building sites also pays dividends. The presence of the design office in the shipyard and the ability of the designers to walk onto the building berth and discuss problems, face to face with the men actually building the ship, is worth a great many drawings and a lot of expensive time.

The ship's accommodation was of a particularly high standard, differing in a number of features from normal practice at that time. This was part of RN policy to make life in the navy more pleasant, thereby attracting more recruits. Efforts were also made in the design of the ship and planning of the maintenance, to minimise the number of crew required to work the ship, and to ease their tasks as much as possible. The MOD(N) required a very detailed standard of handbooks to be produced, and in fact used the project as a test bed to introduce a new documentation system. This was known as DDS: Design Documentation System.

DDS was on the whole a good idea, but somewhat laborious for the designers to implement. The principle was that, when attempting to maintain the ship or to trace and repair faults, the artificers concerned would find their task much easier if they understood the function of each and every sub-system and component. Who better to explain these than the designers? Indeed, would it not be a good discipline for these same designers to write down, as they went along, their objectives and reasons for designing each component the way they did?

To do this of course required another documentation system, whereby everything had to be written down in a particular format so that the whole lot could be developed into DDS in parallel with the building of the ship, and the unfortunate sailors would actually have an up-to-date handbook on the day the ship was commissioned. This latter proliferation of paper was known as DDF; Design Disclosure Format.

DDS in the early days generated rather too much paper, the management of which was somewhat of a handicap to those who were trying to get on with designing and building the actual ship. However, who better to master mind all this than VT's own Support Services department, fresh from its experience with the Iranian and Libyan frigates and ready for a further expansion? An ex-Commander of HMS *Collingwood*, Tom Orr, was recruited to run the enlarged department, which in due course moved into Portakabins in the Woolston Shipyard. Many of its members were ex-RN and Tom was reputed to run his department in proper "Pusser" fashion, with "Rounds" on Friday mornings.

Although many of those concerned more

directly with the design and building of the ships tended to look down on Support Projects as a bunch of paper-pushers, the rapid growth of the department underlined the importance rightly placed by VT as well as MOD(N) upon maintenance and support, without which the most sophisticated and expensive equipment rapidly becomes useless. Proper support is expensive, but vital, and whilst the MOD(N) were inclined to go somewhat over the top, recognition of this fact is one of the reasons which make the RN superior to so many other Navies.

The first ship of the class, HMS *Amazon,* was launched by HRH Princess Anne at Woolston on 26th April 1971. Two more Type 21s, *Antelope* and *Active,* were built by VT, with a further five by Yarrow in Scotstoun. The experience of the Type 21 was undoubtedly the major factor in VT's subsequent success in the Brazilian frigate contract, following the winning of which HMS *Active* was completed by the VT Repairs Division in Southampton to make room at Woolston for the

huge new project, which is dealt with in the next chapter.

Continuing involvement of many MOD(N) departments throughout the design and build period of the Type 21s led to numerous modifications and additions which helped to escalate both the ship's displacement and the cost substantially. There were also numerous MOD(N) specifications invoked which had never been envisaged originally. This could have landed VT in serious financial trouble had it not been for the continual painstaking efforts of Dennis Kemp in keeping track of the situation and negotiating a mutually satisfactory solution with the MOD(N).

The Type 21s were a success and were conceived, designed and built in a remarkably short time for an RN project. The accommodation standards, as well as some of the other features, led to the ships being extremely popular with their crews. Much more about these ships can be read in the book "The Type 21 Frigate" by Commander R. J. Lippiett, RN.

Launch of HMS *Amazon.* Lord Louis Mountbatten, HRH Princess Anne and Sir David Brown.

## Chapter Five

# THE MK.10 - A RECORD ORDER

With the Mk.5, Mk.7 and Type 21 projects all in full swing at Woolston, it might have seemed the time for the salesmen to rest on their laurels. However Portchester was, by now, less busy and in any case selling warships, particularly large ones, is a very long-term exercise.

The team of half a dozen or so VT salesmen consisted exclusively of ex-RN officers who divided up the world between them and spent the larger part of their lives living out of suitcases whilst working their respective "patches". This obviously required a large sales budget, but it was money well spent since it is useless for salesmen only to appear on the scene when the requirement for a new warship becomes common knowledge. A significant part of the task consisted, (as it still does), of casting bread on waters and making VT faces and designs known in the right circles, before the Navy themselves had decided upon their requirements in any detail. The objective, of course, was to ensure that a staff requirement, when it eventually emerged, closely matched a VT design which had already been massaged into shape over months of formal and informal discussion, and many visits by the VT sales teams to the country in question.

As VT designs became larger and more complicated, these preliminary marketing discussions became more and more protracted, and quite frequently some of the VT design team found themselves accompanying salesmen on these visits. Sometimes quite a large team would travel together, since it was usually impossible for any one man to cope with all of the different technical disciplines which were involved.

Foreign travel, particularly among those who do not indulge in it, has a somewhat glamorous reputation, and those who frequently found themselves jetting off to distant and sometimes exotic destinations had to put up with a certain amount of sarcastic comment from their colleagues.

It is true that some trips were adventurous and the opportunity to visit exotic and interesting places was often welcome, perhaps more so in those days when worldwide travel was less common than it now is. There were indeed occasional chances to go sight-seeing or lie on the beach in the sun. There were also some memorable incidents, often considerably stranger than fiction, which occurred in the course of business, and colleagues and families of the travellers were entertained with photographs and stories of the more memorable aspects of such trips. Many such stories have become considerably embellished over the years. However, it must be pointed out that there was another, less exotic side to sales visits, which was more often the norm.

There were the less interesting, in fact downright unpleasant, places which had to be visited. Secondly, the sales trips inevitably kept participants away from home for an uncertain and sometimes protracted period, with consequent disruption to family life. Thirdly, "Montezuma's Revenge" and similar ailments often detracted from any enjoyment, and could also make it difficult to devote the necessary attention to the true purpose of the visit. Finally, a large part of most sales trips is spent just waiting; at airports, in aeroplanes, in hotel rooms or for hours on end in ante rooms (frequently with broken-down air conditioning) for some high ranking naval officer to grant a five minute hearing.

Another interesting dimension to foreign sales is the Agent. Despite the time spent abroad by the salesmen, it is impossible to keep up with developments in every potential customer country at all times. What is sometimes helpful is a resident representative - preferably a native of the country - who keeps abreast of relevant developments and appointments, and can arrange for the salesman at the right time to see the right men. Some representatives would also supply office facilities and transport, and help out with visas and other formalities. Contrary to popular misconception, these functions are not part of the duties of the British Naval or Defence Attaché.

Most attachés were nevertheless an immense asset, and put in a great deal of homework in support of defence sales efforts. A few were less helpful.

Representatives also varied in usefulness, the trick being to spot the good ones in advance. As the normal arrangement was to pay them on results and in arrears and because a successful sales campaign often took years to mature, they might have to work for a long time with no remuneration. To ensure that they remained on the band wagon at the right moment, most of them expected an exclusive arrangement with the Company for a long period. Some became old friends, and prided themselves on attention to every detail of VT visits.

During one particular visit to Indonesia, the representative had arranged to take the VT salesman, Dennis Sitwell, and a supporting cast of designers to meet some very important officers. The weather that day was unusually hot and humid, even for that part of the world, and Dennis, usually attired in neat tropical suit and tie, decided to adopt the dress universally worn in that neighbourhood for even the most formal occasions; an open necked shirt and trousers. The rest of the VT team, on the suggestion of the representative, were sweltering in natty "lightweight" suits. When Dennis met them in the hotel lobby, the representative, himself dressed in the local style, looked at him reproachfully. "*Mr. Sitwell*", he said very politely, "*I think you should dress more formally for this meeting.*"

Dennis surrendered with good grace, and went to change, only to appear a few minutes later in suit and tie, looking somewhat ruffled. "*On my way down,*" he explained, "*a large and rather hairy gentleman got into the lift, wearing only a pair of shorts and a brightly coloured shirt open to the waist. He took one look at me, and said, in a broad Australian accent "Blimey mate, you must be a mad bloody pommy!"*"

Dennis had spent many years in the Far East, and was for some time the sales director of Vosper Ltd's subsidiary company in Singapore, which had been "inherited" from Thornycroft. He later returned to the UK to join the sales team there.

The Far East was one of the more interesting places to visit, although negotiations could be maddeningly slow and often fruitless. The first big sales success of the 70s - if not the biggest of all time - actually took place on the other side of the world.

The Brazilian Navy at the time consisted largely of ageing American ships of World War II vintage, and one enormous Colossus class aircraft carrier, the *Minas Gerais,* (formerly HMS *Vengeance*) which had been bought from Britain in 1956. By 1970 the Navy concluded that within the next few years it would need six new frigates, and set about producing a most comprehensive and ambitious Staff Requirement, which was distributed to all the likely shipbuilders in the world.

VT seized upon this requirement enthusiastically. It was for a ship substantially larger and more heavily armed than the Type 21, and preliminary bids were required in a matter of weeks. Obviously competition would be stiff for such an important order. Could a competitive bid be put together in such a short time, especially as it meant starting almost from scratch, rather than adapting an existing design? The design team accepted the challenge. Since their two latest exercises, as yet unfruitful, had been the design of corvettes designated Mk.8 and Mk.9, the next available Mark number was ten.

Evidently the other competitors either could not design a ship to the requirement in the time available, or did not believe that the Brazilian Navy meant what it said, as virtually everyone except VT offered modified versions of existing ships, none of which were able to meet all the requirements. The consensus seems to have been that to meet the staff requirement exactly as stated would have far exceeded the budget of the Navy (although at this stage nobody knew what this was) and thus be a waste of time. Even VT were a little sceptical, and offered as an alternative a modified version of the Type 21. Moreover, a relatively junior salesman, Charles Reynolds, was dispatched with the technical proposal whilst everyone got on with more important things. Nevertheless, the Mk.10 design was selected. Matters proceeded rapidly and a contract was signed in September 1970. However, long before that, details of the specification had to be settled, and a full VT team visit was required.

Word of this of course soon got round most of the manufacturers of naval electronics and machinery and VT were besieged with eager salesmen all hoping to get their particular speciality into the new frigates. The design department set out to study a very wide range of alternative equipments, in order to assess their suitability and make recommendations to the Brazilian Navy, who would make the ultimate selection. A comprehensive technical comparison was carried out on various major items such as propellers, engines, communications systems, radars and various weapon systems. This involved the VT design department in quite a lot of work in a short time.

The exercise was an unusual one for a shipbuilder to undertake, and parts of it immediately occupied some of the newer members of the design department who had been recruited from the electronics industry.

The staff requirement for the ships enabled the same standards as had been agreed for the Type 21s to be used throughout. The main design task was therefore to increase the size so that the larger weapon load could be accommodated. However, an exceptionally high cruising speed of 23 knots was required on diesels for convoy escort purposes, together with a long endurance at this speed. A somewhat unusual arrangement of two diesels plus a gas turbine on each of the two propeller shafts was adopted to meet this requirement. Controllable pitch propellers were essential to accommodate the wide range of possible inputs from this combination, as well as the astern requirement. This posed a tricky design problem; those interested will realise just how inefficient CP propellers can be when working as far from the design pitch as is required to absorb the full power of one diesel instead of two, or one Olympus.

Some discussion of the equipment selection process may be of interest. Apart from the need to sometimes lean towards the selection of British equipment in order to help ensure that the proportion of UK content remained within the bounds demanded by the UK Government as a condition of providing the customer with a loan, or an Export Credit Guarantee, VT generally had no other axe to grind in the selection of equipment, other than a

purely patriotic one. It was however as much in the customer's interest as in the Company's to minimise technical risks. Technical risk arises not only from the development of new equipment, but in trying to integrate even well tried equipment into a new system. This is nearly always more difficult than it at first appears, and potentially time consuming and expensive to get right. Even in those early days, VT was wary of rushing into such problems, and although they later successfully tackled many highly complicated interfaces between apparently innocent looking equipments, these were always approached with justifiable respect.

Therefore, in the Brazilian project, there was a natural tendency to stick as closely as possible to known territory. The fire control and action information systems selected by the RN for the Type 21s were being built by the Ferranti company, and selection of variants of these systems for the Mk.10s had the added attraction for the Brazilians of providing their ships with a state of the art computer system with a minimum of development risk. But the choice was not so easy for all the equipment.

Sonar, for example, would be a vital component of these predominantly anti-submarine ships. The Mk.5s and Mk.7 had been fitted with what were in effect only slightly improved versions of World War II "Asdic". It soon became clear that in this then rapidly developing field, there were widely differing approaches and the sonar being fitted to the new Type 21 frigates was almost obsolete, for it used thermionic valve technology - which even in 1970 was well on the way out - with its inherent bulk and unreliability. The RN view was that there were far superior things under development which would, perhaps, be available for a later frigate project and it was therefore content to "skip a generation". This may have been right, but VT was naturally as keen as its customer to ensure that the equipment destined for the Mk.10 would be the best and most modern which could be offered with a firm price and predictable performance within the time available.

The Plessey Company had themselves developed a new sonar; the MS 32, using all solid state technology as well as a number of other considerable improvements. Two sets had already

Mk.10 A/S frigate, the Edo 700E variable depth sonar.

Mk.10 frigate, Ikara A/S missile trial firing.

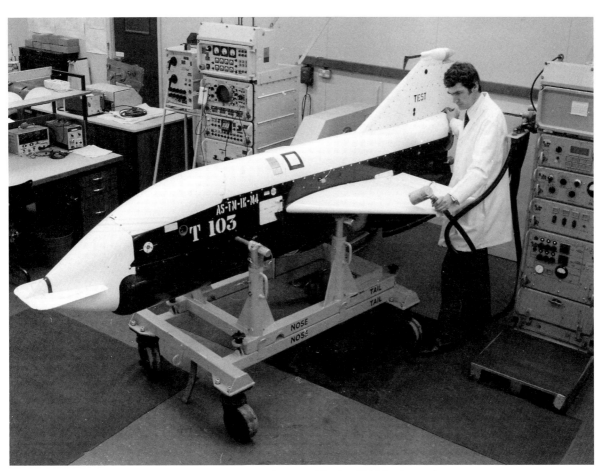

An Ikara A/S missile under test at Hawker Siddeley Dynamics.

been sold to the Chilean Navy, thus substantially reducing the development risk. Plessey however did not have a Variable Depth Sonar (VDS) to offer, an adjunct upon which the Brazilian Navy was very keen. In a variable depth sonar the transducer (equivalent to the aerial) is towed below and astern of the ship on a long cable which permits the depth to be chosen, within limits, to produce a better performance and to keep the transducer away from the relatively noisy environment of the ship.

There were two other competing sonar sets: The Canadian Westinghouse AN-SQS 505, already in service with the RCN, and the American Edo corporation 610E sonar, (the eventual winner of the sonar contract) a version of which was in service with the Royal Netherlands Navy. Both manufacturers also offered smaller sets in VDS form.

The various sonar designers differed quite markedly in their approach to the problems involved and thus provided scope for a series of highly technical exchanges with the various designers. Plessey had a development department in the wilds of Somerset, in the grounds of a large country house near Templecombe. VT made several visits there and on one occasion were invited to stay at Wilkinthroop House itself, where arguments, lubricated by the Plessey director's brandy, continued far into the night on merits or otherwise of transmitting frequency modulated pulses in a high reverberation environment!

At the same time, many similar comparative studies were being carried out on other items of equipment, in order to produce a comprehensive technical assessment and recommendations for discussion with the Brazilian Navy.

The paucity of suitable British equipment, as already explained, was often a disappointment to VT. Even more so was the attitude of some manufacturers, who, although fortunately small in number, nevertheless had monopolies within the UK in important areas.

One such, who shall be nameless, was a well known UK manufacturer and designer of a particular piece of quite important equipment for the RN. At least two foreign companies made comparable items, and were battling hard for the Brazilian order. The British company was reluctant to receive the VT engineers, and decidedly disinterested when they arrived. After some technical discussion and a tour of a factory which seemed almost Victorian by comparison with those in Europe, the visitors were assembled in an oak-panelled Board room to meet the sales department.

The sales department turned out to be an elderly gentleman who made it clear that he had better things to do. Had he heard that Brazil was buying frigates? Had he visited Rio to promote his product?

Of course he had, they were told. Why, he had actually been there in person, only two years ago! The Brazilians were fully briefed on the product, they must therefore know it was the best available, and if they didn't buy it because it didn't fit their Staff Requirement, well, that was their problem!

Having just spent some time trying to get basic data such as size, weight, and power requirements, (all apparently subject to escalation without notice) VT minds boggled somewhat at trying to imagine what the Brazilian Navy could have been told two years before to allow them to reach any conclusion. With great restraint, Terry Grisley pointed out that until recently he had worked in the USA, where the economy was booming, possibly because they approached sales a little differently? At this, the salesman took some umbrage, suggested that Terry should return to the States and left his guests standing outside the gate without even ordering them a taxi.

Fortunately for the British economy, subsequent considerable efforts, mainly by the MOD and VT, ensured that this particular product was eventually selected after all.

Of course, the designers were not the only people who were kept very busy preparing for the new project. Possibly the most vital, and certainly one of the more difficult tasks, was to estimate the cost of the labour and materials which would be required. This required an iron nerve, especially as the estimate for works hours was only about three quarters of that considered necessary to build a Type 42, an apparently comparable task. Although there were some safeguards in the contract a mistake would have been disastrous for VT. It was not until years later that it became evident that Howard Goldsmith and his team of estimators had got it about right. The contract was a commercial success for VT. At the same time the Brazilian Government got good value for their money, thanks partly to the careful control exercised by their Navy.

The VT design department was kept very busy with comparative equipment studies until the end of 1970. On 2nd January 1971 after the customary Christmas and New Year shut down, a large team, headed by Peter Usher, embarked on flights for Rio de Janeiro, with the objective of agreeing the final outfit of equipments for the Mk.10s so that work on the detailed specification could proceed.

For most of the team it was their first trip to South America, or indeed to the tropics, and on stepping out of the aircraft early on the morning of January 3rd, the heat of Brazil hit them like a wall. Coming from the winter climate of Europe, it was not unpleasant, but as the day went on the temperature rose higher still, and they soon collapsed around the swimming pool at the Hotel Gloria.

Meetings with the Navy commenced almost immediately at the Isle of Cobras, close to the centre of Rio. A series of technical discussions were carried on, involving the Brazilian Navy specialists, the VT team, and some of the aspiring subcontractors.

A bus was provided to transport the VT team to and from the hotel and some amusement was derived from observing the very heavy Rio traffic. Most of it seemed to consist of Volkswagen "Beetles", (built under licence in Brazil) driven at high speed with horns going constantly. The team soon discovered that most of the taxis were Beetles too, and their drivers were amongst the more daring of the generally aggressive Rio motorists.

There were other local habits to absorb too. Anxious to please, the team began by turning up at all their meetings punctually at the appointed hour, only to find that the Navy turned up at least half an hour later, in no apparent hurry. It was soon established that, for example, "Half past two" meant "any time after three, depending on the temperature in the afternoon and how long lunch takes". On the other hand "Four o'clock, hora ingles" (English time) meant four o'clock on the dot. This was considered a great joke by the Brazilians.

Certainly the time taken for lunch, for example, was unpredictable. On one occasion, a large party of about twenty VT and suppliers, following a lengthy "wash-up meeting" by the pool, following various meetings with the Navy, marched into the hotel coffee shop for a late lunch, to find it deserted. They were about to leave when some enthusiastic waiters appeared and insisted on serving them. Menus were circulated and much struggling with the limited command of Portuguese eventually resulted in a highly complicated order for twenty lunches being placed; at the insistence of the management, all three courses were ordered immediately. There was a very long pause indeed, punctuated by several rounds of drinks, and repeated assurances from the staff that food was nearly ready. Eventually, well past tea time, when most of the team were on the point of giving up and going back to the pool, there was a sudden commotion and the kitchen door burst open to admit an army of waiters, bearing soups, hors d'oeuvres, main courses, sweets and coffee, all together! By then, some of the local beverages had taken their toll, and nobody could remember anyway what they had ordered a couple of hours before.

Despite spending a large proportion of their time waiting, either for meetings or meals, the team managed to find time to see something of Rio. The statue of Christ on Corcovado, and the cable car to the top of the Sugar Loaf mountain were obvious draws and a great deal of film was expended. One afternoon some of them took a taxi the short distance to Ipanema familiar in name after the popular song about the 'Girl from Ipanema', anticipating a superb sandy beach with an inviting blue sea. These were certainly there, but so was what seemed like the greater part of the population of Rio. On the whole of that vast beach several kilometres long and a couple of hundred meters wide, nobody could see enough room available to spread out a towel!

Meetings proceeded at normal Latin American pace, but steady progress was being made in agreeing the shape of the future Mk.10 frigates. Despite the apparently slow pace, and the casual attitude to punctuality, the team found the Brazilians very much "on the ball" technically and very

Mk.10 frigate for Brazil. Anti-submarine version.

Mk.10 frigate for Brazil. General purpose version.

anxious to make some quick but sensible decisions in order to get the project under way. They also made it clear from the start (and stuck to it throughout the project) that the agreed specification would be final and that neither they nor VT would lightly be allowed to change any details during the build period, this being a sure way of causing interminable delays. This highly commendable approach eventually led to the first ship being delivered in no more than five and a half years from the date of order; a very short time for such a project.

As well as being deceptively efficient in their approach to the project, the Brazilians were charming to deal with and had a great sense of humour. One officer mentioned that the year before, he had set off for a trip into the unknown parts of the Amazon basin, hundreds of miles from civilisation. Making camp one night, just as dusk was falling, he heard what he described as strange unearthly music coming from behind some bushes. Drawing his revolver, he crept up and discovered three Indians with a transistor radio!

Even some of the less pleasant aspects of life in Brazil were treated light-heartedly. Most of the team soon succumbed to the change of climate and diet and suffered from stomach upsets, which generally cleared up after a day or two. However, two of the sufferers eventually appealed to the navy for help, which was instantly forthcoming. A Naval deputation consisting of two medical officers and a sick-bay attendant, carrying a huge white box with a red cross on it, appeared at the Hotel Gloria and recruited the hall porter to interpret. The cure involved treatment with a hypodermic syringe, described later by the victims as "about the size of a bicycle pump". Only national pride (or possibly the Hall Porter) prevented headlong flight. However, whatever the treatment was, it seemed to have the desired effect and both victims recovered quite rapidly.

After only a couple of weeks of discussions in the deceptively relaxed atmosphere of Brazil, the main characteristics of the Mk.10s were agreed. Great credit is due to Admiral Coelho da Sousa, who marshalled the Navy's case with impressive flair. VT were pleased to find that the navy agreed with many of their recommendations.

Two versions of the Mk.10 were to be built; the Anti-Submarine (AS) and the General Purpose (GP) variants. Both were heavily armed. Both carried a 4.5 inch Vickers Mk.8 gun, a twin Bofors AS rocket launcher, two 40 mm Bofors AA guns, two triple AS torpedo tubes, two triple Seacat AA missile launchers, and a full complement of supporting electronics. The AS variant also carried an Ikara AS missile system and variable depth sonar; the GP mounted a second Mk.8 gun, and four Exocet surface-to-surface missiles (SSM); all ships carried a Lynx AS helicopter.

The Brazilians were particularly keen to have a good anti-submarine capability, and the AS version of the Mk.10 was bristling with weapons. During one meeting, Terry Grisley asked the Brazilian Admiral in charge of the proceedings why so many AS weapons were to be fitted. Would not one, or maybe two, be adequate and more cost effective?

"*Aha!*" replied the Admiral, "*We have heard many arguments from many wise men, each explaining why this weapon or that weapon is the best. We do not know which of them is right. We do not think they know either. Therefore we will have them all!*"

Indeed, even depth charge rails were included at one stage, but deleted later when it transpired that obsolescence had completely dried up the supply! The Bofors 375 mm rocket launcher was in any case calculated to terrify any submarine within a large radius of its high explosive charge. Some very spectacular photographs were taken later, during sea trials, of the enormous rockets departing in a great sheet of flame and smoke.

Ikara originated in Australia and entered service with the RAN. A modified version was retrofitted to some of the RN *Leander* class frigates, which necessitated removing the twin 4.5 inch gun mounting. Whilst there were no doubt sound arguments for this, many people felt that a frigate without a gun was somewhat of a liability. Perhaps the diehards felt the same about masts and sails a century before; at any rate, the naval gun is still showing little sign of extinction even now.

Ikara was a very sophisticated system which comprised a guided missile carrying an anti-submarine homing torpedo. Its capability was principally limited by the availability of accurate

The Bofors 375mm anti-submarine rocket launcher.

Mk.10 frigate under construction in Rio Dockyard.

Lysses House - the home of VT Support Services Division.

The covered berth at Woolston.

and up-to-the-minute data on the position of the target submarine. Provided that this was forthcoming, a missile could be launched from the ship and deliver a torpedo to the vicinity of the target in a very short time. To do this, it relied upon a complicated guidance system which kept track of the missile and issued commands. This meant a close and complex interface with the Ferranti action information system. The mechanical side was also quite complex, since it was necessary to store a reasonable quantity of missiles, and then prepare them for launching when required. Wings, fins and missile bodies, the latter complete with torpedo attached, were stored separately, and then assembled just before launch by a lightweight semiautomatic handling system. Finally the missile was loaded onto the launcher by a small railway. The launcher itself was then aimed in the appropriate direction and the missile fired; suitable flashtight doors being required to protect the expensive handling system and its operators from the missile exhaust.

The Brazilian Ikara (quickly christened Branik) was substantially lighter and less expensive than the RN's complex fully-automatic handling system, without significantly compromising the performance. All of the mechanical handling equipment, including the launcher, was manufactured in Australia, and supplied by Hawker Siddeley Dynamics in the UK.

The Branik design obviously benefitted from experiences gained by various people with previous Ikara systems; indeed, similar sentiments could be expressed in relation to the whole of the design of the Mk.10s. There were few, if any, entirely new equipment designs aboard, but virtually all of the major items represented a significant advance in some way over its predecessors, with the result that when the first Mk.10, *Niteroi,* was delivered in February 1976, she was at least as advanced and capable as any operational warship of her size in the world.

The Ferranti computer systems (one for action information, and two on each ship for weapon control) obviously owed a lot to the Type 21 project, but used solid state decoders instead of electromechanical devices, with improved speed and reliability. Many more weapons had to be controlled than on the Type 21s, and an enormous amount of development effort went into the necessary software. The main search radar, the Plessey AWS2, was a development of a well-tried design, but incorporated many improvements to the electronics as well as a new design of stable platform for the antenna, which maintained the accuracy of target tracking when the ship motion became severe in heavy seas. The Edo sonars - the hull mounted model 610E - which incorporated many improvements, and its smaller model 700E variable depth counterpart, fitted to two of the AS ships, employed a new version of a launching and towing winch system made in Canada by the Fathom company.

The machinery outfit also required substantial design work. The maximum speed of 32 knots was obtained from two Rolls Royce Olympus gas turbines which drove into their respective gearboxes. These gearboxes were similar to those in the Type 21 except for minor geometrical differences, thereby keeping the development risk low.

The cruise engines were however very different. The Tyne gas turbines in the Type 21 were replaced by 16 cylinder MTU diesels, two to each shaft. These diesels drove forward through hydraulic clutches into a primary gearbox which not only combined their drives but increased the speed to be equivalent to that supplied by the Tynes in the Type 21. The final drive into the main gearbox was therefore unchanged.

This arrangement of propulsion machinery gave the ship considerable flexibility of operation, it being possible to run on inboard or outboard diesel alone, on both diesels together, or on gas turbine. It was at this stage in the company's history that the port inboard and outboard diesels became known as PID and POD, with SID and SOD the starboard counterparts. This terminology has continued to this day, and you can even hear it used by Kenyans in Mombasa and Chinese in Hong Kong.

An important part of the Brazilian requirement was to build two of the six ships in Brazil, thus not only conserving foreign exchange but obtaining valuable experience for the Naval Dockyard in Rio de Janeiro. The lead yard services, which enabled the Brazilians themselves to build two of these

complex ships with the assistance of VT, therefore became an important facet of the Mk.10 contract for VT too. In addition to supplying all the working drawings, as had been done for Yarrow in the case of the Type 21s, all the necessary materials were supplied by VT and shipped to Rio. "Transfer of Technology" also required a number of VT specialists (some accompanied by their families) to spend long periods of time in Brazil.

To build the other four ships in England in the time required represented an enormous undertaking. Whilst not beyond the capacity of the Woolston Yard, it was clear that the most efficient approach would involve some significant modernisation of the facilities, for example: the erection of an enormous building - a formidable project in itself - to enable the ships to be built under cover.

In considering whether some of the later daunting financial risk should be "laid off", an obvious option was to repeat the arrangements which had been made for the Ghanaian corvette, and for two of the Iranian Mk.5 frigates (all much smaller ships), but Vickers were not interested and so the management boldly decided to build all four ships themselves. This turned out to be the right decision. Protection from the risks which were quite beyond VT's control was negotiated into the contract.

This was ultimately fair to both parties over a period during which, for example, inflation in both countries reached unprecedented levels.

Problems did however occur in quite unexpected areas. A crisis occurred later in the project when a freighter carrying a complete set of Ikara handling equipment, destined for one of the Brazilian built ships, from the Australian manufacturer to Rio as containerised deck cargo was caught in a hurricane somewhere in the South Pacific; some of the containers were washed overboard.

The news reached Woolston at a weekend, and Peter Usher was telephoned as a matter of urgency at the golf club. It was not clear what he was expected to do about a container adrift in the ocean on the other side of the world, but nevertheless bulletins continued to be phoned through at regular intervals:

"*Regret to report that the Ikara containers have sunk!*":

"*No they haven't; they're still afloat but we've lost contact!*":

"*We've found them again; they're still afloat but the sea is too rough to approach them!*".

This sort of thing went on for a day or two, with hopes alternately rising and falling for the valuable equipment on the high seas, until finally, and incredibly:

"*The New Zealand Navy has sunk the containers by gunfire as a menace to navigation!*"

It is to be hoped that this will be the only battle damage ever suffered by any part of a Mk.10 frigate!

The full story of the Mk.10 contract would make a book in itself, with several chapters required to cover the building of two of the ships in the Naval Dockyard in Rio, and the various adventures of the many VT people and their families who elected to live there for several years during the project. The glamorous image of Copacabana and Ipanema, Sugar Loaf mountain and the January Carnival was tempered by accommodation problems, galloping inflation, and daylight robbery, literally. However, on the whole, Rio was a popular posting. Despite their apparently laid back Latin approach to life, the Brazilian Navy made a great success of the project, and became great friends. Even some of the civilian robbers with which Rio abounded were quite polite.

The contract not only kept the shipbuilders busy for several years, but also provided a great deal of work for other parts of the Company, which were beginning to expand. Back at Woolston, the Support Projects Division had outgrown its accommodation again, and moved to Lysses House, a palatial converted mansion in Fareham. In 1975, Terry Grisley took over the General Managership of the division on the retirement of Tom Orr and set about seeking new business which would make Support Projects, and to an extent the Company, less dependent upon the fortunes of the shipbuilding part of VT; a far sighted policy since in the mid 1970s there was no lack of support work coming from that quarter.

Whereas much of the work had been RN-inspired and oriented, with the coming of the Mk.10 contract the division began to adopt a more cosmopolitan and commercial approach. Technical authors were encouraged to attend night school to gain City and Guilds and other formal qualifications. Languages became important since, despite the dominance of English as an international technical language, many of the documents obviously had to be in the customer's native tongue. Soon SPD was dealing with Portuguese, French, Spanish and Finnish, to name but a few.

In addition to pure paper, support also involved training, spares procurement, computer aided support, and the setting up of naval bases overseas.

To do all of this obviously required well-qualified and experienced people, and as well as an expansion in the numbers, a shift in the type of recruit began to occur. No longer was the department dominated by retired RN officers and senior ratings, although they continued to provide a vital contribution. Terry cared little for what people had done - or said they had done - in the past, provided they demonstrated their ability to solve present problems. One or two of the ex-senior ratings suddenly found themselves in jobs previously regarded as the exclusive preserve of Lieutenant Commanders or above. There was an influx of technical graduates, some with little experience, others recruited (in some cases "poached") from the shipbuilding areas of VT. Suddenly, Support Projects was no longer regarded as just a bunch of paper pushers.

In 1976 a very interesting contract was won: the production of a Maintenance Management System for six Finnish built *Kuha* Class Minesweepers, which operated from the Naval Base at Turku, far up in the north of the Baltic between the gulfs of Finland and Bothnia. Les Pratt went there to install and commission the system and to instruct the Finns in its use. Customer liaison involved accepting an invitation to the naval officers' sauna, situated in the forest next to a frozen lake. A hole was cut through the ice through which Les was invited to lower himself before dashing back into the sauna to unfreeze his assets!

Further diversification for Support Projects followed, contracts being won from breweries, nuclear power stations and other heavy industry, and even a commercial laundry.

Meanwhile, the Company as a whole continued to develop, and shipbuilding continued to enjoy a variety of interesting projects.

## Chapter Six

—————— A MIXED BAG AT PORTSMOUTH ——————

As mentioned briefly in Chapter 1, there was a structural reorganisation in 1970 which, strictly speaking, marked the birth of "Vosper Thornycroft" as a recognisable company, rather than a name applied somewhat loosely to the Shipbuilding interests controlled by the David Brown Corporation.

John I. Thornycroft & Co. Ltd had continued to trade since the merger, as a subsidiary of Vosper Ltd. As such, most of the day to day business at board level was handled by Vosper, and JIT board meetings had become mere formalities.

In mid 1970, Vosper Ltd, No.317293, became a non-trading holding company, transferring all its business and associated assets to its subsidiary, John I. Thornycroft, No.70274, which was duly renamed Vosper Thornycroft Limited. Confusingly, for reasons associated with financial legislation, this process was reversed in 1974, Vosper Ltd (317293) became the operating, as well as the holding company, and was renamed Vosper Thornycroft Ltd, whilst 70274 reverted to the name J.I. Thornycroft, and, for a while, became non-trading.

If the reader is not now totally bemused, we will attempt to take this saga one stage further at this juncture, although it means jumping ahead yet again. In December 1975, the dormant J.I. Thornycroft Ltd was again renamed, this time as "Vosper Thornycroft (UK) Ltd", and in March 1977, Vosper Thornycroft Ltd transferred all its shipbuilding and engineering business and assets to VT(UK) Ltd in preparation for nationalisation. Despite further changes of ownership, it is this company, Vosper Thornycroft (UK) Ltd, which is still today the main operating company resident in the Woolston and Portchester shipyards. The holding company reverted to its original name of Vosper Ltd (it became a plc in 1979). Further loose references in this book to "VT" or "the company" will generally refer to the shipbuilding operating company at the time in question, unless specified otherwise!

Returning abruptly to 1970, when "Vosper Thornycroft" (Ex John I. Thornycroft & Co) became the operating company, its board underwent the appropriate changes. Sir David Brown (not involved in the day-to-day business of building ships) and Cdr Peter Du Cane (now virtually retired) resigned their directorships. John Rix became Chairman (as well as Managing Director). The rest of the board comprised Alan Griffith (Shipbuilding), Ken Ford (Financial), John Grant (Company Secretary), Peter Usher (Technical), and Peter Shepherd (Commercial and Sales). In October that year they were joined by David Wilson (Sales) and John Wilde (Ship Repairs).

With the signing of the Brazilian contract in September 1970 there was a lot more reorganisation at working level to meet the new challenge. The board was, as ever, concerned about the effect of the new contract in increasing the numbers of staff, and therefore the overhead costs.

Overheads - the sum total of all expenses not directly related to, and therefore costed in, and directly chargeable to, a particular contract - are a perennial dilemma. The normal way of paying for them is to add a certain percentage to the rate charged for each man hour expended in producing sold work. However, since almost all work has to be the subject of a firm quotation in advance, and since a large shipbuilding contract takes several years, it is necessary to make some assumptions about the total amount of work which will be undertaken in the company over the period of the contract, as well as the total overhead expenditure, in order to arrive at the overhead percentage. This requires inspired guesswork, if not a crystal ball! The temptation, of course, is to make optimistic assumptions about the additional work which may be won during the period in question, and which will therefore contribute to the overheads and keep the ratio low. Such an optimistic assumption permits a lower price to be quoted for any particular contract, thereby enhancing the probability of getting the order. On the other hand, pessimistic

David Wilson.

John Wilde.

Dick Potter.

75 foot Keith Nelson, patrol boat.

assumptions have the reverse effect; fewer jobs are won; overhead costs must be shared between fewer contracts, so the prices go up, leading to fewer jobs being won, and so on, a very vicious circle.

An obvious way out of this treadmill is to cut the overhead expenses; hence the periodic purges on entertaining, travel expenses, office cleaning, photocopying, secretaries, clerks, and even designers and managers! If overdone, such pruning can be counterproductive, leading to ridiculous situations such as skilled technical staff typing their own letters with one finger, or ultimately, the inability to carry out a contract when one is eventually won. On the other hand, unless strict control is exercised, Parkinson's well known Law, or a close corollary, inevitably ensures that, regardless of work input, the effort required always just exceeds last year's budget, thus necessitating additional overhead staff or expenditure.

As the New Year of 1971 approached, the board was acutely aware of these problems. The Design group, and other overhead staff, had not long before been enlarged to deal with the Mk.5s, the Mk.7, and the Type 21s, and already there were prospects of further expansion to deal with the Brazilian contract. Obviously, the volume of work at Woolston would increase substantially to help bear the overhead load, but the future work load at Portsmouth did not look so bright. A number of searching inquisitions were initiated into the (no doubt over-optimistic) costing of some of the contracts already in hand. Moreover, capital expenditure approaching £1.6 million was required to enable Woolston facilities to be updated to build the new ships in the most efficient way, and the projected cash flow for the foreseeable future was almost continually in the red. There were some credit items; the old Thornycroft boatyard at Platts Eyot, Hampton, on the Thames was sold; it had been unprofitable for some time. Thornycroft (Hampton) Boatyard Ltd became dormant for the time being. (It was reawakened in 1977 and handed the ship repairing side of the business in preparation for nationalisation. As Vosper Ship repairers Ltd, it was eventually to be liquidated in 1988).

Nevertheless, although adverse cash flow can be fatal, the medium and long term view looked reasonably healthy and the VT board cautiously considered that a profit of £750,000 for the forthcoming year to October 1971 was "an attainable budget figure". In the event, a year later Vosper Ltd were able to declare an interim dividend of 12% on their 20p shares; the forecast was not over optimistic. The bank was persuaded to extend the overdraft facilities in the light of the new contract. Finance was raised too for the modernisation of Woolston; the largest single item being just under £1 million for the building of an enormous shed, or covered berth, over two of the slipways. This considerably improved production of frigates; work would no longer be slowed by adverse British weather conditions, and VT were to substantially increase the amount of outfitting done before launch, when access was easier and working conditions better.

For this contract, the largest naval export order ever, the board clearly had to take a number of courageous decisions, particularly as it had been decided not to share this order with any other shipbuilder, except of course for the naval dockyard in Rio de Janeiro. This part of the task itself presented another new challenge.

It is however time to leave the Woolston activities for a while and return to the Portsmouth and Portchester yards. Portchester was now entering the heyday of the "Keith Nelson" era. In 1969 the Keith Nelson company had been purchased from Cdr Peter Thornycroft, a cousin of John W. Thornycroft, and ex-Thornycroft apprentice. He had built up a successful business at Bembridge, on the Isle of Wight, building a range of small, tough, seaworthy working launches. John Rix, who had been an apprentice at Thornycroft at the same time, knew Peter fairly well and realised that the popularity of these little boats was likely to outstrip the production capacity at Bembridge. Keith Nelson was absorbed into the Portchester Yard organisation, although for several years there was a separate drawing office team, and the small glass reinforced plastic hulled patrol boats were still marketed under that name. Despite VT's GRP facility at Woolston, of which more shortly, it was not economic to mould the hulls in house, and these were bought as shells and fitted out by VT in a variety of different forms.

Series A 110 foot patrol craft for Singapore.

Series B 110 foot patrol craft for Singapore.

Fast training boat for RN.

Mk.3 Corvette for Nigeria.

*Tenacity*, a private venture gas turbine missile craft as originally built with dummy weapons.

Between 1969 and 1978 over sixty Keith Nelson launches were built by VT. They ranged from 34 feet to 75 feet in length, and were supplied to a wide range of customers, including the RN as well as several small overseas navies, coastguards, oil companies and harbour authorities.

After 1969, several larger contracts had also kept both yards busy. In mid 1968, two 110 foot steel-hulled patrol boats, a stretched and more sophisticated version of the 103 foot design, were ordered by the Singapore Navy. These were both prototypes of two series, A and B, two other ships of each type being built in the Vosper Singapore yard. Series A was a conventional diesel-propelled patrol boat, armed with a 40mm Bofors gun forward and a 20mm Oerlikon aft. Series B however was a similar hull fitted with a powerful 76mm Bofors gun, developed from a coastal defence weapon, and remotely controlled by a radar and digital fire control system which were manufactured by Hollandse Signaal Apparaten (HSA) at Hengelo, in the Netherlands. This gave the VT Weapons Group some more valuable experience. HSA were, and still are, a leading and innovative supplier of military electronics, and the WM26 system supplied for the Singapore project was, at the time, a most up to date example of a real time digital fire control. The Portchester built Series B boat completed its sea trials and was delivered early in 1971, just as the Brazilian contract was getting under way.

What were to be the last of the wooden fast planing type boats HM Ships *Scimitar*, *Cutlass*, and *Sabre*, were ordered by the RN for training purposes in mid 1969, and these too were completed in early 1971. They were derivatives of the *Brave* class, but unlike the latter, they were unarmed, and had only two Proteus gas turbines instead of three. They had a slightly higher deadrise than the *Braves* which had tended to slam a bit in a seaway. This did not save the *Scimitar* class entirely from some damage at the hands of enthusiastic young RN officers who obviously enjoyed driving them very hard. Once again, *"if they don't bend a bit, they're too heavy!"*

In early 1969, the Nigerian Navy had ordered two Mk.3 Corvettes. These little ships were an enlarged version of the Mk.1, but with a slightly less modest performance. The two MAN diesels drove fixed pitch propellers to give a maximum speed of some 23 knots. The ships were fitted with modern HSA radar and fire control; a more capable version than that fitted to the Singapore Series B patrol boats. Owing to the Biafran war then in progress, there were problems in obtaining guns for supply to the Nigerian Navy. The Swedish Government of the day did not wish Bofors to supply their products to people who might actually use them in anger. VT had been forced to shop around elsewhere, and this resulted in the Mk.3s being fitted with some refurbished British built Bofors 40mm guns, of a type which could not be connected to a fire control system. The main armament however was a formidable twin 4 inch Mk.19 gun mounting, two of which were found in a store in Coventry, where they had apparently been for some years. VT themselves undertook the task of refurbishing and rewiring these guns, and of integrating them to the digital HSA fire control.

This was another interesting job for the Weapons Group, and Bob Chase, a young man with some experience of servomechanisms, had the dubious privilege of undertaking it. This entailed tuning up the gun servo system, which relied upon thermionic valve amplifiers. These failed with monotonous regularity, but fortunately could be replenished relatively easily by arrangement with the stores in Portsmouth Dockyard. The main problem was that nobody knew how the ancient guns would react to being driven by a digital system, which, instead of a smoothly varying signal, commanded the gun to move in a series of small steps. The debate was over whether the gun would faithfully follow these steps, thereby probably being progressively shaken to bits, or whether its inertia would make this impossible, thereby causing the servo motors to overheat and burn out. In the event, neither disaster occurred and although the gun shield tended to shake in a rather jelly-like manner, the gun itself was very steady, and put up a splendid performance during trials.

The Nigerian Navy had exactly the same problem as most navies in retaining trained men to operate and maintain complicated equipment. Having been trained by the navy, at great expense, such men could earn much higher wages mending

televisions or motor cars, and would leave the navy at the first opportunity. Nevertheless, somehow the two Mk.3 Corvettes, NNS *Dorina* and *Otobo,* (the Nigerians named their ships with the words for hippopotamus in their various native dialects) passed through the RN's severe crew "work-up" programme at Portland, and sailed back to Nigeria towards the end of 1972. Maintenance, however, must have continued to be a problem. Sixteen years later one of them gently sank at her moorings, reportedly because the bottom had rusted through. A sad end to a handy little ship.

Two of the ubiquitous 103 foot patrol boats were built for Panama during 1970 and 1971, and orders for two more were obtained from Trinidad at the end of 1970, just after the Mk.10 order was secured. Nevertheless, in 1971 concern at the lack of a substantial new patrol boat order was being voiced. In August consideration was given to starting the design work on "the next most likely order" in order to keep the offices occupied, and by November a special board meeting was called to consider the problem of lack of work at Portchester. It came to the inevitable conclusions that another look would have to be taken at overhead expenses, and that efforts to obtain "miscellaneous work" for the shop floor must be redoubled.

This situation had occurred before, and would occur again, illustrating the "lumpiness" of the warship building market. It was not for want of effort by the sales department, nor for lack of efforts by the designers to develop new products for them to sell.

In the heyday of the hard chine fast patrol boats, Vosper had expended a considerable amount of their own money in product development: *Ferocity* had been built as a Private Venture demonstrator boat, and she had also been used as the platform to marinise the SS11/12 missile system. These investments undoubtedly paid off in terms of new orders gained, and in 1968 VT had started another Private Venture by laying down their concept of the patrol boat of the future.

T*enacity* took full advantage of many of the technical lessons which Vosper had learned up to that time. To give her superior seakeeping and weapon carrying capability she was 142 feet long; large for a patrol boat of that era, and had a round

bilge in place of the hard chine, previously a Vosper trade mark for fast boats. She had a welded steel hull and aluminium alloy superstructure, similar to the 103 foot work horses and the fast destroyers. She was propelled by a COmbined Diesel Or Gas turbine (CODOG) system: Three Proteus gas turbines for high speed use, together with two diesel engines for cruising. This gave her an extended patrol range, but a top speed of about 40 knots; fast for such a large boat. She was designed to carry two Sea Killer missiles, on fixed launchers, and a twin 35mm gun, both controlled by a Contraves Sea Hunter system, similar to those then being fitted to the Mk.5s. She would carry better radar, communications, and electronic warfare equipment than any contemporary patrol boat, and would confer on a small navy the capability of posing a significant threat to much larger naval units. She was in fact an ancestor of the modern fast strike craft.

She was launched in the spring of 1969, and completed soon afterwards, a mostly dummy weapon outfit being fitted since a real outfit was neither available nor affordable, although some pieces of equipment as well as machinery were lent by various companies for demonstration purposes. *Tenacity* performed as designed, but was never a commercial success. The problem was rising competition from French and German yards, with strike craft propelled entirely by high speed diesels, which turned out to be more popular than the British built CODOG system. *Tenacity* herself was leased to the RN, who eventually purchased her as a fishery protection vessel, which role she fulfilled for a number of years before being put on the disposal list. Armed with a single, obsolescent 40mm Bofors gun, she performed adequately but was a mere shadow of the powerfully armed warship VT had intended.

There were very sound technical reasons for VT's choice of CODOG propulsion. There was not a lot to choose between the top speed performances of high speed diesels and CODOG, and the former were more economical on fuel. On the other hand, the torque characteristics of the diesel make it prone to "lock up". When the boat becomes covered in marine growth, or if the displacement is increased, (both quite likely occurrences in service) drag increases and a propeller designed for optimum "clean" performance will begin to overload the diesel. Normally, a safety interlock cuts the power down to avoid damage to the engine, and a severe loss of speed can occur. A gas turbine, having in effect a fluid drive between the gas generator and the power turbine, can simply "change down a bit" and is relatively unaffected.

Maintenance of gas turbines should also have been attractive to small navies: the whole engine could easily be removed and replaced in a few hours; the policy of Repair by Replacement. Damaged units could in many cases be repaired "in country" in existing facilities, used to support aircraft engines. Alternatively, being relatively small and light, they could easily be flown back to the manufacturer for major overhauls. Diesels, being much larger and heavier, are a more difficult proposition to remove from the ship or to transport. They are also relatively complicated to work on *in situ*.

However, many emergent navies were used to diesels, albeit to smaller and less complex ones, and found the colossal rotational speeds and very high precision required in turbines rather daunting. Following the oil price explosion, fuel economy became more important. Finally, gas turbines require a large intake through which to ingest enormous quantities of air, which must be very carefully filtered to remove salt water, spray, and other hostile debris. This could take up quite a large area of deck, and with the advent of larger surface to surface missile systems such as Exocet - much superior to Sea Killer - deck space was at an even greater premium than before. CODOG turned out to be the wrong horse to back for fast strike craft. It was therefore some time before VT achieved an order for a strike craft or similar vessel larger than the 110 foot boats.

Meanwhile, another bold development initiative which ultimately did not realise its initial promise had also been started. In the 1960s, the hovercraft seemed to be a new vehicle with enormous potential for the future. Although there have been many developments since then, and new machines are still improving, the number of craft in use today is insignificant compared with what seemed probable

then. VT also envisaged a big market, and considered that a development programme would probably yield big returns. A hovercraft department was formed in 1967 and the first hovercraft began trials in 1969.

The VT1 was 95 feet long with a beam of 45 feet. The payload of about 30 tonnes permitted it to carry a mixture of passengers and cars. It possessed a number of novel features, the principal one being - for a hovercraft - the means of propulsion. Although possessed of a fully peripheral flexible skirt (also of novel design), the vessel was propelled by water screws, mounted on two skegs beneath the main raft structure. Normal water rudders were also fitted. VT1 was therefore "semi- amphibious": she could drive through shallow water and ground her bow on a slipway, thus allowing loading or unloading of vehicles with relative ease. When under way, the water propellers were quieter and more efficient than airscrews and speeds up to 40 knots could be achieved with relatively small, light and economical Lycoming gas turbines. Having skegs in the water also made the problem of manoeuvring much easier by producing a side force relatively simply. In other words, VT1, unlike fully amphibious hovercraft, could corner without struggling to avoid skidding sideways.

The craft performed well up to expectations, and turned out to have remarkably good seakeeping characteristics. In conjunction with the Department of Trade and Industry (DTI), who were encouraging the hovercraft industry with sundry financial support, VT carried out a series of trials during the winter of 1970-71. Based in the Channel Islands, these encountered a good proportion of rough weather, and it was shown that the VT1 could maintain a speed of 26 knots in 12 foot waves.

The VT1 was designed specifically for commercial use, but the company also had an eye on military applications. The steadiness of the VT1 at speed in a rough sea, compared with a conventional boat, had obvious attractions when applied to a weapon platform. This could be convincingly, if frivolously, demonstrated to potential customers by inviting them to drink a glass of gin and tonic (or mineral water for followers of the Prophet) whilst proceeding at speed in

VT1 semi amphibious hovercraft.

VT1 showing a grounding skeg, propeller and rudder.

conditions which, in a conventional patrol boat would have required both hands to hang on.

There also seemed to be plenty of potential for civil hovercraft. Technically, the performance of the VT1 prototype was promising, and two production craft were laid down on the strength of active interest displayed by Hovertravel Ltd, who were building up a lot of operating experience with the smaller SRN5s and SRN6s built by the British Hovercraft Corporation.

Unfortunately, despite various schemes, Hovertravel never acquired a VT hovercraft. A draft agreement to charter VT1 number 001 (the prototype) for operation in the Channel Islands came to nought, and efforts were redoubled to sell the craft elsewhere. In April 1971 the board were discussing the possibility of selling the two production craft (002 and 003) in the USA, in conjunction with a licensing agreement for building more craft in the States, but this too failed to materialise, and by May a hard look was being taken at halting further expenditure on development work; for example, on running the VT1(M), a man-carrying model which was used for various experiments including, latterly, trials with water jet propulsion.

Towards the autumn, proposals for a joint operation involving Rederi Aktibolaget Centrumlinjen of Sweden were beginning to crystallise at last. VT was urgently in need of some solid operational experience with the craft, and there was a clear intention to subsidise the operation with a view to achieving this as soon as possible.

At the same time, there was a firm policy statement to "go equally hard for both commercial and military applications of hovercraft", and there was a proposal to allow the Interservices Hovercraft Unit (IHU) to evaluate VT1.

In October John Rix went to Malmo to sign the promotion agreement with Rederi Centrumlinjen and thereafter things moved ahead. Vosper Limited, as VT's parent company, agreed to the subsidising of the operation, and a joint operating company, Centrumsvavarna AB, was set up to operate VT1 002 and 003 between Malmo and Copenhagen, fitted out to carry passengers only. The craft themselves were sold to a finance company and leased back for this purpose.

The service began in March 1972, and technically was a great success, the craft performing well and reliably. The first week or so of operation showed an encouraging load factor of 50 to 60%, but then the state owned opposition, operating in direct competition with hydrofoils and conventional ferries, cut its fares. The battle was on. A glance at the statistics tells the story only too plainly: the regular commuters could not afford to refuse the cheaper fares, and the average load factor dropped quickly to around 30% during the week, but regularly shot back up again at weekends when Centrumsvavarna seemed to get a better share of the market. Weekend trippers were presumably prepared to pay more for a faster, more spacious and comfortable ride. But despite running two craft and twenty eight scheduled trips per day, the statistics improved only slightly. With the end of summer in sight, and a probable reduction in the weekend demand, Hovertravel were asked to survey profitability and advise. By October the operation was at an end and the two craft back at Portchester, having ferried nearly 200,000 people over the route.

A loss of about £500,000 resulted from the ferry operations, but a great deal of good experience and confidence was gained. The board was, not surprisingly, unwilling to repeat a similar operation which could have provided very little more in the way of worthwhile experience, and one or two such projects were abandoned in the early stages of discussion. It was agreed that further ferry operations could only be contemplated if the craft were actually sold.

Negotiations in April 1973 with British Rail, aimed at operating the craft on the latter's Isle of Wight route, were not promising; calculations suggested that even at the sale price proposed (£600,000, per craft; not a particularly high figure) an operating loss would result. The board considered lowering the price still further, but in the end decided against it.

The salesmen continued to try very hard to find homes for the two VT1 passenger craft, and in the autumn of 1973 there were still hopes of doing so, either on a route between Southampton and Cherbourg; or from the mainland of Italy to Sardinia; or in Hong Kong. Alas, none of these

VT1 (m). Trials hovercraft.

A VT1 in service in Sweden.

The VT2 amphibious hovercraft.

Troops exercising with VT2 in the Hebrides.

ever materialised and eventually the craft were scrapped. People driving down the newly opened M27 spur motorway into Portsmouth were for some months able to view the sad remains in Harry Pound's scrap yard.

But in 1972 hopes for hovercraft were still high. Considerable importance was attached to the future of military hovercraft designs since the board recognised that, whereas Vosper had once enjoyed a significant technical lead, which almost amounted to a monopoly, in the design of the fast gas turbine powered torpedo boats, there was much more competition in the patrol boat markets now being addressed. Investing in hovercraft development was seen as one way of re-establishing a niche. Although hovercraft eventually turned out to be a dead end, it is hard to see how this could have been foreseen at the time.

Just before Christmas 1972, therefore, the Vosper board agreed on expenditure to convert the prototype VT1-001 to a fully amphibious craft, which was to be known as "VT2". The new craft was a VT1 with the skegs and water screws removed, and above-water propulsion substituted. The latter was novel, a good deal of thought having gone into its design.

Firstly, two ducted fans, rather than conventional airscrews were used. They had a relatively low rotational speed and were mounted above the stern, enclosed in annular ducts, which also housed pitch and yaw control surfaces. Drive shafts for these fans emerged direct from the gearboxes in the hull, each of which also drove lift fans: no additional gearing was included to make the thrust line horizontal.

The fans therefore were mounted at a slight angle to the horizontal, but the loss due to this was more than compensated for by the lack of an additional expensive and power consuming gear train, to turn the fan thrust line horizontal. The fans themselves were specially designed and built by Dowty Rotol, and had variable pitch control. This meant that the thrust could be varied without changing the speed of rotation, or, therefore, the speed of the lift fans. Also, at low forward speeds, the craft could be steered by differential thrust alone. This made it, for an air-propelled craft, very quiet and very manoeuvrable.

To drive each of the two propulsion fan/lift fan units, a Proteus gas turbine was fitted in place of the smaller Lycoming. The resulting craft was fully amphibious, with a slightly better payload capability than VT1, and capable of 60 knots, which speed it could maintain comfortably in a sea state which would have been most uncomfortable, to say the least, in a *Brave* class FPB at full speed.

The hovercraft also compared well with conventional boats in its ability to withstand damage; this fact was perhaps not widely appreciated, the uninitiated tending to regard the flexible skirt as akin to a tyre, or even a balloon, to which one bullet hole might prove disastrous. In fact, quite large portions of the skirt and its peripheral fingers could be shot away without having any serious effect upon performance, and damage (arising in practice from wear and tear rather than battle damage!) was quick and easy to repair, without any special facilities.

The VT2 was another technical success, in that it performed well up to expectations. It was at that time the largest naval hovercraft in the world, with a payload of up to 33 tonnes. It proved popular with the Interservices Hovercraft Unit (IHU), who first hired the prototype for evaluation. Some exciting exercises were carried out with the army, on exercises in the Hebrides, when troops and vehicles were delivered rapidly to some most unexpected places.

With this encouragement, VT designed various different configurations for the export market. The Logistic Support Hovercraft was basically the prototype configuration. In this role, it could carry 130 fully equipped troops, together with transport. The latter could comprise four Land Rovers with trailers, or a couple of 4 tonne Bedford trucks, or even three Scorpion light tanks. The Fast Missile Hovercraft was the same raft and propulsion system, but fitted with a 57mm or 76mm gun and two surface to surface missiles.

There was also a great deal of interest in the application of hovercraft to mine countermeasures, largely because, sitting on a big bubble of air, the craft proved almost invulnerable to underwater explosions unless detonated immediately beneath it. A considerable amount of study work was performed on this role, and after a refit, MOD(N) eventually bought the VT2 prototype for extended evaluation as an MCMV support vehicle.

However, the world remained suspicious of hovercraft, unnerved, perhaps, by the unusual operating characteristics. Most small navies (and some large ones) tend to be very conservative and wary of adopting new ideas unless given a strong lead by major armed forces elsewhere. There are few rewards for initiative, especially in peacetime, promotion being dependent mainly upon time and a "clean" record. Association with an unsuccessful project or incident are however quite enough to eliminate, permanently, all chances of promotion for the individual deemed responsible.

Despite the spectacular top speed of the hovercraft, some were put off by the low endurance, (typically about 300 miles) compared with a conventional patrol boat. It was not always clear why this endurance was necessary: when patrolling a stretch of coastline a boat has little choice but to keep moving up and down over the same area at a slow cruising speed; stopping usually results in most unpleasant rolling. On, say, an anti-smuggling patrol lasting several days, sufficient fuel is required to keep under way, and this translates into quite a substantial number of nautical miles. A hovercraft is quite unable to carry enough fuel to cover the same distance at a slow cruise, and yet might be at least as effective since it can stop and drift for a while, without suffering such uncomfortable motion, thanks to its broad beam. It can also go ashore easily on almost any beach, and thus be relatively well concealed, more comfortable for the crew, but ready to move at high speed at short notice.

There were other roles, as well as mine hunting, where the unique capabilities of the hovercraft appeared to offer advantages to those with sufficient imagination, but even today there has been only limited acceptance of such craft. Despite the success of the IHU trials, the British Armed Forces never showed much interest in hovercraft, and IHU was eventually axed in a round of budget cuts. VT2 finally followed her sisters to the scrap yard.

Without a lead by the RN or the British Army, the chances of overseas sales were further diminished, and despite some determined efforts at marketing both the VT2 and other hovercraft

designs abroad, the hovercraft department was eventually run down, and most of the staff absorbed into the shipbuilding departments. VT1 and VT2 were splendid solutions which never found the right problems to solve.

Certainly, neither they nor *Tenacity* immediately led to any solution to the shortage of patrol boat orders which, back in 1971, was giving rise to much concern at Portchester. Two 103 foot hulls were laid down without an order to keep the yards moving, but before these could progress far the end to another "trough" was in sight, and in April 1972 VT won a contract for six 37 metre fast patrol boats for the navy of Venezuela. The partially built 103 foot hulls were "mothballed" for the time being.

The 37 metre boats not only marked the transition from Imperial to Metric measurements, but were also an important step in the development of the relatively simple VT steel hulled patrol boats into modern fast strike craft.

The order was "snatched" from a Scandinavian yard at the last moment, partly because of difficulties with an arms embargo from that country to Venezuela. The weapon systems had already been bought by the Venezuelan Navy separately from Italy in an endeavour to get round the embargo and, when this failed, VT were left with a rather complicated contractual legacy to operate. Fortunately, much of the weapon system was reasonably well-proven and the various Italian companies concerned were well-used to working together. Also, many of the individuals involved were already known to VT from the Type 21 tracker radar contract. A similar radar was included in the Elsag NA10 fire control system fitted to some of the boats, and so Brian Spilman was elected to coordinate the Italian's efforts with VT.

There were two versions of the 37 metre, three "Gun" boats and three "Missile" boats being built in all. Building these kept Portchester quite busy for about three years, after which there was to be another short lull; a further example of the characteristic peaks and troughs of warship work.

The 37m hull design was based firmly upon the well proven 103 and 110 foot steel PCs, with an alloy superstructure. Power was provided by two MTU 16 cylinder 538TB90 diesel engines, which produced a maximum continuous speed of around

37 metre for Venezuela, gun version.

37 metre for Venezuela, missile version.

Italian Oto Melara 76mm gun mounting.

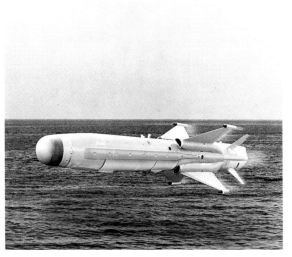

Otomat surface to surface missile.

Supramar designed hydrofoil *Rosa* for service in Hong Kong.

28 knots. The gunboat version sported an Oto Melara 76mm gun, which was then just beginning to dominate the world market for medium calibre automatic naval guns, despite all Bofors' efforts with their excellent 57mm.

The "Oto 76" had the remarkable rate of fire (for a 3 inch calibre gun) of 80 rounds per minute. The remote power control system and automatic loading mechanism eliminated both the need and the space in the turret for human operators and some 80 shells were stored in a beautifully engineered fully automatic magazine beneath the turret, enabling most of the war to be fought by remote control from the operations room, whilst the loading crew were still tumbling out of their bunks. The rate of fire was eventually increased to 120 rounds per minute, giving the crew slightly less time to dress!

These guns were sold throughout the world, and were manufactured under licence in America for the US Navy and Coast Guard. Even the RN, who at one time seemed to be abandoning guns altogether, unbent enough to buy some Oto 76s for their Hong Kong patrol craft. The guns were built to a uniform standard for obvious production reasons, and the Italian salesmen, who seldom missed a trick, were probably not above arranging a little queue jumping to enable undecided customers to be offered a mounting in a very short delivery time. One gun looked identical to another and there was always some "force majeure" available on which to blame the slight delay for the other customers. Who could blame them? Despite the veneer of Latin shambles and the frequent (but usually brief) strikes, it was not hard to see why La Spezia, and not the Royal Ordnance Factory, were market leaders in the field of naval guns.

This, however, was far from being their only forte. Although the French were first in the field with their sea-skimming Exocet ship to ship missile, the Italians were determined to have a slice of this cake too, and (in conjunction with a French partner) set about marketing their Otomat missile. British Aerospace (then Hawker Siddeley Dynamics) were left standing at the post with their SSM, which although based soundly on an existing air to ground system, never progressed beyond the paper phase. Another case of British inventiveness let down by poor marketing and production engineering? The RN bought Exocet, but a significant number of other navies bought Otomat. Amongst these was Venezuela.

The 37m Missile boats had two Otomats each, mounted like Exocet on fixed launching ramps abaft the superstructure. The most obvious difference between Otomat and the French missile was that the former was powered by a small turbojet engine, giving it a much greater potential range. The fact that, when it was first introduced, there was no obvious means available to provide the missile with target information to the required accuracy at such ranges did not detract from its success. Later, of course, it became possible to exploit this by passing data to the missile in flight.

At about the same time as the 37m contract was getting under way, VT obtained an order to build a hydrofoil, under licence, to a Swiss design. This provided some much needed work for the shops whilst the 37m design was still being drawn. It was the first (and so far the only) craft of its kind which VT had constructed, and one of the few which the company did not design, but nevertheless the company's technical expertise was brought into play when, on trials, it proved reluctant to "fly" and even more so to be guided in the desired direction. Klaus Suhrbier and his hydrodynamicists carried out some tests in their cavitation tunnel and established the reason: Air was being drawn down a strut from the surface of the water and "ventilating" the all- important foils. A suitable modification tamed the beast.

As if to underline again the unpredictable "lumpiness" of warship sales, another major order was achieved just before Christmas 1972 when Abu Dhabi ordered six 110 foot patrol boats, followed in February 1973 by its neighbour in the Gulf, Qatar, who ordered another six. Suddenly, Portsmouth and Portchester were heavily loaded again; building a dozen of these as well as the Venezuelan boats kept them busy until 1975, by which time an even bigger and more important order - for two more corvettes for Nigeria - was obtained. However, before dealing with those, the reader is asked to return to Woolston to examine a totally different product, but one which was to be of increasing importance in the years to come.

*Chapter Seven*

# GLASS BOTTOMED BOATS

The popular view of mine warfare is that it is primitive and unglamorous. Antagonists seldom, if ever, come into direct contact with each other. Countermeasures are slow, tedious, and carried out by ships which look like converted trawlers, and move rather slower. Probably for these reasons this branch of naval warfare appears to have been largely ignored by film makers and the popular press, and thus, at least until the events in the Gulf in recent years, has remained a closed book to the public at large, few of whom therefore appreciate the deadly potential of mines.

It may not be entirely coincidental that, with a few notable exceptions, most navies do not place a high priority on the acquisition of Mine Counter Measures (MCM) forces. With limited budgets, the first priority is to acquire a striking force which will impress the taxpayers as well as deter potential aggressors.

Yet more ships were sunk in World War II by mines than by any other means. In the Korean War, they were used with devastating effect by the North, who used fishing boats to sow mines in the path of the United Nations shipping, causing the latter to reflect that they were losing the sea war to a country without a navy, which was using ships that were designed before the time of Christ.

The traditional contact mine is a large buoyant metal sphere containing a substantial charge of explosive and moored to the sea bed. Several horns protrude from the sphere and if any one of these is struck a blow, the mine will detonate. The length of the mooring must be preset to ensure that, when allowance is made for tidal rise and fall, the infernal device neither shows on the surface of the water, nor is submerged too deep to contact a ship which attempts to pass overhead.

Less generally known is that, under the Geneva Convention, such mines must incorporate a device which renders them harmless if the mooring parts, thus reducing the threat to neutral shipping operating away from the mined area.

Such mines can be dealt with by mine sweeping; towing a long steel hawser through the water, either between two ships, or between a ship and some device designed to pull the hawser out sideways at an angle to the track of the ship. When catching a mine mooring, the steel hawser is designed to cut it, either by the action of the hawser itself sawing across the mooring, or by means of mechanical or explosive cutting devices attached to the sweep at intervals. When sweeping an area, the swept paths can be overlapped, so that, except when sweeping the first lane, the minesweeper operates in water which has already been swept. When the mooring is cut, the mine bobs up to the surface, in theory with its explosive charge deactivated by the safety device. It can then be sunk (not necessarily detonated, except in films) by gunfire.

It may well be asked why a crude floating bomb, tethered to a fixed point and unable to either pursue the target or defend itself, should pose more than a token threat. Nevertheless, although the floating mine can often be dealt with relatively easily by ships which are little more than converted trawlers, the task is slow, tedious and dangerous, and can thus cause very considerable disruption. Moreover, a few simple tricks, some of which have been in use for many years, can render the task very much more difficult.

One example is delayed activation. A floating mine when launched from an aircraft, ship or submarine is attached directly to its "sinker", and only after arriving on the sea bed is the mooring deployed and the mine itself armed. This action can be delayed for, say, a couple of days, by which time the MCM forces may have swept over it several times, and declared the area safe. As a more subtle variation, a second mine can be attached to the same sinker, and only released (by a simple automatic mechanism) some hours after the first mine has been successfully swept.

Various anti-sweeping devices can be fitted, designed to allow the mine mooring to cut the sweep, rather than the other way round.

A minehunter at work showing the sonar looking at a mine on the sea bed, special very accurate means of vessel position fixing, special manoeuvring devices to hold vessel in desired position and remotely controlled mini submarine placing charge by the mine.

Many main shipping lanes are relatively shallow, so that an explosive charge laid on the sea bed can sink a ship if detonated immediately beneath it. This dispenses with the need for a moored device, and renders the wire sweep useless. However, an alternative means of triggering the explosion at the right moment is required.

Early in World War 2 the Germans introduced just such a device, the magnetic mine. This lay on the sea bed and was triggered by a magnetometer, a device which detected the disturbance to the earth's magnetic field caused by a steel ship passing overhead. All ships made of ferrous materials become magnetised to some extent, the strength and direction of the magnetism often depending upon the strength and direction of the earth's field at the slipway on which they were built.

The magnetic mine proved very effective. To find out how it worked, it was necessary to recover a mine intact and dismantle it. This task was made more difficult and dangerous by anti-handling devices ("booby traps"). Only when these had been successfully defeated was it possible to discover the secret and devise countermeasures. These took three forms:

Degaussing consisted of winding enormous coils of wire around the ship, and passing electric current through these in such a way as to counteract the magnetic field due to the permanent magnetism of the steel structure. Whilst this was the best method, it was obviously complicated and expensive.

Fortunately, a cheaper and simpler method known as deperming was devised. This consisted of temporarily hanging a coil around the ship and passing a large current through it in such a way as to reduce the permanent magnetism. This was less efficient than degaussing and only remained effective for a limited period, but could be applied to a large number of ships fairly quickly.

Thirdly, a means of "sweeping" magnetic mines was devised, by towing a large buoyant loop of cable behind the minesweeper and passing an electric current through it to simulate the magnetic field of a large steel ship.

These countermeasures reduced the problem of the magnetic mine to manageable proportions, but there were other innovations in mine warfare, all designed to make life more difficult for the minesweeper, and all requiring some new countermeasure. The acoustic mine, activated by the noise of a ship passing overhead, is counteracted by "sweeps" consisting of various noise making devices. More difficult are mine fuses fitted with a counting mechanism, requiring them to be "triggered" a number of times before the charge actually detonates. Thus several ships may pass safely, or a minesweeper may sweep the area several times, before the preset count is reached, and the mine explodes. Since the counter can be set to quite a large number, it becomes impossible to ever be sure that sweeping has been effective.

Whilst in recent times the development of microprocessors has introduced the possibility of even more intelligent mines, over forty years ago devices such as ship counters and delayed arming clocks had made some mines virtually unsweepable, and it became clear that a new approach was necessary.

In the 1950s, the Royal Navy invented and developed a new technique known as mine hunting. The aim was to defeat the anti-sweeping devices not by attempting to trigger the fuse, but by actually locating the mine and then destroying it by external means, usually by setting off a small demolition charge close enough to detonate the main warhead in sympathy.

This technique requires a high definition sonar set to detect and, if possible, identify the mine, and a means of either recovering or destroying it. Headed by MOD(N) (then the Admiralty), a great deal of development work was carried out, particularly in devising a special sonar set. Sonars designed for hunting submarines would be totally unsuitable since instead of looking for a large object entirely surrounded by water at a range of several thousand metres, the target is relatively small and probably lying on the sea bed surrounded by rocks and other debris. To avoid swamping the receiver with too many echoes at once, a very narrow sonar beam is required. This is also necessary to allow some idea of the shape of the target to be deduced. Compared to those used in hunting submarines, very high sonar frequencies are required and one consequence of this is that the range is very short; usually only tens of metres. If

an anti-submarine sonar can be compared to a pair of binoculars, the mine hunting sonar is a microscope. Whilst they work on similar principles, they are not interchangeable.

Having detected a likely looking object on the sea bed, attempts are made with the sonar to identify it. This usually necessitates "looking" at it from different angles, preferably from a steady platform, close enough to get a good view but not close enough to invite retaliation! If the object is still considered suspicious, it is then destroyed, or, if necessary, examined more closely. Both these functions were originally performed by suitably trained and equipped divers operating from an inflatable dinghy. Either an explosive charge could be lowered by hand, with guidance over the radio from the watching sonar operator, or a clearance diver would descend for a closer look. These men and their boats have been replaced by various robot vehicles and TV cameras, for obvious reasons. However, it will be many years before machines are capable of completely replacing a clearance diver, who frequently must operate by feel, in pitch-black mud, to identify, and disable, an enemy mine.

To deploy the mine hunting system therefore requires a ship suitably equipped with accurate navigation equipment and the ability to manoeuvre precisely at very slow speeds under various conditions of wind and tide. Moreover, the ship must present the smallest possible chance of detonating mines, and be well able to withstand explosive shocks, due either to accidental or deliberate detonations. This means a very tough ship with low magnetic and acoustic characteristics.

The obvious solution was to use an existing minesweeper hull, and in 1956 Thornycroft carried out the first conversion of a *Ton* class vessel. Converted *Tons* were used very effectively in this role, but as these ships neared the end of their service lives and the technologies of mines and mine hunting developed, the MoD(N) put a great deal of thought and research into what form their successors should take. As well as further development of mine sweeping and hunting equipments, a major effort was devoted to the design of the first purpose built mine hunting ship itself.

The *Ton* class had been built of wood, on aluminium alloy frames, mainly because of the importance of a very low magnetic signature. The construction and repair of wooden ships was becoming a dying art and maintenance was a considerable burden, particularly in tropical climates, which harbour voracious marine borers. Vosper's Singapore yard was thriving on the repair of *Tons*. Corrosion of the aluminium frames where they had been in contact with wet wood was a particularly severe problem. Also, despite the many merits of wood as a material, its resistance to shock is unpredictable and even suspect. For a ship intending to provoke numerous large underwater explosions in the immediate vicinity, something tougher was to be preferred.

The MOD began a lengthy investigation. One of several alternative materials was Glass Reinforced Plastic (GRP). Hunting mines in a boat made of glass sounds like something out of "Alice in Wonderland", but in the 1960s fibreglass was already well known in many applications, and quite a lot of small boats were successfully being made in this new material. It appeared to be tough, flexible, and almost indestructible. There was no need to paint it, and it could readily be moulded into complex shapes.

True, some of it seemed to burn very readily and one or two yachts had burnt down to the waterline and sunk. Nevertheless, it was certainly worth further study, and the MOD embarked on a research programme.

The characteristics of GRP depend on many things, the most important being the type of resin used, the nature of the glass reinforcement, and the care with which they are put together. For commercial use, in the manufacture of pram dinghies, chairs or similar items, cost is all important and the cheaper resins, used with chopped strand mat, can provide adequate performance at a competitive price. Strength depends quite heavily on the care with which the laminate is laid up, voids and variations in the resin/glass ratio having a considerable effect. There is usually a suitable design factor to take care of such problems. Few dinghies are exposed to serious fire risk, and people have been used to the incendiary qualities of furniture for many years. Thus for everyday

General view of mould for GRP ship - like an aluminium ship built inside out.

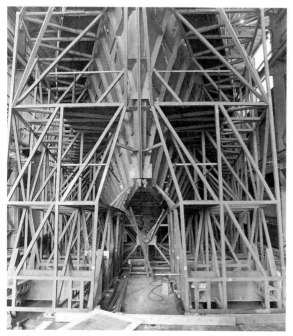

A mould being assembled in sections.

Mould showing space at lower stem for later fitting of
separate section owing to inaccessibility.

Typical section through a frame.

HMS *Wilton* the first ever GRP minehunter.

applications, the advantages generally outweigh these considerations.

The MOD programme succeeded in showing just what could be achieved with different types of resin and cloth, and with careful quality control. Several characteristics of GRP which probably nobody had seriously investigated before were studied and measured; for example, fatigue strength, chemical resistance and creep. Flammability was obviously important: although some resins are less inclined to burn than others, several of them release a toxic smoke or gas in the presence of a fire; being gassed is really just as undesirable as being incinerated!

Eventually an isophthalic polyester resin and a woven roving glass cloth were selected. This produced a material which proved to be about three times as strong as "commercial" fibreglass, (chopped strand mat) commonly used in yacht construction. The new material proved stronger and lighter than aluminium and when compared with an equal thickness of steel, provided over half the strength of steel for one fifth of the weight. In other words, for a steel ship to be as strong as a GRP one would require an impossibly heavy structure. GRP is however relatively flexible, and some care is required in the structural design to take account of this.

It was also established that, whilst the surface resin would burn, the first layer of GRP cloth prevented the flame from propagating further into the material, acting as a sort of built-in fire blanket. This theory continued to cause some unease amongst sceptics until experience in service began to demonstrate its soundness.

After establishing the characteristics of the material, the next step in the MoD(N) programme was to build some full scale ship sections and subject them to various tests, including explosive shock. A GRP section was built in 1967 by the then J.I.Thornycroft company. A similar ship section was built in laminated wood, by Vosper Ltd.

It may seem, in retrospect, that quite extraordinary lengths were gone to in the testing of the material and type of structure, but it must be remembered that, although not then a new material, GRP was much less well known and tried than it now is and that the RN were contemplating applying

a relatively unknown and untried material to an exceptionally arduous and important role. In addition to structural strength, therefore, durability, water absorption, chemical resistance, ease of repair, the effects of heat and cold, and several other areas were thoroughly explored.

In these early studies Thornycroft was in partnership with Bristol Aeroplane Plastics, a company which specialised in high quality aircraft and other applications. The tests on the ship sections convinced the MOD(N) that it would be best to proceed with the development of GRP for shipbuilding. Another test section was built by VT in the single skin configuration which was the form of construction selected as being that most suitable to withstand the arduous life of a mine hunter. As a result of tests on this section, a further construction feature was added which has caused misunderstandings ever since.

The frames and other structural members are formed and bonded to the skin by laying up successive laminations in a "top hat" section over a foam former laid on the skin. The foam, incidentally, remains in place, but plays no further significant structural role. This arrangement has ample strength for all normal conditions, but under extremes of explosive shock, there is a tendency for the "top hat" section laminations to "peel" off the skin, at the "brim" of the "top hat". For this reason, it was decided to reinforce such joints with titanium bolts. Above the waterline, these were not countersunk, giving the first ship a "studded" appearance, and leading to rude (and entirely unfounded) comments about the inability of VT to make GRP stick! This form of construction has proved entirely satisfactory in service, but the cost of the bolts and of drilling holes and fitting them, has always been a powerful incentive to further development, and the latest mine hunters embody a cheaper and even stronger method of joining the frames to the hull.

Even when they had at last developed a satisfactory material and structure, MOD prudence prevailed. Before designing an entirely new ship, the next step was to build a *Ton* class minehunter, identical to the wooden ships, but using the new GRP techniques. A contract to modify the *Ton* design was placed with VT late in 1968, and this

The flat panel tool.

A dispenser laying glass cloth impregnated with resin.

A section of deck with steps cut ready for scarfing to next section.

was followed in February 1970 by an order to build the ship itself, HMS *Wilton*.

If this approach seems cautious, it should be remembered that *Wilton* was to be the largest GRP warship in the world and indeed the first RN vessel (except for small launches and tenders) to be built entirely of GRP. All the machinery and other equipment was to be identical to that used in the earlier *Ton* class ships; in fact, most of *Wilton*'s outfit was taken from HMS *Derriton*, a wooden *Ton* which had succumbed to the ravages of time. A good principle of engineering development is to make only one major change at a time.

Building a GRP ship also required major changes to the shipyard. A traditional open air building berth would have been useless, and even the old covered berth at Woolston, where many of the wooden *Ton* class had been built, was unsuitable. Clean, dry, and relatively warm conditions are essential to achieve the necessary quality control standards: the accidental inclusion of dust in the GRP laminate cannot be permitted, and particular attention has to be paid to fire precautions.

VT therefore designed and erected a special GRP facility on the site of the old *Ton* class berth at Woolston. In addition to two covered building berths, a panel shop was built in which decks and bulkheads could be laid up on either flat or curved panels. Special precautions were taken to eliminate dust and a thermostatically-controlled heating and ventilating system was installed. Compared with the dirt and chaos of a traditional shipyard, it was a surgically clean environment.

It was also necessary to retrain the work force in the new techniques. Some of the "old" skills were still relevant; for example, the shipwright's ability to translate drawings accurately into a complex three-dimensional structure, but recruits from other trades were also retrained as laminators. This was found preferable to recruiting people with experience of commercial boat-building in GRP, even if the latter course had been practicable, the techniques being somewhat different.

There was still scope for steel working skills in construction of the mould, which was virtually a steel ship constructed inside out, with all the frames and supporting structure on the outside. It was built in sections which could be unbolted and removed progressively, and since every kink or blemish would inevitably be faithfully reproduced in the completed ship, it was finished to a very high standard of fairness and smoothness.

Anyone who tries to do minor repairs with glass fibre and resin, for example to car bodywork, will sooner or later be faced with an unmanageable piece of glass cloth, saturated with resin, which insists in clinging to fingers, tools, or any part of the job except the required area. It also becomes apparent that, for best results, the ratio of glass to resin is important, too much resin being as bad as too little. Imagine, then, being faced with a continuous roll of glass cloth, several metres long, which must be saturated to exactly the right degree with resin, and then placed accurately on a smooth, possibly curved, and mostly vertical surface. It makes wallpapering, that favourite theme for slapstick comedy, look like child's play. Moreover, unlike wallpapering, laying up GRP continues layer upon layer, each of which must be added before the previous one has fully cured, to ensure adequate adhesion.

To solve these problems, dispensers were required, which took cloth from the roll and impregnated it with the correct amount of resin before feeding it into the mould. The dispenser was mounted on a gantry, which also supported a number of platforms from which laminators armed with brushes could guide the cloth into place and smooth it down firmly to exclude bubbles and wrinkles. The whole assembly was supported from an overhead crane which could travel up and down the length of the mould as required. In this way the whole of the hull shell except for the forefoot, the very narrow lower part of the bow, was successfully laid up. The forefoot was laid up as a separate unit and scarfed on later.

The technique used to join this bow section is also relevant to the repair of damage. For maximum strength, the joint has to be tapered by cutting back each successive lamination a little further than the last to produce a stepped profile, and then laying up new laminations which gradually increase in size to match. This can produce a joint which is effectively as good as new.

Unlike most other GRP products, there was no surface gel coat, and the resin used was not

A *Hunt* class mine counter measures vessel.

PAP 104 - the French mine disposal vehicles carried by the *Hunt* class.

pigmented, so that the finished product was a translucent pale greenish yellow. The lack of surface gel coat incidentally meant that it was not subject to osmosis, which was then little known, although the resin used for *Wilton* was selected for its low water absorption properties.

Osmosis is a process whereby water molecules penetrate the outer layers of resin and form blisters. This can damage a material which was popularly thought to be virtually impervious to anything when it first came into general use. Although the malady has caused panic in the yachting world in recent years, severe cases are rare and the condition is usually curable.

VT used no coloured pigment in the resin partly because this could have a slightly detrimental effect on strength, and also because lack of it made the all-important quality control easier by making voids and other faults in the laminate visible. Although there was absolutely no need to paint the ship for preservative reasons, the RN prefers most of its ships to be a uniform grey colour, and in any case use of unpainted translucent laminate would have given rise to some novel but unwanted effects, such as the internal lighting causing the ship to glow in the dark, or allowing the crew to see roughly what their mate in the next cabin was up to. The ship was therefore painted in the conventional manner.

*Wilton* was launched on 18 January, 1972. An unusual feature was that the ship was launched bow first. Building the hull pointing towards the river had meant that the high profile of the bow was to some extent offset by the declivity of the slipway, and eased operation of the dispenser gantry and cranes. After being finished off alongside the quay at Woolston, the ship went through contractor's sea trials and was duly handed over to the RN to commence a long series of evaluation trials: she entered service in 1973.

Although *Wilton* was to be a "one-off" experiment, and there was never any intention to build more *Ton* Class vessels in GRP, both VT and the MOD were confident enough to invest substantial amounts of effort and money in the new technology. A good deal of this confidence stemmed from the extensive experiments with the material which had been carried out before building

*Wilton* and, even before she went to sea, few people had much doubt about her success.

The MOD regarded her purely as a step to the next generation of mine countermeasures vessels and, in 1975, approval was given to go ahead with the MCMV project. Later christened the *Hunt* class, like a class of Second World War destroyers before them, they bore the names of English fox hunts, which, in turn, are usually named after a village in their hunting area.

The *Ton* class ships had been designed originally as minesweepers, and some had subsequently had their influence sweeps removed to make room for the mine hunting equipment. Some, like *Wilton*, were therefore basically hunters and others only capable of sweeping. In contrast, the *Hunts* were designed from the outset as combined hunter/ sweepers, to be equipped with full hunting equipment as well as the latest mechanical, magnetic and acoustic sweeps. This meant that they were larger than the *Tons* and, inevitably, considerably more expensive.

Another factor which contributed significantly to the cost was the decision, after considerable study, to reduce as far as possible the magnetic characteristics - or signature - of all the equipment installed on the ship, as well as to construct the hull in GRP. Not only are non-ferrous metals usually more expensive than ferrous ones, but the need to build special versions of many otherwise standard equipments also made for costly short production runs. Nevertheless, the view was taken that to do otherwise could cause the loss of the whole ship and that it was therefore cost effective.

The *Hunts* were 60 metres overall, with a displacement of about 630 tonnes. This made them the largest GRP ships in service, and certainly the most sophisticated mine countermeasures ships afloat. The payload comprised the latest mine sweeping and mine hunting equipment, which required a substantial amount of electrical and hydraulic power to drive all the various magnetic and acoustic sweeps and all their handling and towing winches. With sweeps deployed, a considerable towing effort was required. When mine-hunting, slow speed and good manoeuvrability were essential.

The two low-noise, fixed-pitch propellers could

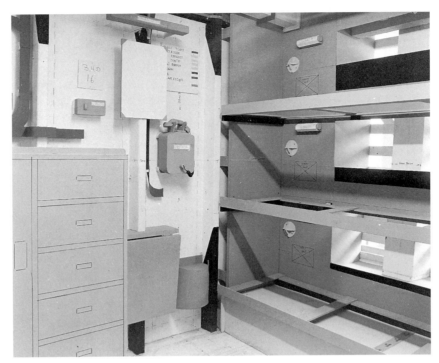

*Hunt* class. A wood and cardboard mock-up of a cabin.

*Hunt* class. The machinery test facility.

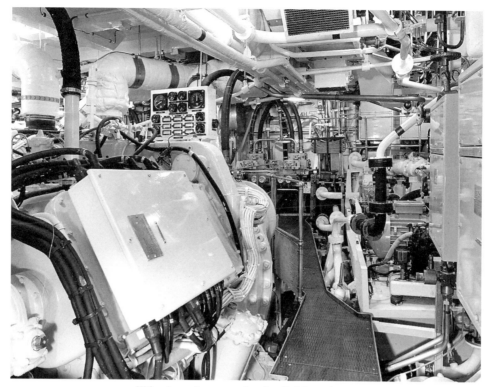

*Wilton*'s engine room showing Deltic engines.

47 metre export minehunter based on *Wilton* but never built.

therefore be driven either by special low-magnetic Paxman Deltic diesel engines, or by a slow speed hydraulic drive. There was also a hydraulically-driven bow thruster to assist in positioning the ship whilst using the mine hunting sonar.

All of this had to be achieved whilst minimising the magnetic signature and the amount of noise generated, and squeezing everything into the smallest possible hull, since the larger the displacement, the greater the risk from pressure sensitive mines.

During the design phase, the MOD(N) had VT build a full size wooden "mock-up" of the whole ship. It is standard practice in designing a new warship to build full size models of the important compartments, such as the bridge and operations room, to enable the operators to get a good idea of the layout and to permit designers to optimise the positioning of various controls and display panels, and to ensure that vent trunks, cable runs and pipe work do not all clash with each other. It is much less common to build a full size wooden model of the entire vessel. This may seem rather an overkill, and certainly VT never felt the need to go so far in the design of any of their export ships. It must however be remembered that the *Hunt* class MCMVs were not only a new design, but the first purpose designed hunter/sweepers, and, except for *Wilton*, the first to be built in an entirely new material. With these design problems to overcome, and with an exceptionally long run of ships foreseen, the wood and cardboard ship, erected in a large shed adjacent to the GRP shipbuilding berths, paid dividends. For example, the accurate location of equipment mounts in advance is important in GRP construction so that provision can be made when laying up bulkheads: unlike steel structures, it is not simple to weld on attachments points as an afterthought.

A machinery Shore Test Facility was also constructed, as is normal practice for all new MOD designs. The STF consisted of a working machinery system which reproduced the main propulsion system and the pulse generator system for the magnetic sweep. This was set up on shore at Woolston to allow the configurations to be tested before being run in the actual ship. It very soon proved its worth by highlighting certain problems

associated with brazing the main hydraulic system pipe work; this undoubtedly prevented a significant delay to the first ship, HMS *Brecon*.

Despite the innovations and various resulting difficulties which arose during the build, *Brecon* was launched on 21st June 1978, and completed alongside the quay at Woolston. Contractor's sea trials were completed within the planned time scale, and the ship was handed over to the Royal Navy in December 1979.

In service, VT's GRP ships were to demonstrate the worth of all the painstaking research and development that had gone into them. *Wilton* was heavily involved in the eventual clearance of the Suez canal of all the various hardware which had been dumped there during the Egyptian/Israeli conflict. Years later, the hull showed every sign of lasting the full predicted term of 70 years, although it is doubtful if the second hand machinery would last so long! However, after spending several months at Portchester in 1991 undergoing major refurbishment of the propeller shafts and bearings, *Wilton* fell victim to the 1994 defence cuts.

In several spectacular but unplanned incidents the *Hunts* too have demonstrated their robustness and confirmed the fire retardant properties of the laminate. A collision with a *Ton* in thick fog almost cut the wooden ship in half. The *Hunt*'s bow was damaged, but she remained seaworthy and VT quickly moulded a new bow section which was grafted on in only a few weeks.

On another occasion, a *Hunt* suffered a serious engine room fire. The engine room was evacuated and the blaze continued out of control for several hours. A wooden ship would undoubtedly have been lost, and heat conduction through the structure of a steel ship would probably have led to a similar fate. The insulating properties of the GRP hull were however so good that not even the paint on the outside of the hull blistered, and the damage was confined to the compartment concerned. This had to be completely gutted, the contents being written off along with the first few layers of GRP. However, beneath these, the structure remained sound despite the fact that the foam core of the frames, originally used to support the laminate during curing but not intended to take structural loads, had melted completely. After removing the

37 metre inshore minehunter for export, based on patrol craft for Venezuela, but never built.

Naval base at Mombasa.

rubbish and cutting back the scorched layers of laminate, fresh layers were replaced and the compartment refitted to make the ship as good as new.

The problem will be how to ultimately dispose of these vessels when they eventually reach the end of their service lives. Like polythene bags, they are non-biodegradable!

Like all warships, the *Hunts* needed comprehensive logistic support and the Support Services division were well placed and well qualified to provide a very large proportion of this.

Although with practice and improved building techniques over the years to come, VT were dramatically to reduce the cost of GRP hull production, it was clear from the start that the complexity and cost of the *Hunt* class MCMVs would not make them attractive for export. On the other hand, a number of foreign navies also had ageing *Ton* class ships in service and it seemed an excellent marketing plan to capitalise on the wide interest shown in the RN programme by designing a modern replacement for the *Ton* class, which could be fitted out either as a sweeper or a hunter and would be substantially smaller and less expensive than the RN's new MCMV.

Thus was born the VT 47 metre Minehunter. A smaller inshore minehunter design was also created in response to a tentative requirement of the Singapore Navy, and later yet another - the 37 metre Minehunter - was developed for export marketing. Despite a good deal of active marketing all over the free world which evoked a considerable amount of apparent interest, none of these designs has yet been transformed into orders. Nor was it only VT who found the export minehunter market very slack. Most navies appeared reluctant to allocate part of their budget to specialised vessels which might never be required. VT made attempts to reduce the specialised nature by proposing various ingenious methods of quickly changing role to that of a patrol craft, but in fact the first export minehunters were still years away, and eventually were to be the most sophisticated and specialised design of all: a vindication of RN policy and years of careful work.

Woolston's GRP facility was kept very busy for the remainder of the '70s and most of the '80s building *Hunts* for the Royal Navy and was so successful in improving techniques that despite the setting up of a rival "second source" of GRP shipbuilding at Yarrow Shipbuilders on the Clyde, VT were eventually to win the orders for all but two of the entire class of 13 MCMVs: after HMS *Brecon*, *Hunts* were rolling down the ways at Woolston at an average of about one every year for ten years. At this rate, the advantages of a "production line" began to be felt, and every ship took progressively fewer man hours to build than its predecessors.

The importance of GRP work was therefore increasing, but through most of the '70s the Brazilian frigates still kept Woolston's steel working facilities busy and there were still more frigate orders to come.

In 1975 two of the Iranian Mk 5 Destroyers, *Saam* and *Zaal*, returned to the UK for a refit. The biggest task was the replacement of the old interim fit 4.5 inch gun mountings by new Mk 8 mountings for which the ships had originally been designed. The work was carried out by the Devonport Naval Dockyard, support being provided by VT. Several engineers who had worked on the ship systems when they were built provided specialist assistance.

The mid seventies were a busy time for VT. In 1978 the Overseas Bases department, part of the Support Services Division, began to make its mark by winning a small design contract for a Marine Base in the Bahamas, followed rapidly by another for a Marine Base in Qatar. During this same period, Support Projects also won a contract to assist Scott Lithgow in the support of HMS *Challenger*. This contract was the forerunner to the Division becoming the MOD(N) nominated support agent for all Type "B" vessels; that is, all vessels other than front line warships. In due course this led to the Division holding the equipment data base for seventeen classes, totalling 82 ships in all.

Portchester too obtained quite a variety of work during this period.

## Chapter Eight

# THEORY AND PRACTICE

In 1974 Woolston was heavily occupied with the Brazilian Mk.10 frigates, had finished putting HMS *Wilton* through her paces and was anticipating the coming workload with the *Hunt* class. They were also still building two Type 21 frigates for the RN - HMS *Antelope* and HMS *Active;* indeed the work load was such that *Active* was handed over to the Ship Repair division in Southampton docks to complete. Portchester was busy with the 37metre patrol boats for Venezuela, and the dozen 110 foot PCs for Abu Dhabi and Qatar. There was no shortage of work, but what was required soon was another export order for sophisticated ships.

1975 brought orders for more 103 foot patrol boats; two for Tunisia and one for Guyana, for once at a reasonably opportune time as the work load on the Venezuelan boats and the 110 footers for Abu Dhabi and Qatar was tapering off. However, more significantly, an order was received from a previous customer, Nigeria, for two Mk.9 Corvettes, to supplement the Mk.3s which had entered service in 1972.

The Mk.9s were larger, faster and significantly more sophisticated than the earlier design. Like all such sales successes, this order was not achieved overnight, but resulted from patient marketing and follow-up of the Mk.3 contract. In a country where, even more than most, skilled maintainers were at a premium and could earn much more in civilian life than in the navy, after sales support was vital and attention to this paid dividends.

The specifications of the Mk.9 had been finalised during a design team visit to Lagos in October 1974, which was not without its lighter moments. Landing at Lagos in the early morning, having spent much of the night trying to play bridge with a Spanish pack of cards in the transit lounge at Madrid, the team was not in good shape. The delay resulting from the non-appearance of Len Pierce's suitcase on the baggage conveyor did nothing to improve matters, and while Len was taken out to the aeroplane and invited to crawl through the baggage hold in a desperate attempt to identify the missing item, the others resigned themselves to a further wait. By the time Len returned, empty handed, the sun had risen and the temperature was beginning to make him regret the thick tweed suit in which he had left the English autumn.

The delay meant that the traffic jam in Lagos had reached the morning peak during transit to the hotel. One reason given for the horrendous proportions of this jam was that the road system had been designed for driving on the left, whereas Nigeria had recently changed over to driving on the right. The logic of this excuse was obscure, although one or two members of the team observed that perhaps not all the drivers in Lagos had been told about the new arrangements. Further delays occurred at the hotel when, one after another, the team tried to change travellers cheques in order to obtain some local currency. This appeared to strain the cashier's mathematical abilities to the limit and it was clear that he had been strictly instructed, probably on pain of instant dismissal, to follow a set procedure for each such transaction. He valiantly stuck to this, despite some incredulous comments and helpful suggestions from the team as, for each transaction in turn, he looked up the exchange rate, wrote it down and solemnly multiplied it by $100, before writing down the result and counting out the Naire notes, all for the fourth and fifth time in fifteen minutes.

It was therefore lunchtime before the team set forth to buy a clean shirt for the now freely perspiring Len, still clad in his tweeds. Fortunately, no meetings were scheduled for that day.

Despite this inauspicious start, the real business of the visit proceeded quickly, the navy apparently being as keen to get on with the project as VT were. The only problems were caused by frequent power cuts at naval headquarters; a large building with many windowless internal corridors, where the VT men kept tripping over temporary cables in the gloom. Nevertheless, by the end of the week all was agreed, and the team arrived back at the airport just in time to collect Len Pierce's suitcase full of

Mk.9 Corvette for Nigeria.

The Broad Street shipyard in its heyday.

— 92 —

tropical clothes before climbing aboard the plane for London again.

The Mk.9s bore many of the characteristics of VT's "Family of Warships". 69 metres overall, with a displacement of around 850 tonnes, they were substantially smaller than the Mk.5 and Mk.7, but although more sophisticated and more heavily armed than the Mk.3, they were spacious and elegant little ships.

The hull incorporated the distinctive flared bow and pronounced knuckle, designed to keep the topsides dry when operating in the long Atlantic swells off Lagos. Propulsion was by four MTU diesel engines, coupled together in pairs to drive the two controllable pitch propellers. This ensemble was controlled by a VT system designed and built by the Controls division. In fact, during the trials of the Mk.9s, the opportunity was taken to try out a prototype digital machinery control system which, although not applied to the Mk.9s themselves, was later to become a major product line.

The ships were heavily armed for their size, with an Oto Melara 76mm automatic gun, a 40mm Bofors, Seacat AA missiles and a Bofors 375mm anti submarine rocket launcher, all controlled by a Hollandse Signaal Apparaten digital weapon control system. There was also a formidable array of electronics, including a large Plessey AWS2 search radar, which would allow the ships to monitor a very large amount of airspace, being able to detect aircraft over 60 miles away at high altitudes.

They were to be the largest ships ever built at the Broad Street yard in Old Portsmouth; indeed, they were almost too large for the cramped slipways. Each ship was built in two sections: after completing the main hull, it underwent a "controlled launch", being lowered down the slipway by hydraulic rams enough to allow the 50 foot long bow section to be welded on.

Like the Mk.3s, *Dorina* and *Otobo*, they were to be known as the *Hippopotamus* class, and the two new ships also bore names which meant *Hippopotamus* in a Nigerian dialect; *Erinmi* and *Enyimiri*; names which Europeans found somewhat tongue-twisting and confusing!

Like their predecessors who had stood by the Mk.3s, the Nigerian Navy representatives in

Portsmouth had a good sense of humour. On one occasion, George Hall, the VT manager in charge of the ships weapon systems, met one of them in his office.

"*Oh, Mr Hall,*" said the Nigerian "*A man came looking for you this morning.*"

"*Who was he?*" asked George. "*He didn't say.*"

"*Well, was he a VT man, or a subcontractor, or Nigerian Navy?*"

"*I don't know*".

"*Well, was he, er, coloured?*"

"*Oh, yes*", said the African.

"*Well,*" said George, "*He must be one of your lot!*"

"*Oh no, Mr Hall, this man was coloured white!*".

*Erinmi* was launched (fully!) in January 1977, followed in February 1978 by *Enyimiri*. They fitted out alongside at Broad Street, and were completed in 1979 and 1980 respectively.

The company was acutely conscious of the importance of obtaining an order to fill the gap which would eventually be left at Woolston by the departure of the Mk.10s, and the salesmen were hard at work following up various enquiries. As far as big ships were concerned, two projects in particular preoccupied the design group at this time: the modification of the Type 21 frigate design for Argentina, and the design of the "Harrier Carrier".

The Armada Republica Argentina (ARA) was one of the few foreign navies who actually showed anything more than academic interest in RN ship designs, having entered into a contract to buy two Type 42 destroyers, fitted with virtually the same equipment as the RN version. One of these ships was built by Vickers at Barrow- in-Furness, and the other, in rather slower time, in Argentina. The ARA was apparently genuinely interested in acquiring Type 21 frigates as well, and from 1975 on, Peter Shepherd, VT's commercial director, spent many long months in Buenos Aires negotiating the deal, which very soon showed all the signs of becoming very complicated.

The original declared intention of the ARA was to acquire a "proven" frigate design, with a view to building at least some of the ships in Argentina with the minimum of development risk. However, this admirable philosophy immediately met

problems, since inevitably some of the equipment fitted to the RN Type 21s would be obsolescent before the new ships could be built and other items would be incompatible with ARA standard practice. This was the thin end of the wedge and whilst efforts were being made to define these essential changes, along with the exact package and modification state of the drawings and other documentation which VT would supply, there was time for lots of other ARA departments, prodded by naval equipment salesman from all over the world, to jump in with their bright ideas and requirements. The ship began to look very different from the original.

Another significant influence was the desire to "Argentinise" as much as possible, so that for ships built in Argentina, as many items as possible would be acquired from Argentinean industry. Whilst this was not possible for many of the larger items which had no Argentinean equivalent, there were plenty of components and materials such as light switches, junction boxes, cable trays, nuts, bolts, valves, furniture, pipes, cables, steel, aluminium and so on which were locally available. However, determining whether they were suitable, or what might have to be done to make them suitable, posed some formidable problems, not the least of which being who would be responsible for the performance of a completed ship which incorporated all these changes?

Discussion of all this, and the drafting and agreement of all the related documentation, took many months and several members of the design team joined Peter Shepherd in Buenos Aires for various lengths of time. The discussions dragged on interminably and huge quantities of paper were generated, mostly defining in some detail the further volumes of paper which VT would eventually produce relating to the new ship, which, as time went on, began to look less and less like the RN Type 21 as study after study was proposed and undertaken on fitting exotic new weapon systems. Indeed, this almost became a self-perpetuating exercise, as more and more weapons manufacturers tried to jump on the ARA Type 21 band waggon, some of them even commissioning VT to carry out studies showing exactly how their equipment could be integrated with the ship.

Fortunately, Peter Shepherd kept his eye on the ball, and insisted that, in order to provide a firm and agreed starting point, the ARA purchased a set of the existing construction drawings of the ship. This was agreed, thereby at least providing VT with some return for what was in the end to prove an otherwise fruitless exercise.

Buenos Aires in the 1970s was an interesting place, and the protracted discussions - made even lengthier by the need for Spanish/English interpreters at every meeting - gave many VT men ample opportunity to look around. The city had a much more European atmosphere than other South American towns with which they were familiar. Indeed, some parts were reminiscent of a Europe of fifty years before: The Teatro Colon offered a superb setting for music and opera, and the magnificent Hurlingham country club (originally an offshoot of its namesake in England) offered splendid facilities for anyone who could afford them. Although welcomed as occasional visitors, the VT team clearly did not belong to this category; a notice on the club board reminding members that no individual might keep more than ten polo ponies on club property at one time made this clear.

Despite such signs of affluence, there was also evidence of severe poverty and of civil strife between the authorities and their political rivals. Police stations were heavily sandbagged and there were constant rumours of "disappearances" on both sides. One of the VT interpreters, an Anglo-Argentinean lady, was kidnapped for a brief time, but fortunately released unharmed. Another friend, a charming ex-ARA officer, also had a few hair raising tales to tell. Whilst still in the navy, he had been driving home alone late at night when the car in front stopped at traffic lights and two men with guns jumped out and rushed towards him.

*"Who were they? What did they want?"*

*"I didn't stop to find out"* he said. *"I shot them both through the windscreen and drove off quickly."*

Luckily, VT saw nothing of such incidents: most of the Argentineans were extremely friendly and hospitable.

On a lighter note, the Buenos Aires traffic was even more exciting than that in Rio de Janeiro, especially at weekends when everyone would take to the countryside. All four lanes of the motorway would be packed nose to tail with cars, all striving desperately to gain a few inches advantage on their neighbours. Leaving more than a tiny gap between one's vehicle and the one in front was an open invitation for another car to squeeze in, even if it meant crossing several lanes of traffic to make the attempt. The hard shoulder was fully occupied at all times with crawling cars, and on reaching open countryside, many vehicles would literally take to the fields in an attempt to circumvent their rivals. This ploy seemed to work until reaching a "spaghetti junction", where it became essential for at least some of them to rejoin the proper carriageways, which ensured total chaos. On one occasion, a VT party in a taxi were going through a one way, single lane underpass at such a junction, when they met a bus coming the other way! It was not at all clear who was in the right!

Another little problem was the tremendous inflation, even worse than in Brazil, which was afflicting the Argentinean economy. Newcomers at first found it difficult to realise that the very impressive banknotes were worth less than the paper on which they were printed and could not understand the ungracious attitude of hall porters or waiters to whom they had just given what seemed to be a most generous tip. Paying of hotel bills was difficult, since there was a limit on credit card transactions and a suitcase full of Pesos was required to pay even a fairly modest account.

Another memorable feature was the Argentinean beef and the enormous steaks which would be served dangling over the sides of the plate. For less conventional appetites, it seemed that no part of the animal was allowed to be wasted.

However, after two or three years of negotiations, the ARA Type 21 project eventually fizzled out. In retrospect, it seems possible that the reason was based on the political situation over the Falkland Islands which even then was a bone of contention.

The "Harrier Carrier" project was another ambitious design and marketing exercise.

One reason for VT's success in the export market was its policy of "bespoke" warship building to the requirements of the customers. Since few of the potential customers had design organisations,

or even naval staff with significant time or skills to spend on specifying future requirements, a major part of the VT marketing effort was spent in dreaming up new designs which could be used as "talking points" with potential customers, with a view to them becoming staff requirements which could be fed back from the customers to VT. The Harrier Carrier was a rather extreme and ambitious case of this, which came about partly because of the remarkable Hawker Harrier V/STOL aircraft and the decision by the RN to carry it aboard their new "Command Cruiser", and partly because of Ron Crook's passion for aeroplanes.

Oddly enough, Thornycroft had designed a "pocket aircraft carrier", designed to carry nine Seafire fighters in 1943. This too never got beyond the drawing board but, like the Harrier Carrier, was inspired by the enormous cost of "conventional" aircraft carriers and the desire to do something practical about it. Being only a young Vosper electrician in 1943, Ron had had nothing to do with this earlier project, but some of the faded drawings played a small part in interesting the 1975 design team in a reincarnation of the idea.

The cost of building a carrier capable of launching, recovering and supporting conventional fixed wing aircraft had long since become prohibitive. Indeed, the RN project for a flat topped ship to carry a number of helicopters was referred to as the "Command Cruiser" or "Through-Deck Cruiser" lest casual reference to it as an "Aircraft Carrier" should lead to a political outcry and cancellation. There was never any question of the ships (the *Invincible* class) being large enough to operate conventional jet aircraft, but as the project came closer to fruition it also became obvious that the remarkable Harrier did not require a larger ship in which to be deployed at sea. All that was needed was some slight modifications to the aircraft itself, the principal one being the installation of a radar set in the nose, to adapt it to a maritime role.

Nevertheless, the RN requirement still called for a large ship and large ships are expensive. Despite careful analyses which prove that large steel boxes are no more expensive than small ones, something akin to Parkinson's law always ensures that the eventual cost per ton is at least as much;

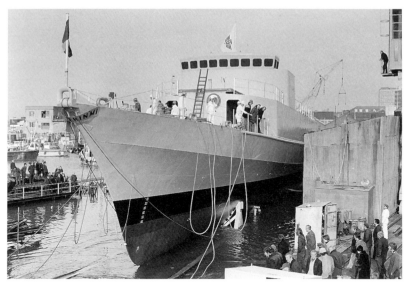

Launch of *Erinmi* at Broad Street.

The Harrier Carrier.

Hawker Siddeley, Sea Harrier.

An Exocet missile in flight.

HMS *Wilton* in Suez Canal.

© Crown Copyright/MOD.

possibly because someone will always find a cast iron reason for filling every available space with expensive gadgetry.

VT began to consider whether Harriers could be launched and recovered by a smaller ship, which might be inexpensive enough to appeal to the export market. It was of course not possible to make much progress without consulting the designers of the Harrier, and the VT team soon made the acquaintance of the Harrier team, led by the chief designer (Harrier), John Fozard. The two groups immediately got on very well together and began exchanging ideas. It was not long before the Harrier Carrier concept began to emerge.

The objective was to design the smallest ship capable of operating and supporting the Sea Harrier effectively. The result was a ship of about 8000 tonnes, only slightly longer than a Type 42 destroyer, and capable of carrying eight Sea Harriers and two Lynx helicopters in a below deck hangar. The length was partly governed by the take-off performance of the aircraft; although capable of taking off vertically, the Harrier can carry a much greater load of fuel and weapons if a rolling take-off is possible; the longer the better, up to a point. Like most such complicated problems, there was no clear cut answer to the required deck length for maximum take-off weight, since it depended upon relative wind speed, air temperature, and future developments to the Pegasus engine, amongst a host of other factors.

A length of 445 feet (135 metres) was decided upon as a good compromise, and one which would also permit sufficient hangar space below decks. At this point, John Fozzard tentatively introduced VT to the "Ski Jump" concept.

"Ski Jump" at first sight seems an obvious way of getting an aeroplane off the ground in a short distance by simply running it up a ramp which ends in mid air, roughly equivalent to driving it over a cliff. The reason why this idea has not been pressed into service many years ago is that, until proper flying speed has been achieved, there is insufficient airflow over the control surfaces to keep the aeroplane pointing in the desired direction instead of performing an inelegant cartwheel or similar prelude to disaster. The Harrier, however, is equipped with thrust jets to permit the pilot to maintain attitude control even at zero airspeed, thus control can be maintained after leaving the ramp, whilst still in a brick-like ballistic trajectory. Provided flying speed has been achieved before hitting the sea, no solid runway is necessary.

However, in 1975, the idea was untried and some careful development work was required to prove it before proclaiming its merits to the world. Nevertheless, John Fozard permitted the VT naval architects to incorporate a modest ramp in the forward end of the flight deck, the "cover story" being that it was to ensure that the aeroplane could not leave the deck in a nose down attitude, even in the severest sea conditions. This gave the ship a much more elegant profile than a flat deck. Later on, when the concept had been proven, the ramp was made more pronounced. Eventually, of course, a ski-jump was incorporated in the *Invincible* class.

A good deal of thought went into the design of the Harrier carrier in order to ensure its viability; in particular, to make best use of the available space. Probably the most unusual feature was the propulsion system, which was turbo-electric.

This was mainly the brain child of Ron Crook and his department and caused a certain amount of scepticism among the uninitiated at first sight. It was however soundly based on existing technology and although it came under critical examination from several quarters, nobody was, in the end, able to fault the design. No doubt there would have been some teething troubles had the Harrier Carrier ever been built, but these would have been worthwhile for the enormous benefits which the system conferred on the ship.

Firstly, of course, there was considerable flexibility and redundancy. No less than nine Rolls Royce Tyne gas turbines were to drive individual generators, each of which could either supply electricity, at a constant frequency of 60 hertz, to the ship services and electronic systems, or, at a variable frequency, to the two electric propulsion motors which drove the propellers. This meant that whatever ship speed was required, the number of gas turbine generator sets allocated for propulsion could be chosen so that they ran at their most economical load. Thus three sets could push the ship along at a comfortable 19 knots, whereas six would achieve 24 knots and eight the full 25 knots. Generator sets not in use for propulsion could be used for power generation, remain on standby, or be under maintenance. The ship's normal electrical load could be taken by a single generator. An interesting consequence of this arrangement was that, in a disaster relief situation, the ship could supply some 25 megawatts of electrical power; enough for a small town.

Since the gas turbines themselves needed no mechanical connection to the propeller shafts, they could be situated much higher up in the ship, at any convenient location. This meant that simpler shock mounts could be used and that there was no need for large air intake and exhaust ducts penetrating deep inside the ship, taking up huge amounts of valuable space. Access for the replacement of machines was also easy.

A consequence of using gas turbines as prime movers instead of diesels was that it would be possible to run the ship and its aircraft on the same fuel. This meant that, with a full load of some 1300 tonnes of AVCAT either the ship could have a range of over 8000 miles, or could trade some of this for a huge number of aircraft operating hours.

The design was "launched" at the 1975 Royal Naval Equipment Exhibition (RNEE), in those days held at Greenwich. It is roughly the naval equivalent of the SBAC airshow at Farnborough, but less well known since it is not open to the public. The Harrier Carrier concept created real interest, not least from the MOD(N), some of whom clearly considered it an attempt to upstage their Command Cruiser. There was a definite air of "not invented here" and considerable scepticism, mainly centred on the small size of the vessel. This had not been unexpected, but VT and the Harrier team had done their homework and had no doubts about the project's viability. Later studies, in which various MOD departments were involved, confirmed this view.

One marketing target was the Royal Australian Navy, and there was a joint VT/Hawker sales visit to Sydney in July 1976. The formal technical sales presentations created a certain stir in RAN circles, but this was nothing to the stir in less formal circles created by John Fozard wherever he went. He was not only a clever engineer, but had the unusual talent of being able to explain his ideas to laymen (and women) in simple, non-technical, and highly amusing language. This of course came in very useful when talking to politicians. His impromptu lectures he illustrated with rapid and brilliant sketches, using any materials which came to hand. These drawings became sought after souvenirs, and it was said that one lady, after a dinner, took home a plate from the restaurant covered in felt-tip sketches of bits of Harrier.

In the Canberra hotel, the mirrors opposite the lift doors mysteriously became covered in little sketches of aeroplanes and suitable slogans.

Not long after, John moved from the chief designer (Harrier) seat to exercise his talents full time in sales. VT could not resist sending him the following ditty by way of acknowledgement. It should be explained that by this time the Labour government was making progress with its ridiculous plans to nationalise both the aircraft and shipbuilding industries, which diverted a good deal of senior management effort from both industries for a considerable time. Hence the slightly bitter note:

Amongst the talents of young Foz
Was talking, nineteen to the doz.
Whilst illustrating, with his pen
His thoughts, for slower thinking men.
To draw attention to some grouse
He one day visited The House
And, lest they should forget his coming
Left his mark around the plumbing.
Months passed; a MP rose from slumber
And went to 'call upon the plumber.'
Whilst contemplating Georgian china
His thoughts aspired to something finer:
His gaze rose heavenwards and then
He spied the marks of Fozard's pen!
*"Great Scott!"* he cried (and wet his shoes)
*"What a curious place to choose.*
*"J. Foz was here'- that must be him; "I'd*
*better go and wake up Jim.[1]"*
*"Ah, yes" said Jim "I know that chap.*
*"He talked an awful load of crap.*
*"Why, everybody - even I*
*"Knows aeroplanes must move to fly:*
*"Yet Hawkers say there's no one finer;*

[1] Callaghan, the Prime Minister

*"I understand he's Chief Designer!*
*"Fancy having such a clot -*
*"We'll have to nationalise the lot!*
*"Mind you," he said, eyeing the wall*
*"It's not that he's no use at all.*
*"He must be worth a hundred tons*
*"Of stuff for giving bulls the runs:*
*"With such a fund of doubtful tales*
*"We'd better make him Head of Sales!"*

Another potential customer for the Harrier Carrier was Iran, and the sale of even one carrier to the Shah would have been a considerable achievement. At one time, this looked like a distinct possibility, but Teheran had other things on its mind, and during their last visit to the naval headquarters there in September 1978, the VT design team detected a definite air of unease. There were armed soldiers on the streets and occasional distant gunfire. Visitors were warned not to venture into the older part of the city.

There were other attempts to sell the Harrier Carrier, but with the rapidly escalating price of naval weaponry worldwide, the chances were always slim and the very few nations who could afford an air capability at sea were unlikely to buy a carrier from abroad. There was also the problem of selling an idea which did not have the demonstrable and whole hearted backing of the MOD(N), who remained sceptical, particularly as the long awaited launch of HMS *Invincible*, the first Command Cruiser, at last approached. The Harrier Carrier gradually faded from the marketing programme as more urgent - and less ambitious - items cropped up. As a vehicle for new ideas it was not entirely wasted, and, (who knows?) it may yet see a third, and more successful incarnation in future years. It is hardly necessary to note what a great success the Sea Harrier eventually became in the Falklands war, which almost certainly could not have been won - or even contemplated - without it. VT can claim no credit for this, but some of the ideas which were discussed between the Harrier design team and VT and not all of which were originally incorporated in the "Invincible" class, were successfully put into practice, largely thanks to the efforts of John Fozard and his team.

In 1976 the company bid successfully for the

contract to build a Type 42 destroyer for the Royal Navy. HMS *Southampton* was ordered just as the first Mk.10, *Niteroi*, was completed, and a year later Woolston landed an order for a second Type 42, HMS *Nottingham*, just as the second Mk.10, *Defensora*, was completed - an example of fortunate timing which kept the Woolston steelwork departments continuously busy.

Portchester too had an eye to continuity, and although the Mk.9 Corvettes and the various 110 foot and 103 foot patrol boats provided plenty to do, the company was still striving to achieve an order for large patrol boats, or strike craft as they were becoming known. The *Tenacity* project had not led anywhere, whereas foreign competitors had managed to sell a number of diesel patrol craft in the 40 to 50 metre size range. Although the Venezuelan 37 metre boats had been a welcome step in the right direction, it was important to establish a firmer foothold in this market.

The sales director at that time was David Wilson, one of the most successful salesmen in his field, although anyone less like the archetypal arms dealer would be hard to imagine. A charming ex-naval officer, well over 6 feet tall and a devout Roman Catholic, he was equally adept at dealing with foreign Admirals, over-enthusiastic VT engineers with technical axes to grind, and the sometimes dubious characters who invariably emerged from holes in the woodwork offering assistance whenever any large arms deal seemed remotely possible. Few people, if any, can remember David losing his cool in any of the very trying situations in which he continually found himself, and yet he usually got his way and succeeded in keeping the shipyards busy.

Under his direction the sales department were working patiently in a number of areas. In 1974 they began to make headway with a new potential customer, who was eventually to give them the opportunity that they were seeking.

Egypt was recovering from the wars with Israel and various Western powers were gearing themselves up to clear the long-unused Suez Canal of all sorts of wreckage, much of which was of an unknown nature and was thought to include all manner of dangerous ordnance. The Royal Navy's contribution to the international effort to clear this

Unconverted Egyptian built *Komar* boat.

*Komar* after conversion.

lot included HMS *Wilton,* and VT naturally took a keen interest.

It was also clear that the Egyptian Navy was in sore need of re-equipping. It possessed a number of very old ships, including at least one ex-RN second world war frigate, but during the penultimate Arab-Israeli war the more effective vessels had been ex Russian patrol boats armed with Styx surface-to-surface missiles. It was some of these which, although obsolescent, and apparently without needing to leave harbour, had sunk the Israeli destroyer *Eilat* and, rather belatedly, awakened the free world to the threat of these weapons. The ensuing panic accelerated the development of, and vastly increased the demand for, a number of western SSM systems such as Exocet, Otomat and Harpoon, which by 1974 were just becoming available. Like Styx, they worked on the "fire and forget" principle; the range and bearing of the target being set on the missile's autopilot before launch. This not being sufficiently accurate to ensure a hit on a small, distant and mobile target, the missiles were fitted with their own on-board homing radar which was switched on automatically near the end of the flight to detect the target and steer the missile home. This meant that once having launched the missile, the firing vessel could turn away and make itself scarce, probably before the target knew anything about it.

Exocet and its contemporaries were all fast, low flying and small, with an explosive charge smaller than many first world war naval shells. Flying at high subsonic speeds, they relied for much of their effect upon the large amount of kinetic energy, frequently compared by journalists to that of an express train, which they possessed. Even the largest modern frigates and destroyers, being unarmoured, smaller, and more vulnerable than a first world war battle cruiser, would suffer very severely from a single hit, as convincingly demonstrated years later during the Falklands war.

Styx - as the Russian missile was known to the West - worked on a slightly different principle. An RN tactical school instructor who described it as "the size of a Pusser's bus, with a warhead big enough to blow a ship in half", was exaggerating only slightly. The missile launcher was more appropriately referred to as a "hangar", and yet two

or more of these were successfully mounted by the Russians on numerous small, and some not so small, patrol boats. It was some of these that the Egyptian Navy had employed so effectively against the *Eilat.*

By the time of what will, hopefully, be the last Egyptian-Israeli war, the Israelis had not only got the measure of Styx, but had produced their own SSM, Gabriel, which was rather more deadly. The ageing ex-Russian boats and missiles were nearing the end of their lives. This situation, coupled with the fact that the Egyptians had fallen out with the Russians and were therefore "respectable" again in the eyes of Western governments, made the Egyptian Navy in 1974 a prime target for almost every naval weapons salesman in the free world.

As experienced negotiators and with limited funds available, the Egyptians were in no great hurry.

VT submitted proposals for strike craft, based somewhat loosely on *Tenacity,* in 1974. Following Egyptian Navy reactions to this, the design was revised, and then revised again. Originally 49 metres long, with CODOG propulsion, the boat became all-diesel propelled in early 1975. Weapons changes were going on continually as the customer revised his ideas. David Wilson patiently went on resubmitting revised proposals to match.

For some time VT had been trying to encourage more British companies to develop weapons equipment suitable for patrol craft. At last, two British companies, Marconi Radar Systems and Sperry, had got together to develop a suitable radar directed gun fire control system. They too spent a great deal of sales effort in Egypt.

Sufficient funds for the new strike craft that the Egyptian Navy wanted were not being made available as soon as everyone had hoped. The navy decided to take matters in its own hands. Amongst their worn out ex-Russian fleet were several *Komar* class boats; hard chine wooden fast patrol boats slightly less than 100 feet (30 metres) in length, equipped with two Styx missiles each. Impressed with the potential of these small and inexpensive ships, the Egyptians set out to build some new hulls themselves. This they succeeded in doing very effectively, using traditional boat building methods, in Alexandria. They acquired some lightweight, high speed, Isotta Fraschini diesel engines from Italy. Thus was born the *October* class.

The problem of arming these boats remained, and Marconi saw an opportunity to sell some fire control systems. The Egyptians were enthusiastic but wise. They knew the difficulties of fitting such equipment to a small boat, and of making it work. By 1975, instead of simply selling electronics, Marconi found themselves making proposals to fit the equipment, integrate it with guns and missiles provided from elsewhere, and run a series of proving trials on the completed boats, as well as the weapons. As radar manufacturers rather than naval architects, they called in VT to assist.

By 1976 VT had taken the lead in the *October* Boat project, which was becoming progressively more complicated. But success was near. The contract between VT and Egypt for the 'refit' of six boats was signed at last in September 1976, after over two years of patient sales campaigning.

The task was, in fact, almost as long and complex as building new boats from scratch; indeed, there were times when some thought that the latter would have been easier! It was necessary to remove the existing superstructure of each boat entirely and to design and build a new deck house, bridge and Operations room. As ever, the manufacture of most of the electronic equipment took many months, or even years and there was then a complicated programme of installation, testing and trials to be undertaken. Moreover, the Egyptian Navy expected VT to guarantee the performance of the boats themselves when refitted just as VT normally did with new ships of their own design. This of course necessitated establishing a reference by carrying out trials on the boats as they arrived from Egypt, an event which was not scheduled to begin until almost two years after the contract was signed.

Since dynamic stability was a matter of no little importance, VT suggested that these trials included the application of full helm at full speed. This the owners politely declined to do! The boats were smaller and more load sensitive than the VT 103 foot steel patrol boats, which, with very few exceptions, were fitted with little more than a hand operated gun and a navigation radar. When the VT

designers were presented with the task of fitting not only two 30 mm gun mountings, together with a fire control radar and computer system, but also two Otomat missiles and a very sophisticated electronic warfare outfit, there was some sceptical shaking of heads at first.

However, the battle-hardened Egyptians, having first hand experience of seeing quarts squeezed into half-pint boats, could see no problem, and cared little for RN accommodation standards - or magazine regulations for that matter. If VT couldn't do the job, there were any number of other shipyards eager to try. Those same shipyards were also very anxious to oust VT from the position they were gradually achieving of being the preferred supplier of new boats, if and when these eventually materialised. The designers set to, trying to forget many of their traditional taboos.

It was surprising what could be achieved by ignoring some fundamental inhibitions! For example, a problem arose over where to put a 400 hertz electrical power supply converter; a large ugly cable-festooned box which emitted a loud and irritating whine when switched on. All the operational compartments and lobbies were already crammed full of cabinets and panels. The crew's 'accommodation' in the forecastle was clearly going to have to double as a 30mm magazine, and the First Officer's 'cabin' was so full of electronic units and junction boxes that there was scarcely room to stand in there, and no chance whatever of lying down.

The Egyptians couldn't see the problem:

"*There is plenty of room*", they insisted. "*Look here; there is room for three such units at least.*"

The VT designers gulped slightly and complied. After all, the Captain probably would not have time to visit his cabin anyway!

The highly-strung Italian engines required frequent overhauls which necessitated their removal from the boats. The Operations Room, which housed all the radar displays and weapon control consoles, was sited on deck immediately over the engine rooms. Since there was no chance of resiting the Ops room elsewhere and less still of manoeuvring large oily bits of machinery up through a cramped compartment filled with expensive electronic equipment which was

supposed to be kept clinically clean, a different approach was required. The whole operations room was made removable. In fact, it consisted of a container which was partially fitted out before being joined to the ship, and which had most of the radar and other antennae mounted on its roof. This might have been a positive advantage if it had been possible to install the entire weapon system in this single module, but unfortunately there were many electronic 'black boxes', in addition to the missile launchers and guns themselves, which had to be fitted elsewhere. This meant that a huge number of electrical connections had to be reliably unmade and remade every time the Ops room was removed for an engine change. Finding room for, and installing, the necessary plugs and sockets, was no mean task.

This was not all. The six boats had been built by hand, skilfully but piecemeal. There were drawings, but the boats differed from them and each other in detail, so that no two were exactly alike. This meant that the new superstructures and many of the new equipment mountings also had to be individually tailored.

This challenging project would therefore provide a significant work load for Portchester for some three years. However, David Wilson kept his eye on the main objective of achieving an order for new strike craft, and the patient marketing discussions continued in Cairo and Alexandria.

The Egyptians also had ideas for much larger ships, and although there was some discussion of new frigates, most efforts focused on ambitious proposals for refitting various old vessels. On one occasion I found myself in Alexandria with Jim McEwan, from the VT ship repair division in Southampton docks, who had been called in to assist.

The Egyptians possessed an ancient destroyer, purchased from the RN after the second world war, of which they were very proud. We were invited to inspect this ship with a view to making proposals to install all sorts of modern equipment. We followed the Admiral in his smart white uniform, with an entourage of similarly clad officers, on a tour of the ship. Everywhere there was neatly polished brass work, and a number of dockyard labourers were at work on deck, painting all the bollards and fairleads with black paint. We tactfully remarked on how well kept the old ship was. Jim, however, was sceptical about its true condition, and kept uncovering signs of corrosion behind linings or in dark corners. Returning to the weather deck, he suddenly stopped and stared at the metal plating beneath his feet. The Admiral and his entourage stopped too. Watched by a number of painters, we all waited expectantly. Jim turned to me.

"*Jump up and down a bit*", he said.

Puzzled, I complied. After a few moments, "*Right,*" said Jim, "*You can stop now. As you're still here, this bit of deck is probably OK*".

During the pause, one of the Admiral's immaculate white shoes had somehow got painted black, which caused much more of a stir than Jim's rather unscientific structural testing. We hastened ashore, uttering promises to return with proposals for packing the old ship with modern equipment, and doing our best to conceal our misgivings. Fortunately, the Egyptians too thought better of this idea which was not pursued further.

A lot of time in the early part of 1977 was spent in considering the purchase and modernisation of various newer RN frigates, and even a *County* class destroyer, which were then coming up for sale, but these too came to naught. VT continued to persist in following the main goal of a strike craft order.

Meanwhile, by 1977 the long delayed threat of nationalisation really began to materialise. VT, busy, prosperous, and with good prospects for the future was less receptive than ever to the idea.

## Chapter Nine

# NATIONALISATION

In an attempt to put nationalisation in context, it is necessary to pause and look outside VT at the background of the British Shipbuilding Industry.

Poor productivity originated as long ago as the late nineteenth century. Rapid growth of international trade, much of it under the control of the British Empire, provided a huge home market for British shipyards, who were also first in the market with new iron and steel ships. This virtual monopoly, coupled with the vigorous defence by each trade of what it saw as its own work, was an ideal breeding ground for demarcation disputes and inefficiency. Between 1890 and 1893 demarcation led to an average of one major strike per month on the Tyne.

By the early 1900's management effectively condoned restrictive practices by instructing which trade should do which work in an effort to pre-empt further disputes.

That same management, most of whom were themselves steeped in traditional "practical" methods and had little scientific training, failed to invest in new plant developments. The slump between the wars therefore found them ill equipped to compete with more progressive European and American yards.

The Second World War, and the rearmament programme just before it, necessitated a vast expansion in merchant ship and warship building, as well as in conversion and repair. It was a concern of the War Cabinet that widespread restrictive practices made this so difficult. In 1942 Ernest Bevin complained "how difficult and backward the shipbuilding industry has been from a labour point of view ever since I have been in office".

Over the past fifty years there have been several Government sponsored reports on the industry. In 1942 Oliver Lyttleton, the Minister of Production, appointed Robert Barlow to head a committee of enquiry into shipyard labour conditions. This led to a study by Cecil Bentham which resulted in some capital investment in production methods and equipment. In 1960 and 1961 two more Government committees reported, and in 1962 the industry itself set up yet another under James Patton to examine productivity and research. His report in February 1962 identified eight features of the European yards, most of these being ways in which they were superior to their British counterparts at the time. It is possibly because Vosper in Portsmouth took more notice of these than many other yards that their subsequent opposition to nationalisation was so strong.

In particular, Patton highlighted sales; overheads and their relationship to throughput; flexibility of labour; control of suppliers; training; and a better identity of purpose between management and the work force.

By 1964 Vosper alone in the UK had a dedicated ship sales department. Thanks to the large order for 14 identical Patrol Boats for Malaysia, the Company had become much more conscious of productivity, and been able to make real progress in quantifying it. Their Unions were more enlightened and better managed than elsewhere and the importance of material costs was well appreciated. The need for training both apprentices and managers had been recognised. Finally, and most important, there was an excellent spirit which showed itself in many ways; the exceptional communication within the Company from those early days was only one example.

To a lesser extent, Thornycroft applied the lessons of Patton, but British shipbuilding as a whole continued to go downhill. In 1955 Britain had completed 1.32 million Gross Register Tons of merchant shipping out of the total of 4.23 million GRT built in Europe. Japan had built 0.56 million GRT. But by 1970 Japan had taken the lion's share of the boom in seaborne trade by building 10.0 million GRT - an eighteen-fold increase. Europe other than Britain managed 7.15 million GRT - two and a half times its 1955 total. Britain built precisely the same tonnage that it had fifteen years earlier. It was this performance that first gave rise to calls for nationalisation.

By this time however, the message about investment had begun to sink in. Facilities in the best of the British yards were similar to those overseas. But we had still failed to create the cooperative atmosphere between management and employees which was essential to reduce the labour content of production. Even to this day there are some trade unionists who prefer the short term extra employment provided by restrictive practices to the long term job protection underpinned by efficient and unfettered use of labour. The fact that this also improves job interest is only slowly being accepted as an important ingredient.

The merger of Vosper and Thornycroft coincided approximately with the findings of yet another Shipbuilding Inquiry Committee; the Geddes report. One conclusion of this was that groups should be formed to specialise in ship types. VT was to become the southern area group specialising in small surface warships. Geddes' recommendations on industrial relations led on the 14th August 1967 to the signing of an agreement between the Shipbuilders and Repairers National Association (SRNA) and the Confederation of Shipbuilding and Engineering Unions (CSEU) - the first time in the history of the industry that all nineteen unions had signed a common agreement.

A fortnight later the new VT management and most of the Woolston unions followed this up with a further historic agreement designed to radically streamline and modernise the labour force. All labour was to be divided into five groups; metalworkers; woodworkers; engineers; finishing trades and ancillary workers. Any worker would perform any of the normal work of his group and work necessary to further their job. Moreover, there would be temporary interchange of workers between groups to make more efficient use of labour.

This was known as the Blue Book agreement, and had it been implemented would have made VT outstandingly competitive. But in spite of being signed by twelve unions, and three sections of the Amalgamated Society of Boilermakers, it was necessary after prolonged negotiations to include this sad epilogue:

"It is further agreed that at the date of signing this agreement the provisions whereby there is:

(a) flexibility between shipwrights and joiners

(b) freedom for tradesmen in Groups other than the Metalworking Group to undertake simple drilling aboard ship, and

(c) an extension to the existing practices for tradesmen in the Engineering Group to do their own tack welding
are not yet operable."

Yet another case of Unions clinging to demarcation because of inter-union rivalry. With the prospect of ample work, no amount of persuasion could convince the officials that they were putting the long term survival of the company, and therefore their member's jobs, at risk. Not surprisingly, the subsequent agreement at Portchester (the Red Book) became little more than a new pay deal.

VT was not immune from the ills of the industry, and thus failed to derive as much benefit as it might have from Geddes. However, a much less successful attempt to implement Geddes was the formation of Upper Clyde Shipbuilders, which only partially followed the recommendations. UCS collapsed in 1971 after only three years, the first monument to Government intervention in the industry. That same year, at the Annual Conferences of the Labour Party, the TUC and the CSEU both adopted resolutions calling for the nationalisation of shipbuilding.

In 1973 the consultants Booz, Allen and Hamilton International, commissioned by the Department of Trade and Industry, produced what was to be the final report on the industry. It identified overcapacity in warship building and suggested that MOD(N) should concentrate its orders on the yards which it wished to continue in this sector. Vickers, Yarrow and VT between them, it said, provided the whole range of design, lead yard and production capacity likely to be required by MOD(N).

It was a major mistake that this suggestion, made 20 years ago and still so obviously true today, did not become a strategic aim of British Shipbuilders when the nationalised corporation was eventually set up a few years afterwards.

Following Booz Allen, a joint working party of the Labour Party, TUC and CSEU listed the following grounds for the nation to acquire the assets of virtually all yards of any significance:

"*1. No other industry has failed to increase its absolute output for 25 years.*

*2. No other industry, with the exception of the aircraft industry (upon which they also had designs) has received so much public finance; it will continue to need that support.*

*3. Few other industries have failed to modernise and re-equip to the disastrous degree of shipbuilding and ship repair. . . . . only one third of government subsidy has actually gone on capital modernisation.*

*4. The history of labour relations . . . . has been poor; this has largely been a reflection on managements.*

*5. Finally it is clear that the coming few years will continue to be difficult for shipbuilding internationally. . . . . The Booz Allen report. . . shows that the government will need to intervene massively in the next decade to ensure a viable industry. The report itself makes the case for nationalisation. . . . . a clear and firm national strategy can only come from a nationalised shipbuilding organisation.*"

The Trade Unions and the Labour party recognised some of the problems but remained silent on the central issue of restrictive practices. The history of industrial relations had been an unhappy one and the working party believed that the creation of a National Corporation would eliminate the old attitudes of management and provide an opportunity for a new start. The efforts of the Upper Clyde workers in their campaign to save their jobs had demonstrated their self discipline and their desire to share in decision making. Nationalisation would provide for a proportion of the Board to consist of worker representatives, and would facilitate greater worker participation in decision making at all levels. The industry "could thereby emerge in the vanguard of the extension of industrial democracy".

Perhaps it was no coincidence that the issue of restrictive practices was ignored, when one of the authors of this brave new policy was the General Secretary of the Boilermakers Union, Danny McGarvie.

The Labour Government, elected in 1974,

brought in a bill to nationalise the shipbuilding, ship repair, and aircraft industries. Mr. Wedgewood Benn, the minister responsible for this monstrous undertaking, justified it by reference to the indifferent record of the industry despite substantial financial support from various governments.

In his eloquent letter to the shareholders dated 7th August, (see Appendix 1), Sir David Brown utterly refuted this in respect of VT, pointing out that the company had received very little financial assistance from the government, had invested substantial sums of its own in new plant and development, and by implementing many of the other recommendations of the various government committees had achieved notable success. He maintained that not only was there no justification for nationalising VT, but that it would positively damage the company.

There was ample evidence for this latter point. A serious article in Fortune magazine in December 1975, entitled "The grim failure of Britain's nationalised industries" set out the inherent characteristics of the industries which had been nationalised by the Clement Attlee government: relentless government interference, poor productivity, more (rather than less) labour strife, and the safety net of public funds, always there as a last resort, which Fortune referred to as "the high cost of coddling". This dismal record was, alas, to be repeated in shipbuilding from 1977 to 1985.

Vesting day, - the day on which each company had its assets compulsorily transferred to the state - was meanwhile delayed by sundry lawmaking technicalities as well as by spirited opposition from various quarters. Except by Ross Belch of Scott Lithgow, there was little apparent opposition from the merchant ship yards, but the specialist warship builders fought hard. Sir David Brown, whose holding company had by then acquired 23% of the equity of Yarrow shipbuilders, worked together with Sir Eric Yarrow and with Len Redshaw of Vickers.

The possibility of MOD(N) sponsoring this cooperative group was mooted. Had the Booz-Allen proposals for warship building been adopted as government policy this would have been an avenue down which to approach the problems of the future.

Another potential approach was through the unions. Westlands, the helicopter builders, had escaped being nationalised with the rest of the aircraft industry, apparently because their trade unions had objected. Was a similar escape a possibility for VT, at least? The unions however, although they wanted to retain both VT's autonomy and existing management, drew the line at opposing nationalisation as a whole.

So whilst a few sympathetic supporters had been found in DTI and the local Chamber of Commerce, it soon became clear that the government would not listen, and that efforts would be better concentrated on lobbying to maintain autonomy of the company within a nationalised corporation, when it was eventually set up.

The case for nationalisation of ship repairers - including Vosper Ship Repairers, who had recently absorbed Harland & Wolff's repair interests in Southampton docks, - was even weaker. Unlike some of the merchant building yards, the repair companies were unanimous in their opposition to a state take-over, and the ship owners seemed to agree. A Chamber of Shipping paper predicted a disaster.

Despite all this, it must be said that there was never the slightest indication of Benn budging from his original stance. Moreover, it soon became clear that the proposed terms almost amounted to confiscation. This situation was highlighted by another statement made by Sir David Brown at the AGM of his company on 17th April 1975, (also reproduced in Appendix 1).

Benn's basis for valuing the companies to be nationalised was intended to be the price which would have been paid by a willing buyer to a willing seller on 31st July 1974. In the case of VT this was interpreted as the London Stock market capitalisation of the company. At that time some 85% of the shares on issue were directly or indirectly under the control of Sir David Brown, so that the market in these shares was stultified to the extent that their price represented only about a third of the nett company assets per share. An examination of the accounts of Vosper Ltd and VT shows the net assets at just over £13 million in October 1974, and climbing steadily from £8 million in 1972 to £28 million in 1976. The price offered by the government in 1975 was initially a mere £4.2 million, at a time when, in addition to the known asset value, there were firm prospects of growth already in the pipeline.

Although this price was subsequently raised to £5. 2 million, it was poor recompense for a company which had reported pre-tax profits of £6. 2 million for the year to October 1976 (the last full year before being taken over), and hardly in line with the Act's pious reference to "a willing buyer and seller". Sir David claimed compensation of some £40 million. Remarkably, this was eventually turned down after appeal to the Court of Human rights in Strasbourg, although some of the Judges from the European court wrote a minority report recommending special consideration for VT and Brooke Marine, which had suffered a similar fate.

As already explained, some restructuring of the company had been carried out for technical reasons, and it was necessary to partially reverse this and carry out further changes to prepare for nationalisation. The net result was that by vesting day the original J. I. Thornycroft & Co. had become "Vosper Thornycroft (UK) Ltd" and acquired all the group's shipbuilding interests, including the peripheral activities of Support Services, Controls and Hydraulic power. Ship repairing, because it had looked for a while that it might escape nationalisation, was separated and transferred to the old Thornycroft (Hampton) Boatyard Ltd, which had been dormant for some time, and which was renamed Vosper Ship Repairers Ltd. The holding company, (which had been renamed Vosper Thornycroft Ltd in 1974) reverted to its original name of Vosper Ltd.

Vosper Ltd, together with the old Thornycroft shipyard at Tanjong Rhu, Singapore, and a small offshoot, Vosper Offshore, formed under Alan Griffith to exploit the growing offshore oil industry in the UK, were the only parts eventually to escape nationalisation.

Regardless of VT's misgivings and in spite of delaying tactics by the Opposition, the Aircraft and Shipbuilding Industries Bill inexorably made its way through parliament (by a margin of one vote) and on 17th March 1977 received the Royal Assent.

Vesting day was on 1st July 1977. To readers

who have witnessed the collapse of communism and its centrist doctrine, it may come as no surprise that nationalisation was doomed to failure, but this was not the political mood in 1977. Admiral Sir Anthony Griffin, the first Chairman of British Shipbuilders, touring the yards at the time said that this was to be nationalisation with a difference. The successful yards would get little more from headquarters than a card at Christmas time, so they need not fear a heavy bureaucracy. Even before the first of those cards was due, however, central departments had been set up requiring to know how many cables, pipes, plates and so on had been installed in each and every ship under construction, and on a monthly basis!

The unions were also due for disillusionment. Pay bargaining, the heart and soul of industrial relations, was conducted centrally, and common rates of pay were agreed with national officials of the Trade Unions by the BS director of personnel and his staff. The deputy chairman of BS would commonly attend these negotiations to emphasise their importance, along with the ceremonial beer and sandwiches in emulation of similar set piece rituals which then also took place at No. 10 Downing Street. In the shipyards, industrial relations therefore became a dogged game of management insisting on working to the agreements, and shop stewards endeavouring to extract any concessions possible. Pay levels slipped gradually over eight years to 15% below the average employment rates. The role of the full time officials, the local area Trade Union representatives across the country, was gradually usurped by the shop stewards who of course were paid by the company but who did less and less work until many of them too spent all of their time on so-called trade union business. These were the heydays of trade union power which led to the "winter of discontent", and, later, to Arthur Scargill's miners strike, when it seemed that the only thing that mattered was bringing down the government - any government - without regard to Britain's ability to buy and sell wares in the world market place.

The result was that British ships remained uncompetitive and there was a need for a growing subsidy in the industry. This in turn created a strategy of progressive redundancy. There had

been 88,000 people in shipbuilding and repair in 1977. By 1987 despite a huge reduction, no pattern for the future emerged: Virtually no yards were closed and each ran on with fewer employees and consequently higher overheads. Naval work was seen as jam to be spread thinly across all and sundry. The advice in the Booz-Allen report, to effectively concentrate this on the three specialist warship yards, was ignored; not because it would have imperilled the MOD(N)'s procurement policy, but presumably for the very reason predicted by Booz-Allen, namely that it would reduce employment prospects on the Tyne, at Swan Hunter; near the BS establishment which housed most of the 900 Headquarters staff. Many others were based in London at 197 Knightsbridge.

Eliminating Cammell Laird, Swan Hunter and Scott Lithgow from warship building could have helped MOD(N) to encourage Vickers, Yarrow and VT to cooperate more fully with each other and in particular to establish a common export marketing organisation since even these three firms could not rely wholly on the RN programme for their continued viability. There was already a certain air of comradeship between the three when they occasionally came together at working level.

As time went on more and more people were employed at headquarters, whilst the working yards were continually pressurised to cut their overheads, regardless of whether they brought in work. Tolerance changed to bitter frustration as more and more power moved to the centre.

The feeling grew that VT, in the over employed sunny south, could be sacrificed to northern interests. MOD(N) recognised that VT designers were more experienced than any in the UK. Having placed the Type 22 Frigate at Yarrow, it was the intention of a number of influential officers to develop the next, and smaller, frigate at VT. This plan became obscured in about 1980, although VT's proposals for the machinery fit were eventually adopted. The call to keep Yarrow busy won the day: It was decided that VT, who had gained the lion's share of UK warship exports for many years, could stand or fall on such work. Anyone who has ever been involved in the business will know this to be a fatuous proposition since the first question from an overseas buyer is "What do you do for the Royal Navy?". It doesn't have to be the same design, but the seal of approval from MOD(UK) for recent work is essential.

No sales advantage came to VT from nationalisation; indeed, the Company suffered a good deal of bureaucratic interference. It was fortunate therefore that, the Company began the period of nationalisation with a significant export coup.

In 1977 VT's long relationship with the Egyptian Navy was at last showing signs of achieving the sought after contract for strike craft. While VT was being swallowed up by British Shipbuilders, the final specification for the 52 metre *Ramadan* class had been negotiated in Alexandria and Cairo, and in September 1977, two months after vesting day, the contract was signed for six boats.

This was another major export achievement by any standards, and more so because, like the *October* boats, the new ships were fitted with predominantly British electronic equipment. In addition to two Marconi/Sperry fire control systems, each ship had a Racal-Decca electronic warfare system similar to those installed on the *October* boats but with a substantially increased capability. It was unfortunate that development problems with this very advanced equipment were a constant source of worry and eventually the cause of late delivery for some of the boats.

The *Ramadan* class boats were also fitted with a Ferranti Action Information System, based on the CAAIS system originally fitted in the Type 21 frigates, but very substantially modernised. The guns, a 76mm and a twin 40mm, (both fully automatic), and the Otomat missile system were all supplied from Italy, there being no suitable British equivalents.

The whole weapon system was a very powerful one even for this large strike craft, and the task of weapon system engineering, led by VT themselves, a very considerable one. There was a large proportion of additional development work required, not only with the new CAAIS system, but also with the fire control and, in particular, the electronic warfare system.

The EW system for the *October* boats was already suffering delays due to the development problems, as were parts of the Otomat missile

system. It was becoming clear that some of the *October* boats at least would be delivered late because of these problems, and that strenuous efforts would be required to avoid similar delays with the *Ramadans*.

The boats themselves were indeed the sales breakthrough that VT had been seeking ever since the building of *Tenacity*. The *Ramadans* were however all diesel powered; each with four high speed engines made by MTU in Germany. Each engine drove a separate fixed pitch propeller via a reversing reduction gearbox. This gave the ships a top speed in excess of 40 knots, and the fact that VT were confident enough to guarantee this in the contract played an important part in winning the order. In the well-tried VT fashion, the hulls were of welded steel, with mainly riveted aluminium superstructures in order to save weight.

This order ensured that the company began its nationalised existence in good shape, with plenty of work in hand, unlike many of its newly acquired sister companies.

It was, however, the end of an era. Sir John Rix, as well as being chairman and chief executive of the now nationalised Vosper Thornycroft (UK) Ltd, was also the managing director of the old private sector holding company, Vosper Limited, together with its few remaining subsidiaries. It was clear to everyone that Sir John could not long remain in both camps, and on 31st January 1978, he resigned from the nationalised company.

British Shipbuilders replaced him by appointing Andrew Shaw as managing director and chief executive. Andrew had been successfully running the Controls and Electrical Division for some time and had been appointed to the board of VT in June 1977, at the same time as Hugh Melvin, who in October had become financial director to replace Ken Ford on the latter's retirement.

The last new appointment to the board before Sir John's resignation was that of Nigel Tunnicliffe, the General Manager of the Portchester Shipyard. Nigel was an experienced and very dynamic manager who invariably called a spade a spade. Son-in-law of Peter Du Cane, he was an ex-Guards officer and looked it. Nobody who did not know it would have guessed that he relied on a heart pacemaker to keep him alive: certainly he never appeared to allow it to restrict him in any way.

These organisational changes, which had to be approved by British Shipbuilders, were the first of a series of changes at board level which continued throughout the period of public ownership.

Another significant change coincident with the departure of Sir John was the splitting of the ship repair business from the rest of VT. On paper, the two had been separate companies since the former had become Vosper Ship Repairers Ltd when the organisation was restructured to allow for the possibility of ship repair being treated separately, or even, it had been vainly hoped for a while, escaping nationalisation altogether. Until the end of January 1978 the two companies had continued to share the same board meeting. Thereafter, John Wilde, the chief executive of Vosper Ship Repairers Ltd, presided over separate board meetings, although he and the new chief executive of VT remained members of each other's boards for a while.

An important consequence of the *Ramadan* order was the need to modernise the Portchester yard in order to deal with larger patrol boats. This of course necessitated obtaining the approval of British Shipbuilders; a somewhat lengthy process. The project involved the building, in two stages, of a large new workshop at Portchester and an associated ship lift and wet dock. These were all sited on reclaimed mud flats adjacent to the then existing yard. The new building was not ready in time to accommodate the first *Ramadan*, which was built in the old hovercraft facility, No.3 shop. However, before the completion of the second phase, two more *Ramadans* were taking shape in the first half of the new No.4 shop.

It might perhaps be thought that the building of this splendid new modern facility at Portchester so soon after nationalisation demonstrated the advantages of the new organisation. The fact was that VT had to fight hard for the approval required to spend its own money (particularly favourable payment terms had been negotiated with the Egyptians), and in fact the company was to remain a substantial net contributor to British Shipbuilders throughout public ownership.

The ship lift, which was part of the second phase of this development, was a novel addition

which was to prove most valuable in the years to come. Three parallel wide gauge railway tracks ran the full length of No.4 Shop and out of the shop onto a large concrete apron. The centre track continued onto the ship lift platform. Using special trucks and moveable rails, complete ships could be moved transversely from one track to another, and thus onto the ship lift, which could lower them into the water. The lift could carry ships of up to about 800 tonnes in weight. It moved extremely slowly under the control of a series of synchronised electric winches, which supported the huge steel and wooden platform on wire hawsers. The speed of operation made the launching ceremonies of new ships painfully tedious to watch, but it had one enormous advantage over the traditional rush down the slipway: the whole process could be reversed. This meant that ships could just as easily be brought out of the water, and, in many cases, back into No.4 Shop, for inspection, repairs or painting. Both quality and productivity benefited from the ability to work under cover.

British Shipbuilders approved the ship lift in September 1978 but insisted on it being leased. This was more expensive in the long run than outright purchase, but was due to the already critical cash flow situation of the new corporation. Nevertheless, during the autumn of 1978, VT was also able to obtain approval for further new developments at Woolston, which included a new fitting out complex and a highly mechanised pipe shop facility.

Changes at board level continued. In August, Dennis Kemp, who had been in overall charge of shipbuilding, resigned and was replaced in this role by Peter Usher. British Shipbuilders appointed Dr. Peter Milne as a non-executive member of the board.

In October, Andrew Shaw apparently fell out with BS headquarters and vanished virtually overnight. Mr. W. Richardson was appointed as chairman immediately.

Bill Richardson had been chairman and chief executive of Vickers Shipbuilders for a long time. Whilst to the shocked employees of VT he was still an intruding foreigner, appointed by the unwanted BS headquarters in Newcastle, he was at least an experienced warship builder, and, moreover, one

52 metre *Ramadan* class for Egypt.

Portchester shipyard: No. 4 shop, ship lift and new wet dock.

*Ramadan* in No. 4 shop.

Tanjong Rhu shipyard - Singapore.

who had been forcibly nationalised like themselves. If there had to be an outsider at the helm, there could have been many worse choices.

Bill, however, was still expected to continue his duties at Vickers shipyard at Barrow in Furness as well as to "pull VT together". A glance at the map should be enough to confirm that this meant that he was required to travel a very large number of miles if he was to visit both of his charges sufficiently frequently and although he set about doing this, it was clear that a new chief executive would also be required.

Amid the disturbance and speculation that these upheavals at the top created, the resignation of John Grant, on reaching retirement age, after many years as company secretary of VT was yet another blow, although John remained on the board for a further year before actually retiring. Nobody could have known it at the time, but the appointment of his assistant, Keith Brown, as company secretary was a significant milestone. Keith nominally shared the post for a while with the assistant secretary of British Shipbuilders, but single-handed was to carry out the role with distinction throughout the difficult transition to privatisation, the eventual flotation, in a new form, on the Stock Exchange, and beyond. All of this would have tested the patience and ability of any company secretary to the full, but Keith remained calm throughout and never seemed to be at a loss to provide advice on the most obscure aspects of company law and the complex procedures which inevitably arose.

The company could obviously not continue long without a full time chief executive, and, much to the relief of many, David Wilson was appointed to the vacancy with effect from the 16th February 1979 under Bill Richardson as chairman.

Morale amongst the staff was however suffering, one reason being that Sir John Rix and Peter Shepherd, who had also left VT, were busy setting up a warship design consultancy under the name of Vosper International, in Fareham, just down the road from Portchester. Frustrated by British Shipbuilders and lured by the better salaries being offered by Vosper International, several valuable and senior design staff left VT. The intention was to design warships which could be built by the Singapore yard, and although this plan never really succeeded, it had many of the necessary ingredients; certainly there was no lack of competent designers. The Singapore yard had built many small patrol craft under VT guidance and was, at the time of nationalisation, building three quite advanced 37 metre patrol craft, fitted with gun fire control and Exocet missiles, for the Sea Wing of the Brunei Defence Force.

The changes at VT board level continued, the next to resign, on 31st May 1979, being Nigel Tunnicliffe who felt that life would be less bureaucratic and more productive building patrol boats in Italy. On the day he left Portchester there was a ceremony in the old boat shop at which Nigel kept everyone in fits of laughter with a lengthy and complicated story of how, when he had been much younger, Jean Carpenter (who had for years been Cdr Du Cane's secretary and still organised all company travel) had organised a business trip to Hong Kong for Peter Du Cane and himself, and had, in the interests of economy, booked them into an inexpensive hotel which, unknown to Jean, turned out to be a house of ill repute. The fact that Jean herself was listening to the story and laughed as loudly as anyone suggested that Nigel had embellished the facts quite considerably. He was popular and his departure was another blow to the morale of those remaining, some of whom were beginning to feel as though they were clinging to a sinking ship.

Although VT still had ample work, it was clear that not many other British Shipbuilders yards had, and the general state of the Corporation was obviously poor. Pessimistic rumours abounded. Despite the introduction in the summer of 1979 of a bonus payment scheme, productivity was suffering too.

British Shipbuilders continually urged all subsidiaries to economise and yet in November the VT board felt obliged to express its concern at the continuing growth in the numbers of staff employed at headquarters. By the New Year of 1980, British Shipbuilders had decided to reduce the numbers employed by the Corporation by constant percentage cuts in all subsidiaries, apparently regardless of profit performance, cash situation, or the needs of production and growth. They also employed some outside consultants to consider how all warship sales should be handled in future.

However, the gloom was not entirely unrelieved. Peter Usher, who had been a successful shipbuilding director at Woolston for some time, was awarded an OBE in the New Year Honours list, and there were signs that the government of Oman was almost ready to sign a contract for a new design of fast strike craft, 56 metres long.

Best of all, in some people's view, was the fact that in Britain a Conservative government had been elected and had announced its intention of privatising the nationalised industries. At last there seemed to be light at the end of the tunnel, but if they had known how long privatisation was to take, the mood at VT might have been less cheerful.

*Chapter Ten*

## WHEN A HORSE GROWS HORNS

Although the new decade offered little apparent comfort to British Shipbuilders, and VT was entering another spell of worrying about shortage of future work, there was plenty of activity. The *Ramadan* project proceeded apace, with the new Portchester building facilities being completed around the new strike craft. Early in 1980 the order from Oman for a larger, 56 metre, strike craft was confirmed, consolidating VT's foothold in this new market.

Another new market also appeared to be opening up. During 1979 British industry was beginning its first tentative contacts with China for many years. The first of many delegations from China appeared at Woolston, and the first of many lengthy discussions as well as social meetings with the Chinese took place.

After so many years of isolation, nobody in the West knew what to make of China, but natural curiosity and the desire to perhaps make a new ally were powerful incentives to fraternisation. More powerful still was the possibility of business with a vast and untapped market. In particular, the Chinese Navy was huge and thought to be very much in need of modernisation.

Initial contacts indicated that the Chinese were well aware of this and appeared to have a vast shopping list for naval equipment. The first naval mission to the UK included shipbuilders and engineers, and the resulting party of twenty or thirty set the pattern for all future contacts; the Chinese always operated in large groups.

There were reasons for this; everything in China seemed to be conducted in committee. Possibly, no single individual was empowered to make any decision, but it seemed more likely that the system had evolved so that no individual within a group could take all the blame for an incorrect decision; not only could responsibility for mistakes be more widely spread if more people in the group were involved, but fewer would be left to criticise the guilty.

We also discovered that there was no unemployment in China. This problem was eliminated by detailing several individuals to do a job which in the West would barely be enough to occupy one.

All of the Chinese appeared to closely watch all of the others, and nobody was permitted to be separated from the group. Whether this was due to fear of defection or of corruption by foreign devils was never clear.

Finally of course there was the language problem. Particularly in the early days, few of the Chinese spoke or understood much English (although some did so much better than they would admit), and so most were obliged to stay close to one of their interpreters in order to understand what was going on.

Fortunately there were a few Mandarin speakers on the British side. One of these was Ken Sly, an Australian ex-Air Force officer working in Ministry of Defence Sales, who very soon found himself occupied full time on the China project.

Ken was an enthusiast who spoke excellent Mandarin, which of course everybody regarded as an impossibly complex language. A few who made the effort to learn soon discovered that, compared to most European languages, it is sophisticated but simple in structure. However, it has several peculiarities, not the least of which is the writing, which tend to put off the casual student!

Although it seemed very likely that most, if not all, of any new ships bought by the Chinese Navy would be built in China, there was a possibility of selling ship designs, systems engineering, and support. It was generally agreed that the interests of British industry would best be served by a coordinated response, and that British Shipbuilders were best placed to provide this coordination.

Initially this task fell to Ian Wright, another ex RN Captain recently arrived at the Knightsbridge office of British Shipbuilders to coordinate warship sales activities. In November 1979 he led the first British Naval Armaments Team (BNAT) visit to China.

56 metre *Dhofar* class for Oman.

Another 75 foot GRP Keith Nelson, this time for St. Vincent.

In addition to Ian himself, BNAT comprised seventeen representatives drawn from a cross-section of the British Naval equipment industry. There were four from VT, three each from Vickers and British Aerospace, two from Rolls Royce and one each from Ferranti, Marconi, Plessey, Graseby and Westland Aircraft. BNAT arrived in Beijing in two waves, on the 11 and 12 of November 1979, and for three weeks were involved in a very busy programme getting to know China, the Chinese and their Navy. It was the beginning of a fascinating, frustrating, exhausting and eventually quite fruitless relationship which lasted for several years.

After being isolated from the outside world for so long, China was full of interest, both on the professional level and, even more so, all around us wherever we went. It was soon apparent that the average Chinese felt the same about the odd-looking foreign devils; in the early days it was all too easy to attract attention simply by walking down the street, and if one side or the other plucked up enough courage to try to converse, a huge crowd would rapidly gather. The first time this happened, it was rather frightening. However, we very soon found that the people were universally friendly and polite. A few were keen to try out their English, and when some of us responded in halting Mandarin, the ice was broken and we would spend a long time answering the same questions: *What country are you from? How many people in your family? How old are you? How much money do you earn?*

The last was a most difficult one to answer. Had we translated our salaries (relatively modest by Western standards) into Ren Min Bi at the tourist exchange rate, we would have seemed multi-millionaires to these people. Although the exchange rate was artificial and Chinese notes which we bought for our pounds were foreign exchange tokens, acceptable only in certain shops open to foreigners, we were indeed opulent, even compared with the most senior Chinese whom we met. Luxuries such as motor cars and superior living accommodation were evidently provided free to the latter, who could probably not have begun to pay for such things with their meagre salaries.

Our hosts were very hospitable, and keen to take us sightseeing to those places which were deemed suitable for foreigners. Over the years, we were to become familiar with the Forbidden City, the Ming Tombs, and the Great Wall at Ba Da Ling; its nearest approach to the capital. The Summer Palace became almost a second home since, remarkably, a British friend who worked for the Shell oil company had actually been allowed to move into one of the pavilions by the lake to live with his family, suitable accommodation for foreigners being in short supply. The Chinese had provided servants, and furnished the place with new, and perfectly ghastly, modern plastic furniture to make him feel at home. He had somehow managed to tactfully dispose of the latter, and furnished the old building, whose single storey was capped by a "curly" tiled roof and adorned with dragon gargoyles, the way it should have been; with old Chinese furniture and rugs, presumably acquired in some magical way from the maze of old shops which were still to be found in back streets of Beijing.

Later, we overcame our initial trepidation, and wandered far and wide in the older parts of the city without our guides. They were at first quite concerned, probably in case we got lost or were not properly treated as important guests. Certainly there was no danger of coming to any harm; more than could be said of a city of almost any other country in the world. We were often greeted with friendly smiles and unintelligible enquiries. Although the older parts of the city were poverty stricken, the streets, houses and people were usually scrupulously clean and tidy. Wandering through the narrow alleys amongst the picturesque old buildings was a rare experience. Suddenly, one would emerge into an enormous boulevard, flanked by huge and rather ugly modern buildings. The contrast was startling.

Another part of our education was travelling on the Beijing Underground. This was exciting because one first had to negotiate for a ticket. Getting on the right train was easy; usually there were only two platforms to choose from, and it was difficult to avoid getting on the first train that arrived: the mob surged forward in a body as soon as the doors opened. The trick was to know how many stops to count before trying to get out again;

even if one could remember the name of the station in characters or Pinyin, some skill was required to arrive at the doors at the right moment to be swept out onto the platform.

On that first visit we were new to all this, and in any case were soon borne off to Shanghai to visit shipyards. This journey was rather more alarming than the Underground as it involved flying in a Chinese aeroplane. We walked across the runway and queued for the steps, being given ample time to inspect the worn tyres on the undercarriage whilst waiting. Being unused to Chinese queues, the BNAT party were almost the last to get aboard, whereas their reserved seats were at the far end of the aeroplane. As soon as the last man stepped through the door, it was shut with a bang and the aeroplane began taxiing. Some managed to get to their seats before take off, only to find that most of the seat belts had lost their buckles. Should one ignore this, and hope that the pilot, who was already displaying aerobatic tendencies, would refrain from looping the loop? Or was it better to tie a knot and hope to be able to undo it in a hurry if it became necessary to abandon the aircraft? Somewhat relieved, we landed fairly safely in Shanghai, and were immediately whirled off to our hotel (a military run establishment) by another cohort of Chinese friends.

In Shanghai we were kept busy visiting shipyards and factories and attending crowded technical discussions with scores of Chinese "experts". We were also taken to theatres and entertained on a lavish scale at several Chinese banquets.

Banquets were a regular feature of our visits to China. We were invariably invited to one on arrival and, during longer visits or excursions to other areas, repeat performances were laid on. We would reciprocate by organising return fixtures at appropriate intervals. The meals were, of course, invariably Chinese, and consisted of innumerable courses of the most exquisitely prepared and delicious food which we had ever tasted. This was doubtless in sharp contrast to our host's normal daily fare, although the hotel food which we normally ate was usually good (unless one risked the European menu!). Certainly the cost of one banquet for twenty or thirty people would have fed

a Chinese family for weeks or even months on end. As there was always far too much for us to eat, we felt rather uncomfortable about this, but our hosts certainly enjoyed themselves.

Banquets also involved obligatory drinking sessions. Everyone always had at least three glasses at once; beer (which was very good), wine (which was not) and Mao Tai, (which was indescribable). At regular intervals, one or other of the senior Chinese present would rise to his feet and propose a toast; "*To Anglo-Chinese friendship!*", or "*To the British Navy*", or "*To Project 051*", and so on. One then had to rise to one's feet and drain the glass of Mao Tai in a single gulp (to drink it any other way would have unnecessarily prolonged the taste), crying "*Gan Bei!*" (Bottoms up!, or literally, dry glass). One was then supposed to prove that it was indeed dry, by inverting it or showing it to one's neighbour, whereupon it was instantly recharged in readiness for the next sally. Of course, the guests were expected to reciprocate, and the proceedings became quite merry. The Chinese all gave Mao Tai a fearsome reputation, maintaining it was "very strong". In truth, it did not appear to have an exceptionally high alcohol content; however, it certainly had a fearsome taste!

Our first visits to Chinese industry were also an eye-opening experience. The shipyards were huge, somewhat crude by modern standards, but turning out acceptable albeit somewhat dated ships. The warships in particular were obsolescent, mainly copies of Russian designs of the 1950s. The electronics factories were much the same; turning out, for example, serviceable but rather crude black and white televisions in hundreds. In one establishment we saw an old blacksmith's forge turning out waveguides and similar microwave components for radar in the most "agricultural" of conditions. Clean room conditions for "precision" components were almost laughable. However, here and there, presenting an incredible contrast, were small pockets of genuine modern technology; for example, one small, clean and well equipped factory was producing microchips, apparently with some success.

One day, we were invited to visit the ship research establishment at Wu Xi. This involved

getting up at about 5 a.m. and travelling for most of the morning by train. The journey was more interesting than flying, and a lot less frightening. The establishment was also very interesting, possessing a number of enviable test facilities such as towing tanks, a cavitation tunnel, a wave generating tank, and a rotating arm tank, all built on a lavish scale. Any Western research establishment would have been proud to own any of these. However, the weak point was the instrumentation which was for the most part crude, and could in no way have done justice to the rest. The Chinese were clearly acutely aware of this.

After admiring this establishment, we were taken sightseeing by boat on a huge shallow lake. In the distance, fishing junks under sail were most picturesque, even in the pouring rain.

Lest the reader by now has the impression that visiting China was just one long orgy of banquets and sightseeing, let me hasten to add that we were also worked quite hard as well. There were constant group discussions, in which two or three of us were cross-questioned by twenty, thirty, or more Chinese. The discussions began with us giving outline presentations on our various products, but soon centred in on proposals for modernising Chinese *Luda* class destroyers. As proposal details grew, with alternate massaging by both sides, so did the level of detail in the questioning.

The speed and effectiveness of the proceedings was of course greatly influenced by the competence of the interpreter. A few of these spoke better English than we did and had an excellent technical grasp of the subject matter. Others were not so good, and still more were clearly terrified and could make very little sense of what either side was saying! These latter were relatively easy to recognise and explanations could be slowed up and simplified accordingly. The dangerous ones were those who exuded confidence and immediately burst into voluble Chinese as soon as - or sometimes before - we finished a sentence. After a while, from the questions that were being asked and by catching a few words of Mandarin here and there, it sometimes dawned on us that these gentlemen had not the faintest understanding of what we were talking about and were misleading all the others. By then, a lot of time might have been wasted.

An average session would start with lengthy introductions. One by one, our "new friends" would stand up, beaming, whilst the interpreter explained: "*This is Mr Chen Gao Lin. He is antenna expert from Fourth Shanghai Radar factory. He wishes to say how honoured he is to meet foreign friends. He has several questions he wishes to ask. . . .* " and so on, until all twenty or thirty had been introduced, whereupon we felt obliged to introduce ourselves and explain our various roles. Then the questioning itself would begin, starting again with the first Chinese:

"*Mr Chen's first question is. . . .* " (here would be a lengthy technical question, sometimes concerning quite frivolous detail). We would take notes, lest we forgot the beginning before the end was interpreted. When the interpreter at last fell silent: "*Right*", one of us would say; "*I will now answer the first question*".

"*Excuse me,*" the interpreter would answer "*but first Mr Chen would like to ask five more questions*".

These would be expounded and translated at great length, until at last Mr Chen sat down. But before we could open our mouths:

"*Now Mr Pan has some questions to ask. Mr Pan's first question is. . . . . .* "

And so it went on, question after question, as fast as we could write them down. After a while, a question would recur, and then another. Originality would all but vanish, but each Chinese had to ask his quota of questions.

Eventually, after several hours, the last Chinese would sit down and the interpreter would fall silent.

"*Right,*" we would say. "*Shall we now answer question number one?*"

Murmuring and whispered consultations among the Chinese; then the interpreter would say:

"*We think it is now very late. Now it is xiu xi (rest) time. We will meet again later. Thank you very much.*"

At the next meeting, we would answer the questions, grouping together many similar or identical ones in the hope of cutting short the proceedings. At the end, after more discussion, the interpreter would say "*Thank you very much. We wish to study your answers. Please could you let us have them in writing tomorrow.*"

After a day or so, back they would come for the postmortem:

"*Mr Chen does not agree with your answer to question number thirty seven. He considers that. . . .*"

In this way, round one could be kept up for days before anybody could start on round two. A slight variation on the theme was when we were persuaded to put together a proposal, or a draft agreement, or memorandum of understanding. We would then explain it to the audience, and the questions and answers would start all over again.

During that first trip to Shanghai, we were relieved when Sunday came round; everyone was ready for a rest. There was some relief when the Chinese announced that Sunday was for "xiu xi". "*Who would like to come sight seeing?*" they asked.

Ian stuck his heels in. "*I shall have a rest and write up my report.*" he announced. "*You lot can go*".

Most of the rest of us decided to accept the invitation, especially when it was announced that the proposed trip was to Hang Zhou (Hangchow), a famous beauty spot, and that it would be entirely informal, with no meetings, speeches, or banquets. "*Yes please*", we told the interpreter.

"*Very good*" he said. "*All please meet in hotel lobby at 5 a.m. Bus will take you to station*".

We hadn't realised how far it was to Hang Zhou.

Nevertheless, next day we all appeared, dressed very informally in jeans and heavy sweaters and armed with cameras. Again the morning was spent straining cups of Chinese tea through our teeth, and watching mile after mile of agricultural countryside go by. Some of us bemused a group of Chinese by starting a game of liar dice, but they then got out their game of Chinese chess, which we found quite incomprehensible. At last we reached Hang Zhou station, but for those of us at the back of the coach, there seemed to be a hold up at the front. No one was being allowed to disembark. At last the reason emerged: The Leader was expected to disembark first, and Ian was back in Shanghai. Everyone tried to hide behind everyone else; some of those at the front could see out of the window.

"*Today*" announced our chief guide "*Hu Ke is leader. Please ask him to come forward*". My colleagues knew that this was the nearest most Chinese could get to pronouncing my name, and pushed me forward. Drawn up on the platform was a large reception committee, headed by a gentleman who was introduced as the Leader of the Peoples Liberation Army of Hang Zhou. So much for informality; and me in my old jeans and sweater!

In the bus, it soon transpired that my new friend spoke no English, so summoning up my few words of Mandarin, I said something like "*We are all very pleased to be in Hang Zhou*".

"*Ah*" he said "*You speak Chinese?*"

"*Not too good*".

"*Very good! Very good*".

Clearly more was required of me; the bus had fallen silent around us. I summoned up all my limited powers of conversation gleaned from 'Elementary Chinese, lesson three'

"*Er, last week we went to Wu Xi.*"

"*Ah, Wu Xi*" he said. "*Good, good.*"

Emboldened by success, I tried again. (Stick to the good old British ploy of discussing the weather - can't go wrong).

"*In Wu Xi it rained very hard. . . .*"

Suddenly there were roars of laughter and applause. Ken Sly came to the rescue:

"*You said 'lots of oil came down'*" he explained, "*They're all saying 'hurrah, we're rich!'*"

The full story of our experiences in China could probably fill another book. During the many visits spread over three to four years there was boredom and frustration, hundreds of hours of patient negotiation, dozens of banquets, and the production of tons of draft documents, mostly amid the bitter winter cold or dusty summer heat of Beijing. There were memorable occasions too, such as Christmas 1981 when the team enjoyed a fabulous traditional British Christmas lunch as guests of Commander Mike Farr, the British Naval Attaché, and his wife, and then had to follow it up with a Chinese banquet to end all Chinese banquets in the Great Hall of the People. The Chinese obviously appreciated the fact that we would rather have gone home for Christmas and did their best to make it up to us; we could not possibly have refused their kind invitation, which was also a great honour. Xia Tong, the cheerful little leader of the shipbuilders who spoke almost no English

but drank volumes of Mao Tai, explained most apologetically that he could find no "fire chickens" in Beijing. *"We do not eat them in China"* he explained. He meant turkeys.

Then there was New Year's Eve at the Summer Palace when the British contingent skated and let off firecrackers at midnight on the frozen lake, whilst a few puzzled Chinese looked on.

There is little point in dwelling further on what in the end turned out to be a blind alley. The project eventually grew into about the most complex and expensive weapon fit ever proposed, and although the Chinese kept saying they were appalled at the price, they did eventually sign a contract "subject to ratification by the Chinese Government".

The Chinese have a disarming way of expressing themselves in a roundabout fashion, which appears even more ingenious when expressed in Mandarin. Ken Sly was always coming up with linguistic gems. One evening in the Bei Jing hotel, several years after our first visit to China, when we were, as ever, chafing at some delay, he produced an old book of Chinese epigrams, and began to explain their subtlety.

*"Look at this one"* he said, *"Ma sheng jiao: When a horse grows horns".*

*"What does that mean, Ken?"*

*"Well, how many horses have you seen around with a set of horns? It means NEVER!"*

The Chinese Government never ratified that contract.

Back at VT during the early 80's it did indeed seem as though horses might grow horns before VT was released from the clutches of British Shipbuilders, despite the Government's declared intention of denationalisation. Initial approaches to the Government by some of the previous owners of the nationalised warship builders who wanted their property back had not been discouraged, but British Shipbuilders were, understandably, reluctant to part with virtually the only profitable parts of the Corporation. It was to be some time before the Government was to grasp this particular nettle.

Whilst some of us were wasting much time and money in China, changes and reshuffles at board level continued. In October 1981 British Shipbuilders decided to strengthen its central

marketing of warships, and appoint a senior man to take charge. David Wilson was undoubtedly the best man for this job, but unfortunately it meant that he had to leave VT, the company which he had served so long and so successfully. Peter Usher was appointed managing director in his place. Although nobody knew it at the time, this was at least one appointment which was to remain unchanged for several years.

Under Bill Richardson, a two tier director system had been introduced whereby some senior managers were appointed "local directors"; not full members of the VT Board, but frequently "in attendance" at Board meetings. When Peter Usher became managing director, Tony Dorey (Technical), Terry Grisley (Support Services and Products division), and Dick Potter (Sales) were elevated to the status of full VT board directors, and Gordon Dodd, who took over the running of the Woolston Yard from Peter Usher, became a local director.

A steady stream of MCMVs was being turned out with ever increasing efficiency. Despite this success in GRP, there was continuing concern over steel working productivity and competitiveness, and rumbles of possible redundancies. There was talk of building further 56 metre strike craft hulls for stock at Portchester, where steelwork was running short, although other trades were quite busy fitting out the 52 metre "Ramadans", and an order for a 75 foot Keith Nelson patrol boat was received from St Vincent in July 1980.

Woolston too was hungry for more steelwork, although an order for a further Type 42 had been received: HMS *Gloucester*, despite being a "stretched" version of the MOD design, was not enough to fill the available space left in the covered berth after the launch of HMS *Southampton* and HMS *Nottingham* in January 1979 and February 1980 respectively.

The former deserves special mention. Launches are normally a routine matter, although exciting occasions and a good excuse for a party, but the launch of HMS *Southampton* was exceptional. There had been a dispute with the workforce during the period leading up to it, culminating in the refusal of the Trade Unions to launch the ship. All the preparations for the event and the accompanying celebrations had been made, but there was no way out of the deadlock. With due propriety, the ceremony took place and the lady Sponsor named the ship, which stayed firmly on the slipway as the guests all trooped off to celebrate at the Southampton Guildhall.

The ensuing luncheon, like all such events, occupied most of the afternoon. Between the speeches and toasts, small groups of people conversed with each other in low tones, with the result that in the early evening most of the management returned to the yard. The ship was launched at midnight, without the assistance of the workforce. Those present will never forget this occasion which must stand in the record as a success, even though there was anger in addition to the astonishment when the yard opened in the morning.

In December 1980 there was a novel finale to the *October* boat contract. The Egyptians, always with an eye for a bargain, had negotiated for a somewhat dubious shipping company to transport two of the newly completed boats from Portsmouth to Alexandria as deck cargo. The ship met heavy weather in the Bay of Biscay, and one of the boats fell over the side in the middle of the night. Unmanned, and still attached to its shipping cradle, it survived the storm alone for many hours, until it was pounced on by a Dutch salvage tug and towed into Corunna. Here it remained for several weeks whilst the Egyptians negotiated with insurance agents and the shipping company over who was to pay for the damage. Although the engine room had been flooded, the boat had survived remarkably well and it proved impossible to represent it as a total loss; apparently the only eventuality against which it had been insured. In due course, it returned to Portchester for repair.

In February 1981 the Sultan of Oman placed a very welcome order for two more 56 metre fast strike craft; sister ships for the first of this design which was by then half completed at Portchester. The 56 metre, which was named the *Province* class in Oman, was designed to meet the arduous requirements of patrolling the Sultanate's 1000 or so miles of coastline. The ships were required to remain operational in the heavy weather encountered in those regions during the monsoon.

The hull form was based on the 52 metre *Ramadans*, but with increased length, beam and draught. The freeboard forward was also increased, and model tests carried out to optimise the profile of the bow for these severe conditions.

Like the *Ramadans*, the hulls were of all-welded steel with alloy superstructures, but unlike the 52 metre, the decks too were of steel and the joint between them and the alloy superstructure was made with explosively bonded bimetallic strip.

Usually, if unlike metals are in contact with each other, particularly in the presence of sea water, a galvanic cell is formed and severe corrosion results in a very short space of time. To prevent this, VT had previously riveted steel and alloy components together, taking suitable precautions to ensure that the two materials remained electrically isolated from each other and the joint was so designed that water could not lodge in it. This is however a tricky and labour intensive form of construction. If a sheet of aluminium and a sheet of steel are laid together and forced into violent contact by detonating an explosive charge, the two become firmly welded together. The bimetallic sheet can then be cut into strips, which are used at the joint between the two types of structure. Provided that water is kept away from the joint, corrosive action does not take place. In this case, the steel deck was welded to the steel half of the strip, and the aluminium deck house to the aluminium part.

The 56 metre also had a new propulsion system. They were the first vessels to go to sea with the new Paxman Valenta 18 cylinder high speed diesel engines. Four of these were fitted in each craft, each one developing 3,394 kW and driving a fixed pitch propeller through a reversing gearbox. Even more novel was the auxiliary electrical propulsion system, developed by VT in conjunction with Mawdsley Ltd. This allowed the ship to be propelled at speeds up to 8 knots by using power from the ship's generators, thus providing a quiet and very economical means of propulsion for extended patrol work.

VT also used the 56 metre to try out another innovative idea. One major advantage which bigger warships possess over strike craft is their ability to carry a helicopter, which can undertake

Wallis Autogyro operating from a 56 metre strike craft.

Hong Kong ferry.

Landing craft for Algeria.

Launch of HMS *Gloucester*.

many useful roles. The company approached the redoubtable Wing Commander Ken Wallis to investigate the possibility of giving strike craft their own indigenous aircraft in the shape of the Wallis autogyro. This rugged and reliable little "flying motorbike" was flown successfully from a 56 metre at sea, and could have provided a practical and useful addition to future strike craft. However, attempts to sell the idea usually met with incredulous smiles and remarks about James Bond films!

1982 opened with negotiations with an American company for two high speed monohull ferries for the Hong Kong to Macao route. These were a departure from VT's usual product line, but sufficiently similar to fast strike craft to tempt the company into bidding for the badly needed work. Another unorthodox (for VT) job was received in the form of a subcontract from Brooke Marine to build a landing craft which they had designed for Algeria. Woolston's appetite for steelwork was also slightly assuaged by a further subcontract for a patrol craft hull.

1982 also brought the Falklands war, and Woolston carried out some very rapid refit work, including fitting a helicopter deck to the liner *Canberra*.

The design group continued to produce designs for light frigates and to assist the sales department in marketing them around the world. There seemed real possibilities of frigate sales in Greece, Indonesia and Pakistan, and much effort was expended in these directions. Egypt continued to be regarded as a "hot" sales target for frigates as well as more strike craft, but money was, as ever, the problem. Egyptian credit in Britain was hard to obtain, and in 1982 the Egyptians signed a contract with Spain for frigates, but this too foundered for lack of finance. With pressure from VT, British finance was arranged for Pakistan to procure some VT Mk.7 frigates; these turned into Type 21s at an early stage of the ensuing discussions, which, like China, were also to continue, fruitlessly, for several years to come.

In July 1982 the first 56m strike craft ordered by the Sultan of Oman was completed and delivered on time, only thirty months after the order had been placed. SNV *Dhofar*, as she was called, carried out

proving trials in the Arabian Sea in the monsoon of 1983, when she operated successfully in force 7 winds and an unpleasant 8 metre swell.

VT then was still proving its ability to design and build modern warships, and to deliver them on time. Nevertheless, it was still a desperate struggle to maintain competitiveness against foreign yards, although wage and salary rates were held low by British Shipbuilders. Because of this, the work force was becoming disenchanted, and it was increasingly difficult to recruit well qualified technical staff to replace leavers.

There were several changes at board level too during this period. Hugh Melvin, the finance director, decided to seek his future outside the shipbuilding industry and left in September 1982. Barry Jones, who had been managing the financial affairs of the non-shipbuilding divisions of VT, stepped ably into the breach but British Shipbuilders insisted on seeking to fill VT's vacant financial directorship from elsewhere. This too took some considerable time. In March 1983 John Gray joined VT and British Shipbuilders appointed him finance director a month later. At about the same time, Gordon Dodd was appointed a full member of the VT Board. Two weeks later Terry Grisley was appointed managing director of Brooke Marine, the smallest of the British Shipbuilders warship builders, located at Lowestoft. Terry had been running the Support Projects division of VT since 1975 and in 1980 had become a director when he had also taken over the other VT non-shipbuilding divisions; Controls and Hydraulic Power. On moving to the East coast yard, Terry remained a non-executive director of VT.

George Cameron had replaced Terry as general manager of Support Projects when the latter joined the board.

Support Projects continued to develop and in 1982 designed and built a maintenance base in Barbados for the Defence Force. In mid April 1983 George took over Terry's other executive responsibilities at VT, and was appointed a director. Peter Usher gained a seat on the British Shipbuilders warship building divisional board. British Shipbuilders appointed Geoff Fuller, an ex-Ministry Naval Constructor to the VT board, and in August appointed him chairman of VT to replace

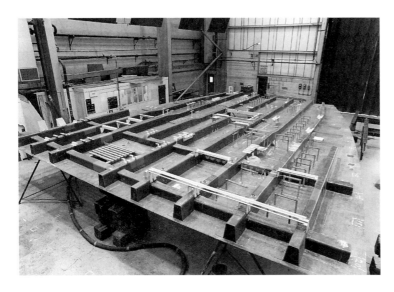

GRP deck section upside
down for easy fitting of pipes
and cable hangers.

Lower hull GRP module
showing fittings under
deck and on bulkhead
prior to fitting to ship.

GRP main bulkhead ready
to go to the ship.

GRP superstructure unit being placed on a trolley for transport to ship.

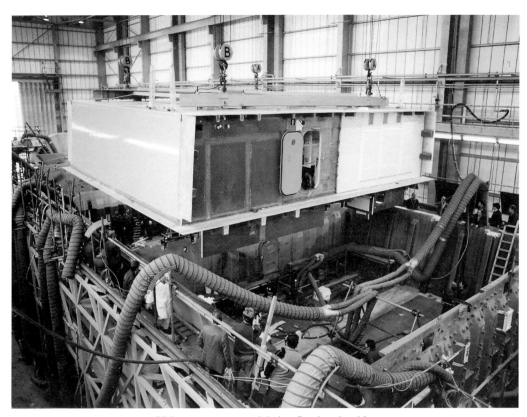

GRP superstructure unit being fitted to the ship.

HMS *Sandown* lead ship of single role minehunter class.

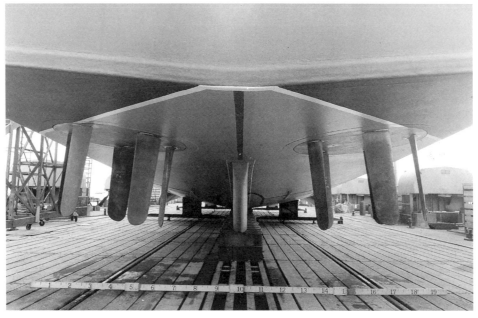

A *Sandown* on the Portchester ship lift showing Voith Schneider propulsors.

Bill Richardson, who was finally retiring from his remaining duties.

Negotiations for the two high speed ferries for Hong Kong were successfully concluded and construction commenced at Portchester. These ships were similar in many ways to the strike craft, but rather larger at 62.5 metres overall. Also powered by four 3000 HP 16 cylinder Paxman Valenta diesels, they were to carry 700 passengers on three decks, in some comfort, at a speed of 27 knots. The intention was to compete with the existing hovercraft and hydrofoil ferries which were smaller, and slightly faster, but relatively expensive to run.

Portchester needed the work badly at the time, and an over-optimistic estimate was made of the number of man hours required to build a ferry, as compared with a strike craft. Although the fitting out, which normally accounts for a substantial portion of the effort required to build a warship, was relatively simple, Portchester had little recent experience of this type of work, and there were unexpected problems. Also, these were high technology vessels rather than simple ferries. The company overran its budget on both ships. Nevertheless, things looked better on 12th July 1984 at the combined ceremony at which the ships were named *Cheung Kong* and *Ju Kong*, after Chinese rivers. At the crucial moment, a sharp shower of rain soaked most of the assembled crowd of spectators. Many of the most important guests were Hong Kong Chinese, who regarded this as a most impressive omen of good luck, and were delighted despite their wet clothes.

Unfortunately, however, problems continued to plague these vessels. In the autumn, successful trials in the Solent followed completion, and eventually they were loaded aboard a container ship for the journey to Hong Kong. The ship went via Copenhagen, where it encountered severe European winter temperatures. Considerable frost damage was caused to the ferries' engines, which had not been completely drained before departure, and this fact was not discovered until they arrived at Hong Kong. This was the principal cause of delay in entering service, but, not surprisingly, there were other teething troubles.

The efforts to rectify the various problems and

deal with the ensuing legal actions by the owners, who were in any case apparently in some financial difficulties, continued for a considerable time. It was a cautionary lesson on the dangers of stepping outside the normal product range without due care; the landing craft subcontract taken by Woolston, which also ran into unexpected problems, was another. At least such lessons were noted and strenuous actions taken to prevent repetition of the mistakes.

British Shipbuilders had also been deeply concerned for some time at the low level of productivity throughout the industry, and were making serious efforts to improve matters by studying the production methods used abroad; notably by the Japanese. VT, although it may not have been among the worst in the UK, had much to learn from this exercise, and a lot of effort was put into studying "Common Core Technology".

Without going into details, the techniques involved radical changes to production methods which would allow easier access to otherwise difficult and time consuming jobs. Traditional shipbuilding involved building a metal box and then squeezing all the machinery, pipe work, cables, electrical equipment and furnishings into that box through small openings and along cramped passageways. They then had to be fitted to bulkheads and deckheads in awkward or cramped positions. Different trades would get in each other's way, and the whole situation could be further aggravated by demarcation between them.

The solution was to fit as much as possible of the internal equipment to bulkheads and decks before these latter were added to the ship, thus allowing much easier access for all the workers concerned. However, a moment's thought will show that this requires a very great deal of additional planning; detailed installation drawings are required at an earlier stage of the build, and a high degree of accuracy in installation is essential: part of a pipe run fastened to a bulkhead must meet up precisely with its counterpart on the adjacent deck if time consuming reworking is not to negate the whole process.

VT had, to a small extent, been applying such principles already, as well as gleaning improvements which should in any case result from repetitive production runs. Nevertheless, everyone agreed that there was still plenty of scope for further improvement.

By 1982 the *Hunt* programme was in full swing, HMS *Brocklesby* being launched in January to join *Brecon*, *Ledbury* and *Cattistock*. In December *Dulverton* followed, launched the day after HMS *Gloucester*, which turned out to be Woolston's last Type 42. But although steel shipbuilding in the yard was in for a bleak time, GRP production was only just taking off. Seven more *Hunts* were to follow before the class was complete, each one being produced with fewer and fewer man hours. VT was improving with every ship, but to further reduce the cost of production would require a determined effort from the initial design stage, as well as an enormous investment in production planning and drawing. Full benefit of Common Core Technology was therefore only to be felt in the next major project.

The RN too was gaining experience from operating the ships and the MOD(N) was beginning to consider how the lessons learned should be applied to the next generation. In broad terms, they reached three conclusions.

That the type of stiffened single skinned GRP construction developed for the *Hunts* was the best available, being superior to both the sandwich and monocoque methods being practised abroad.

That the next generation should concentrate exclusively on hunting, as opposed to sweeping, mines.

That great emphasis should be placed on unit cost, but without degrading performance.

In 1982 VT was asked by the MOD(N) to carry out a pilot study on the form which the next generation minehunter should take. Having already put considerable thought into their design for the 47m export minehunter, and with the involvement of the VT2 Hovercraft in various Ministry trials and MCM studies, the company were uniquely placed to do this. Both the 47m and the VT2 were initially put forward as possible solutions, together with other hovercraft. However, although air cushion vehicles had demonstrated a remarkable invulnerability to underwater explosions, as well as other relevant talents, they were eventually rejected by the RN in favour of a more conventional

solution. It was also considered that in the light of more recent technology and experience, the 47m design could be substantially improved, and an entirely new outline design was developed. This was eventually selected by the MOD(N), and christened the Single Role Minehunter, or SRMH.

VT was then awarded a detailed design contract for this ship, with the object of producing a design which could then be built by a shipbuilder of the MOD(N)'s choice. This was of course right and proper and in accordance with the established principles of competitive tendering. The Ministry were clearly keen to avoid the establishment of a GRP shipbuilding monopoly by VT, and, in theory at least, the new ships could be built in Glasgow by Yarrow Shipbuilders, who had built two of the eventual total of thirteen *Hunts*. Nevertheless, with VT's efficiency improving with each *Hunt* built there was not much doubt about who would be able to give the MOD(N) best value for the taxpayer's money. The MOD(N) however did not relax the competitive pressure.

After a lengthy and very thorough design period, the embryo SRMH began to emerge. It remained very firmly a mine hunter only, although space allowed on board for future development meant that the addition of sweeps or other equipment for an export customer would be possible.

Development of the mine hunting system itself; the special sonar and the mine destruction equipment, represented some considerable advances over the capability of the *Hunts*, but at least as significant was the design of the ship and its propulsion and control systems, as well as the great efforts that were taken throughout to keep the costs of these down.

A major design aim was to optimise the slow speed manoeuvrability of the ship, so that when hunting mines it could be positioned accurately over a given spot, and remain there regardless of wind and tide. The profile of the hull and superstructure were determined with the effects of windage in mind, and considerable study went into the selection of the propulsion system. Eventually Voith Schneider propulsors were selected. This device comprises a series of vertical paddle blades, each shaped like an aircraft's wing, rotating about a common vertical axis. As they rotate, the angles

Computer Aided Drawing (CAD) office at Woolston.

RN *Tribal* class refitted for Indonesia.

110 foot patrol craft for US Coast Guard, built by Bollinger to VT design.

56 metre fast strike craft for Kenya. Project *Shark*.

of incidence to the water are varied in order to produce thrust in any desired direction. With two of these propulsors, the ship can be moved ahead or astern, and rotated virtually on the spot to point in any direction. The ship was also fitted with bow thrusters; small propellers mounted forward in transverse ducts in order to provide a powerful yawing moment.

With the two thrust vectors from the Voith Schneiders being infinitely variable in both magnitude and direction, and the bow thruster as well, the helmsman would have a variety of options in any given situation. The exploration of these by means of a computer model, and the design of an appropriate automatic control system occupied VT Controls division for some time, but their efforts were eventually rewarded by winning the contract from the MOD(N) to design and build this system.

Considerable efforts of course also went into minimising the magnetic and acoustic signatures of the ship, in order to make it as safe as possible when approaching magnetic or acoustic mines. The achievement of the severe standards set for these was no easy task, especially as great emphasis was also placed on minimising the cost of so doing.

Production engineering considerations probably had a greater influence on the shape of the SRMH than on any other previous RN vessel. This was the first complete ship design carried out by VT since their study of "Common Core Technology" techniques, and an enormous amount of effort went into production engineering and planning. This was all to pay significant dividends.

Unlike the *Hunt* class, the ship was built of flat deck panels to ease production, and an enormous amount of pre-outfitting was planned. When VT eventually won the contract for the first ship, HMS *Sandown*, the operations room was, for example, built separately and largely fitted out with equipment before being installed in the ship.

Another first for the SRMH was that it was the first RN ship completely designed and drawn on a computer system. VT had installed a Computervision drawing system at Woolston and had for some time been training draughtsmen in the new techniques. Whilst the system took quite a lot of learning, and in no way replaced the need

for original and innovative design work by humans, it made modifications or adaptions to existing designs created on the system very much easier. It was also ideal for presenting the mass of design information in the new formats demanded by the techniques of Common Core Technology.

These innovations in drawing and production techniques were introduced fully for the first time on top of the need to develop from scratch not just a new design, but an entirely new type of warship. All three main elements; hull, propulsion system, and payload, were radically new, and moreover the interaction between them was complex. It would not have been surprising if the original programme had eventually stretched to delay the delivery of the first ship by many months, or even several years! But this was not so. The feasibility study completed in mid 1982 envisaged the Contract Acceptance Date of the first ship being in early 1989. Following the basic design phase in mid 1983, this planned Contract Acceptance Date had slipped by about a month, to the end of the first quarter of 1989. But there it stayed throughout the project; an amazing feat.

This is not to say that no problems were encountered, or that there were no delays or changes of plan; there were, but they were overcome. Inevitably, it was the production department which bore the brunt of the accumulated delays in commercial negotiation and design. Production of the mould also took longer than planned, but laying up the new hull went faster than had been expected. The actual launch was, on paper, eight or nine months late (depending upon which of the early draft programmes was considered), but to some extent this was deliberate. Following experience with the *Hunts*, even more fitting out was completed before the ship entered the water, so that the time required to completion was dramatically reduced. The first ship was eventually accepted on 17th March 1989. The new methods of project management, within both the MOD(N) and VT, were beginning to bear real fruit. But the narrative is jumping ahead again.

Although no order for new steel ships had come in 1982 to fill the empty berth left by the launch of HMS *Gloucester*, VT did secure an important order from Indonesia to refit three ex-RN *Tribal* class destroyers. This task provided some much needed work for Woolston, but, like many such jobs, did not prove to be profitable. Quoting for refits is always difficult and dangerous, since the exact nature of the work required cannot usually be determined and costed until much of it is already in hand. There are various arrangements intended to protect the shipbuilder from having to do more than he quoted for, and the customer from running out of money before the ship is seaworthy, but almost invariably there are disappointments and unpleasant shocks on both sides. This large contract for the extensive repair of three elderly and quite complex vessels was no exception.

On a different front, another project which was to have far reaching results in the future was the success of a small American shipyard, Bollinger Machine Shop and Shipyard of Lockport, Louisiana, in selling the VT 110 foot patrol craft design to the US Coast Guard.

The Coast Guard had an urgent requirement for a number of patrol craft to combat drug smuggling. There was no time for development and they insisted on a well proven design. Bollinger approached VT for a licensing agreement, and, after the usual American round of court cases with their rivals, eventually won the contest to build what became known as the *Island* class in the USA.

VT was astonished at the speed with which the Americans built these ships. Although their first efforts appeared a little rough and ready by VT standards, quality soon improved without any concessions to productivity. There were clearly useful lessons to be learned from these wild men from the swamps of Louisiana! It was the beginning of an important link between VT and the USA.

The first contract was for a batch of sixteen boats, an unheard of number by VT standards, these were to be followed by a second order for twenty one more and eventually a final order for a further twelve.

Although VT secured some useful sub contracts to supply certain components and other support, very little of the shipyard work came to the UK, and Portchester was getting hungry again.

However, salvation was at hand. For many months the sales department, in the form of Dennis Sitwell, had been working patiently with an old Vosper customer who had a requirement, and a welcome order for two 56 metre fast strike craft was received from the Republic of Kenya, who christened it Project *Shark*. Support Projects also won some important contracts to design and, later, build a base for the Kenya Navy. VT was set to leave public ownership in a similar way to that in which she joined it: with a very valuable order for Portchester.

## Chapter Eleven

# PRIVATISATION AT LAST

Whilst VT was busy with the early phases of the SRMH programme and desperately pursuing the *Shark* project and other warship export orders, the Conservative Government was moving very slowly but nevertheless surely towards the declared goal of privatisation.

On 9 May 1983 the British Shipbuilders Act received Royal Assent. Thoughts at VT began to turn to the reality of the Company regaining its independence. Most people welcomed the prospect of simply being free of British Shipbuilders, but there had been little serious conjecture at what might replace the nationalised holding company. Vosper Ltd, under the executive leadership of Sir John Rix, had taken over Hovermarine, and was now established as Vosper Hovermarine, a few hundred yards up the Itchen river from VT's Woolston shipyard. Would Sir David Brown, who continued to be the power behind Vosper Ltd, which was still engaged in litigation over the terms of the original compulsory purchase of VT at Nationalisation, bid to regain his lost property? If not, who would?

The Government put in hand a "vigorous programme of denationalisation" despite the protests of Labour MPs. For those in the yard, the vigour of the programme was imperceptible at that time, though gradually dates emerged. In April 1984 the then Chairman of British Shipbuilders, Graham Day, said he expected that privatisation would be "up and running" in 3 months time and would be all over in 12 months. By October a more cautious programme was publicised where the aim was to complete by 31 March 1986, and this programme was in fact held. The warship builders were to be taken one at a time and would be sold off to the highest credible bidder. In the event, it was November 1985 before Vosper Thornycroft was free. The intervening period was used by British Shipbuilders to "put the best gloss on the apple". Apart from overhead reductions, for all of the yards were witnessing a reducing workload, the age profile of the directors was to be reduced by some aggressive pruning and firmly encouraged voluntary redundancy.

At VSEL Barrow, Greg Mott, the Managing Director was invited to leave in April 1984. A new British Shipbuilders-appointed Chairman, John Steele, took over at VT. Reducing the age profile became a struggle to stop the VT heart being torn out of the company and an alien transplant inserted in its place.

Len Peacock, James Pardoe, and Gordon Dodd for a different reason, were all invited to resign.

Even Peter Usher was put under intense pressure to "consider whether he wished to stay." It was probably the fact that he had declared his intention to lead a Management Buy Out (MBO) some 6 months earlier that protected him from the clean sweep of the elderly; he was within a month of his 58th birthday.

It was a difficult time. Overheads were reduced using Priority Based budgeting and more redundancies declared.

The first independent assessment of the company as it approached privatisation was made by Lazards on behalf of BS. They came to the yard under the chairmanship of Sir John Nott on 5 May 1984. A document summarising the activities and assets of the company had been produced for their benefit, and this stood the management in good stead for the many subsequent visits of merchant banks and potential bidders over the 18 months which followed. One golden rule which applied throughout the drawn out privatisation era was that there must be absolute equality of information to all who might reasonably need it. Thus for a year and a half the directors assembled and collated a mountain of facts, from the capacity of each machine tool to the latest move in each enquiry for a ship or product from any part of the world, and made this available for inspection.

Touche Ross came as Lazards' accountants in June 1984 and over the next 12 months produced a comprehensive report on the company.

Two new directors, Peter McNeilly in place of

Len Peacock for personnel and Brian Chapman as production director taking over from Gordon Dodd and James Pardoe, together with the earlier British Shipbuilders appointed Finance Director, John Gray, were invited to join the Usher led Management Buy Out team. The "old guard" members of this team were Tony Dorey (Technical), Barry Stobart-Hook (Sales), George Cameron (Systems) and Terry Grisley (Commercial), the latter now back from Brooke Marine following another British Shipbuilders initiated upheaval. The allegiance of these four to Peter Usher went back to the 1960's when they were members of the VT Design Department with Peter as the Technical Director. This distinction was to become a schism a year later.

From early 1984, efforts were made to learn what was involved in an MBO and which of the possible sponsors should be employed. Visits were made to the directors of two quite small firms who had bought their companies and the team became aware of the awesome risk they might face. The debt, the uncertainty of the order book ahead, the application required from everyone and the sheer hard work of being your own boss were clearly demonstrated, and starkly sobering. As they talked to some of the Banks, to Candover and later to 3i, egotistical thoughts quickly evaporated. The phrase "we shall be an under-bidder" came into parlance. In other words they would never raise the sort of money that a large company could offer if it really set its heart on buying VT.

The combination of such grave doubts over a successful bid and an uncertain and prolonged programme in the run up to a sale dampened any optimism that one day the company would be in the hands of the MBO team. But the other side of the coin was that the very thought of buying a shipbuilding company in 1985 was so far from the minds of most large companies, so the MBO just might win through.

If at this stage there was any price in mind, it was in the region of £10 million, based upon the value of 55 acres of prime Hampshire countryside. Set against this, redundancy costs were running at an average of £5,000 per person and VT employed in excess of 4,000.

The principles of the type of buy-out needed were becoming apparent. Clearing banks were willing to give competent managers leverage in the form of term loans, provided venture capitalists, who would of course require thoroughly convincing, were prepared to sponsor the proposition. The managers would be loaded with a significant personal debt, such as the value of their house; daunting, but not such a burden as would detract from their whole time and attention being devoted to the success of the business.

Even so, if the management team were to own a significant proportion (around half) of the shares in the company, the total amount of share capital inevitably had to be small. The purchase price would come, in the main, from a loan and from deferred payments. Protection for the Clearer would come from a charge on the assets, and comfort for the venture capitalist from preference shares. The MBO team had to make a success of the privatisation in order to keep a roof over their heads.

It did not take long to decide that County Bank (later County Nat-West) were the sort of venture capitalists with whom the team could have a good rapport. Andrew Davison and Sydney Donald led for County Bank Development Capital Ltd and it was their professional approach which galvanised the MBO, enabling the relationship to survive the traumas which were to follow. It is a pleasure to record the appreciation which is felt in the company towards the city and its institutions as represented and focused by County Bank and its officers.

The Board of British Shipbuilders issued guidelines on the financial assistance which would be made available for Management Buy Outs. In the event of an approved bid being unsuccessful, 50% of the promoters costs would be refunded by BS. This was to get as many bids as possible, but it was made clear that internal bids would not be valued more highly than external ones. The first public announcement of the intention to mount a buy out of VT was carried by the Financial Times on 15 December 1984 following an announcement to employees.

The employee buy-outs at Yarrow and Hall Russell which were envisaged at that time, did not materialise; Bob (now Sir Robert) Easton at Yarrow was unable to carry the Trades Unions with the

management and the yard was bought instead by Lord Weinstock (GEC). Hall Russell at Aberdeen were privatised for a short while but succumbed to a shortage of work and eventual closure. Brooke Marine, the first of the warship yards to be sold, soon closed the main part of its works and traded for some years as Brooke Yachts on a much reduced scale from that of earlier years. It was eventually only at VSEL, originally the Vickers yard at Barrow-in-Furness, that an employee buy-out succeeded, and the conditions which were applied to it differed considerably from those at VT.

The VT sale was set up to be a competition with two criteria; the bid price (to be a maximum) and the number of employees to be made redundant at British Shipbuilders expense (to be a minimum). As planned, it was competed for by a number of parties with sealed bids. At VSEL all the employees and many residents of Barrow in Furness were invited to buy shares in an employee buy-out. This would require a completely different approach; a prospectus was necessary, the cost of which was substantial, and County Bank consequently advised VT that a small team was the only practical way ahead. Moreover, an eagle eye was being kept on equality of information for all bidders which meant that the VT team could not involve even senior managers let alone the whole work force in their plans, though most would have preferred to do so. It was therefore decided to proceed on the small team basis but, in the event of winning, to allocate 10% of the total shares to employees. In the event they gave, or virtually gave, 15% of the equity to the employees.

The first six months of 1985 saw the Touche Ross report on the company gradually licked into shape, but the date of the intended sale remained unclear and County Bank expressed concern that the programme for the sale was so protracted.

A fortuitous development at this time was to have enormous beneficial consequences. The VT search for a chairman, in the event of a successful management buy out, coincided with Roy Withers' search for a non-executive directorship and the catalyst was Andrew Davison at County Bank, who knew him well. Roy had been Managing Director of the Davy Corporation for 10 years and

had recently been appointed Deputy Chairman to Lord Jellicoe. Andrew Davison brought Roy and Peter Usher together; the chemistry was right and the bond has been a close one ever since.

Roy Withers brought major industrial contracting experience, business acumen, knowledge of overseas markets, contacts in Government and the City, firm discipline, a wealth of common sense, and not a little engineering know-how to the group. Though his role in the privatisation process itself was not large, his remark when there had been a set back will be long remembered by those who were in Old Broad Street at the time: "*Gentlemen we are not here to play, we are here to win*".

A similar robustness was shown by Peter Usher in July 1985 when he decided that one of the team would not, in his view, meet the demands of a privatised company. Concerned that any mismatch after a buy-out would damage the new enterprise Usher forced the issue. Whether this triggered latent thoughts in the minds of the three 'new' directors Gray, McNeilly and Chapman is not known but by the end of the month the city heard of a 'rival bid from Vosper Thornycroft'. The incredulous old guard promptly responded to the medicine prescribed by Dr. Andrew Davison by each writing a cheque payable to County Bank for 10% of their risk capital, which would not be returned to anyone found to be in a rival bid. The cure was immediate and from 28 July until 21 October 1985, there were two management buy-out teams running a company for which at least three other groups were interested in bidding. All had to be provided with the latest accurate information.

Strength cometh from adversity and for the Usher-led group of Cameron, Dorey, Grisley and Stobart-Hook, (all engineers) it came in the form of Barry Jones, to whom British Shipbuilders had preferred John Gray as successor when Hugh Melvin had resigned as Financial Director. Barry was fortunately still in the post of deputy and willing to join the Usher team. This blessing exceeded at the time even that of finding Roy Withers. Barry Jones' grasp of the business was without parallel and his rigorous analysis of the cash flow of each contract proved crucial to winning the confidence of County Bank after they had set Peat Marwick to work on the projections. The lesson to be learned was to look on the 'downside' of every marketing forecast - to consider the very worst conceivable case and to be prudent about cash flow. In other words to be utterly pessimistic by the normal lights of enthusiastic managers. For example, it seemed, at the time, quite inconceivable that the company could be run without building frigates. Forced to consider that possibility, which regrettably came to pass, VT has traded more profitably than was forecast.

With Barry Jones making the team up to six, plus the chairman, and driving now towards a bid date of noon on Friday 18 October 1985, the pace hotted up very considerably.

Having witnessed the informal but effective and rapid communication in the city over the rival bid affair, it was also interesting to see County Bank operating risk management. They offered Gresham Trust half of their share of the equity. It was agreed at this stage that the management team would take 51%, County 24.5% and Gresham Trust 24.5% of the shares. Norman Baldock, the then managing director (now chairman) of Gresham Trust plc, came to see the company, met the team, weighed up the projections and within 48 hours took up the option. It was refreshing to see top financial people at work with their penetrating questions and a propensity to unearth half hidden realities. As a consequence of the Gresham Trust shareholding, Norman Baldock was appointed to the Board and remained as the "City" non executive director.

British Shipbuilders appeared to have a number of potential buyers for VT, so negotiated a provisional contract with each party in advance of the sealed bid. The Usher team used only top class professionals for this process by engaging Slaughter & May as solicitors and Peat Marwick as accountants. There were five or six different meetings with British Shipbuilders during September. The main issues were the numbers of employees it would be necessary to make redundant, the liability for claims on current contracts (in particular the frost damage to the Hong Kong ferries) and the funding of the employees pension scheme.

In recent years we have all come to realise the extent to which the London banks have been exposed to risk associated with either foreign loans, company failures or the recession. It was however a bolt from the blue when in 1985 National Westminster Bank informed their subsidiary company County Bank on 27 September, three weeks before the bid date, that they were unwilling to make a loan of £10 million as leverage for the buy-out. Shipbuilding having been in decline in this country for 40 years it was not, perhaps, an unreasonable decision, but it was made very late in the day for the VT sale. The hunt for a bank willing and able to act quickly, was top priority. Standard Chartered Bank and Banque Français both reacted extremely positively within days, even though the rates of interest they required were on the high side, and a loan could have been secured from either. Standard Chartered had a branch in Southampton so they were chosen, and the team were home with days to spare.

When some years later Standard Chartered were in trouble and instructions from Singapore made them terminate their links with shipbuilders, the company chose Barclays, which has our cash balance now.

There was a fearsome array of bid documents and agreements drawn up by the legal representatives of the parties as the 18 October approached. These were worked through at late night meetings in Old Broad Street and a host of amendments would appear retyped first thing the following day.

The management team engaged a Portsmouth solicitor, John Cobbett of King and Frankeiss, to guard their interests in the light of the personal commitments being made to County Bank and Gresham Trust.

Not a little stamina is one essential feature of bidding to buy a company. Some of the team found remarkable restorative powers in the fast food products of Casey Jones on Waterloo Station, frequently snatched between meetings whilst awaiting trains. Indeed, there was a suggestion, as yet unfulfilled, that Casey Jones be selected as the venue for a reunion dinner!

The price to be bid for VT was decided at the very last moment. The team had no idea what the

other bids would be, - indeed were not sure who else would put in a bid, and there was a tendency to increase the figure which had been in mind. They didn't want to lose for the sake of a million pounds they didn't have! Finally, and with varying degrees of anxiety, it was agreed to offer £18.5 million. In addition, a further payment would be made if Pakistan ordered a frigate within a specified time.

In all some fourteen agreements, guarantees, statutory declarations, letters regarding covenants and deeds were signed during the bidding process.

Bids were due at Lazards office at noon on 18 October. At 1155, the phone rang at the County Bank office, just up the road. It was George Cameron, who had had to stay in Portsmouth to 'hold the fort', but was naturally on tenterhooks.

*"Did they get it away in time?"* he asked.

*"Just going now, George"* he was told, as Peter Usher and two of the bankers rushed past the phone on their way to the door.

*"Oh no!"* said a shaken George, *"They've left it too late!"*

But the bankers knew what they were doing, and exactly how long it took to reach Lazards along the crowded city pavements. The documents were delivered on the very stroke of noon.

Suddenly there was nothing left to do except wait. Withdrawal symptoms set in. Back at Woolston, relations with the John Gray team continued on an established polite and slightly formal note. Did they know something the rest didn't? Certainly they appeared confident of their success, as they had insisted on attending various works meetings and being briefed on matters in which they normally took little interest, but over which they would have to take control if their bid succeeded.

The suspense lasted only three days. On the 21 October, Trafalgar Day, just as some of the Usher team had resigned themselves to failure and were wondering what to do with the redundancy money, the phone rang. Peter Usher and his team were declared the preferred bidders. Subject to a few last minute formalities, Vosper Thornycroft Holdings, the shelf company which the team had bought for the purpose, originally with the princely capital of £2, would shortly own Vosper Thornycroft (UK) Ltd.

On 1 November, 1985, the formalities were completed at a final meeting with the heads of British Shipbuilders at Knightsbridge. Public ownership was over at last. There were few people in the country who mourned the end of this unfortunate era, and even fewer in VT. It was a hugely expensive experiment which stultified the company and failed, and which VT was lucky to survive reasonably intact.

There were, of course, mutual congratulations and celebrations to say *"thank you"* to all the City helpers, but, as everyone had known would be the case, there was very little time for rejoicing. There was an urgent need to further reorganise the company, and inevitably this meant more severe cutting of the overhead budget.

However, by way of a very welcome start to the privatised company, the Sultan of Oman placed an order on 12 December for a fourth 56 metre fast strike craft. Nevertheless, despite this and the *Shark* contract and the GRP work at Woolston, there was still over-capacity in shipbuilding and little prospect of a further large order in the immediate future. Something would have to be done.

There had already been one round of redundancies at VT under British Shipbuilders, and although the nationalised company had held back on further cuts to allow the new owners to decide how best to implement them, it was recognised in the run up to the sale of the company that further redundancies were inevitable. The Government had legislated for exceptionally good severance terms to those made redundant from the shipbuilding industry up to a certain date, and British Shipbuilders had agreed to continue to meet the costs of such redundancies after privatisation. However, not unreasonably, they had required all prospective purchasers to state how many redundancies they would declare during the period in question. The cost of this to British Shipbuilders would be discounted from the purchase price offered; there was therefore an incentive to quote a low figure. On the other hand, if the new owners were forced to declare additional redundancies in excess of this figure, they would be obliged to meet the costs of these themselves.

The Usher team had done their sums on overheads and forecasts, and reached the reluctant conclusion that there would have to be cuts at almost every level in the company. Negotiations with Pakistan for Type 21 frigates (by now heavily modified) were still dragging on, with no successful conclusion in sight.

To explain their plans 'live' to everybody, the new owner-directors of the company called two meetings at theatres in Southampton and Portsmouth respectively. Every employee was invited to one of these and most of them seemed to appreciate being asked to the performance, even if not everyone applauded at the end.

Implementing redundancies was, as ever, a painful affair. The stage had been reached where it was just not possible to rely entirely upon volunteers. Probably there would not have been enough in any case, but although severe thinning down was necessary in almost every area it was important to ensure that a hard core of expertise was retained. This meant that some volunteers could not be allowed to go but that, sadly, a number of very competent people, some of whom had been with the Company for many years, had to be selected by the management.

As well as thinning down the organisation, the new owners carried out a further drastic reorganisation. Basically, it involved splitting shipbuilding into two almost separate organisations, making Portchester and Woolston virtually independent of each other, and each with their own sales, design, estimating and commercial departments. This meant that it was necessary to spread some of the expertise very thinly indeed; some "departments" were one man bands!

The idea was to create small, close-knit units where everyone knew everyone else. Communication lines were short and other people's problems could be more readily understood. A better team spirit could be fostered. Less time would be wasted typing and sending memos to the other site, fifteen miles away: The man one wanted was at the next desk, or in the next room and in the time required to compose and type a memo one could walk to his desk and either have the action under way, or at least some appreciation of why it couldn't be done and how one's request might be modified to solve the problem.

In this new organisation there was clearly no room for the Broad Street yard. Old fashioned, with a cramped and awkward layout imposed upon it as a result of outgrowing its original confines in an already overcrowded environment, its only merit was the relatively deep water quay and proximity to the mouth of Portsmouth Harbour. Despite access to Portchester's new facilities - the wet dock, ship lift, and number 4 shop - being limited by tides, their advantages far outweighed the assets of Broad Street. The old yard would have to go.

In any case, it was mostly leased from the local Council and, after some negotiation, the entire site was sold for development. Apart from a few sentimental sighs from some of the older employees, this caused little disturbance as the site had closed some months before privatisation and the work force had moved elsewhere. A few of the remaining machines were moved to Portchester, the older ones were sold and the site and its buildings left in the sole possession of the ghost of a previous employee, who was reputed to appear in the old mould loft from time to time. Whether he emigrated or moved into one of the desirable modern residences now erected on the site is not known!

One technical consequence of the loss of Broad Street was that the profile cutter, a machine used for cutting thin steel plates into complicated shapes, was lost too. It would not have been economic to move it, despite the fact that it served both Woolston and Portchester. During the closing months of British Shipbuilders' reign much effort had been put into trying to procure a more modern cutting system. If an oxyacetylene, or similar, flame is used to cut steel plate, the flame takes some time to burn through the plate, and considerable heat is conducted away from the edge to the rest of the component. This causes buckling and a certain amount of 'shrinkage' of the plate on cooling. Neither of these are conducive to neat and accurate shipbuilding, and much time can subsequently be spent applying agricultural brute force to persuade what should be accurately crafted components to fit neatly together. The problem is particularly acute in the case of the relatively thin steel plates

Roy Withers,
Director.

Norman Baldock,
Director.

The GRP module hall at Woolston.

used for building patrol boats. Moreover, the gas flame can leave a ragged edge upon which further work is necessary before the plate can be successfully welded to its neighbour.

Modern methods include the use of plasma jets or lasers instead of a gas flame for cutting. The methods still rely on melting the steel to cut it, but the heat is applied in such a concentrated way that the plate is cut through before the surrounding area has time to warm up. The whole process can also be carried out in a water bath, which further inhibits undesirable heating. The result is - or should be - a neat, accurate and undistorted component. VT had selected the laser option, but unfortunately this turned out to be a little too near the forefront of technology at the time, and much delay ensued while the would-be suppliers of the machine struggled unsuccessfully to make it work. Eventually the order had to be cancelled.

Elsewhere plasma-based machines were working successfully, even leaving a neat and accurate bevelled edge to the cut plate, ideal for welding without further preparation. In fact, the intermediate solution to VT's plate cutting needs was to subcontract to specialist companies who serve many different manufacturers and can thus afford to invest heavily in state-of-the-art plant. With the eventual advent in 1992 of further substantial orders for steel ships, a fully developed laser cutter was installed at Woolston, perhaps demonstrating that the original project, although premature, was on the right lines.

By mid 1986, the organisation was settling down again in its new form and both yards were earnestly continuing the search for work. In Pakistan, the long-standing negotiations for much modified Type 21 frigates were looking less and less promising and eventually they petered out, with the Pakistanis in effect deciding to start again. VT withdrew, hurt, having again spent considerable amounts of time and money on an abortive project. Reviewing their requirements, the Pakistanis had concluded that they required a different ship after all and began to show interest in the Royal Navy's new Type 23 frigate. Yarrow took their turn in Islamabad, but this too eventually came to nought.

This of course caused gloom at Woolston, where the huge shed built for the Mk.10 Contract

had stood almost empty since HMS *Gloucester* had been launched. It began to look as though there might be no more frigates, at least for some time and, alas, another round of redundancies was necessary.

Whilst this was regrettable, it was by no means disastrous although VT was having to tighten its belt by an amount which would have seemed utterly unthinkable even a couple of years before. All the calculations and predictions made before privatisation had wisely excluded the Pakistani frigates, to the extent that the price actually paid to British Shipbuilders had assumed that this order would not materialise. There was, however, a clause which would have entitled British Shipbuilders to a share of the predicted profits if it had been achieved. VT were therefore well able to weather the loss of this notional project. There was, however, a good deal of discussion and heart searching at board level as to how the prevailing level of work could justify keeping open two shipyards.

Far more important than the Type 21s was the need for further orders from the MOD(N) for GRP ships, in particular, for further Single Role Mine Hunters to keep the GRP facility busy when the work load on the prototype, HMS *Sandown*, began to slacken. Should the expected orders for more ships not be won, the consequences would indeed be serious. There had been a big investment, in terms of both money and effort, in the development of the SRMH design and the relevant production facilities at Woolston, which had to yield returns. To enable the prefabrication techniques which had been worked out for SRMH production to be employed to full advantage, a new production facility, on which work had begun before privatisation, had been specially constructed at Woolston. This was the module hall; a production line for ship units where the building blocks would be built in ideal conditions and fitted out almost to completion, before being taken to the building berth and assembled as a ship.

This was advanced production engineering which would cut the time and cost of building GRP ships even further, but VT nevertheless expected keen competition for the next batch of SRMHs from Yarrow and meanwhile there was still an

*Lord Nelson* on Portchester ship lift.

The VT/Flight Refuelling air target system passing over a Ramadan.

urgent need for other work - any work - and Woolston and Portchester were both scouring the countryside for jobs to keep their workshops going.

There was competition, because others were hungry too. Some were willing to cut their prices below cost. Estimating the true cost of unaccustomed jobs was difficult; sometimes the results would be wildly wrong, usually on the high side due to building in too large safety margins. Ship repair and refit jobs, for which the yard facilities, particularly the ship lift, were best suited were also hotly contested by other shipyards. Although offering more familiar work, repair jobs are always difficult to estimate: One never knows what to expect when the 'can of worms' is opened up! On the other hand, more straightforward, non-marine metal fabrication work was less familiar and competition was sometimes fierce from smaller or less sophisticated competitors whose overheads were much lower. Despite these problems, both yards began to win a variety of small jobs. Although these were never expected to be a substitute for genuine shipbuilding orders, they were a useful background load, providing some interest and helping to keep the works occupied. After a while, some of them even began to show a modest profit as well as recovery of overheads.

One unusual and interesting job which fell to Woolston was the completion of the sail training ship *Lord Nelson*, which had been left unfinished by the liquidation of an east coast yard. *Lord Nelson* was especially designed to give handicapped people the chance to go to sea and to help navigate and sail the ship. There was even provision for taking a wheel chair along the bowsprit. Portchester also contributed by putting the ship on the ship lift for some essential underwater work, thus providing an opportunity for some picturesque photographs of a sailing ship and a strike craft together in the wet dock, which made an attractive and unusual Christmas card.

Times were quite hard, but although VT appeared to be struggling somewhat to stay afloat, parts of the old Vosper organisation from which VT had been separated when nationalised, were actually sinking. First to go under was the old Singapore shipyard, which had remained part of the Vosper holding company which escaped nationalisation. Their assets were purchased by a local company and became Vosper QAF and the use of the Vosper name continued to cause confusion with VT in the Far East.

Meanwhile at home, the rest of the old Vosper Ltd possessions, still run by Sir John Rix, was also soon in difficulty. Their acquisition of Hovermarine, with premises just up the Itchen from Woolston, made them close neighbours, but as their main interest was in sidewall hovercraft there was no direct competition with VT. However, in February 1986 they, too, had to call in the receiver.

Vosper Ship Repairers, separated from VT during nationalisation and privatised first, were the next to go under. Administrators were appointed in February 1987. They struggled on for a while but were eventually liquidated towards the end of 1988. Part of their facilities in Southampton docks were taken over by Thew Engineering, a local rival of VT for some ship repair work, but later, Thews also went under.

Vosper International, a subsidiary of Vosper Ltd formed to produce ship designs for offshore build, reduced simply to a name and was eventually bought by Brian Morrison, who had for many years been the technical director of Vosper Singapore. Brian left Singapore and began to practice as a naval architect in his native Scotland under the name of Vosper International Ltd.

The failure of several organisations with the Vosper name made some of VT's suppliers and customers decidedly nervous; a great deal of careful reassurance and explanation was required to convince them that none of the unfortunates had had anything to do with VT itself for several years and that despite the hard times, VT was in very healthy financial shape.

Indeed, under the careful management of Barry Jones, the Company was in a very strong financial position. Although the actual sales achieved since privatisation were disappointing compared even with the modest forecasts upon which plans had been based, the final instalment of purchase money to British Shipbuilders, which was not due until over a year after the buy out, was in fact paid early and the company soon had a healthy cash balance to its credit at the bank. Inevitably, forward cash

Coastal defence Exocet missile system engineered by VT for the MOD.

A luxury yacht on the ship lift at Portchester.

*Gentry Eagle* on trials in the Solent.

*Gentry Eagle* on the ship lift showing water jet unit.

flow predictions always showed this melting away to nothing about a year ahead, but as time went on, this disaster seemed to recede ahead at the same rate. VT was alive and very well, even if work was hard to find.

The heavy reliance upon shipbuilding had always been recognised as an Achilles heel and this was partly what had led to the development of the 'non-shipbuilding' divisions; Support Projects, Controls and Hydraulic Power. These divisions had grown over the years and although they had originally obtained most of their business as spin-off from shipbuilding contracts, they were by now much less reliant upon the fortunes of the shipyards. VT machinery control systems and roll damping fins found their way into ships built by other yards all over the world and Support Projects produced handbooks, maintenance schedules and spares systems for all sorts of outside concerns. Even the shipbuilding division itself had sometimes contributed to this policy: The small but efficient air target system operated jointly with Flight Refuelling Ltd had originally been set up to conduct ground to air gunnery trials for the Egyptian contracts, but then, thanks largely to the expertise and enthusiasm of Dave Hartung, an ex RN Chief Petty Officer, went on to earn its keep by flying targets for the RN and even for foreign weapons trials. Portchester also engineered and built a naval Exocet surface to surface missile system to be carried and fired from a series of road trailers.

Diversifying further away from shipbuilding had been against the policy and aims of British Shipbuilders, but under the new management there was a positive intent to do so and the company began to look around for suitable ways of broadening its interests and product ranges.

Of course, there was no intention to abandon shipbuilding itself and the search for diversity in the shipyards was also on. With the merchant ship industry being so different from warships and in a parlous state anyway, there was no point in looking in that direction, but some attention was turned to the luxury yacht market.

Large yachts, from about 25 metres in length upwards, were more compatible with VT's existing facilities and skills. One or two had already appeared on the ship lift for repair jobs and it was clear that the latter was ideal; quite large vessels could readily be moved out of the water and into No.4 shop at Portchester, enabling high quality painting and other such tasks to be carried out in a dry and warm environment.

This luxury yacht market was, however, specialised and intensely competitive. It was clear from the start that large profits could not be made and that, indeed, substantial losses could result from inexperience. The Board was divided as to the advisability of entering this market.

At the end of 1986, an attractive entrée to the yacht market appeared in the shape of an invitation to bid for a challenger to Richard Branson's transatlantic speed record, which had been established by *Virgin Atlantic Challenger* the year before. Branson's boat had been built by Brooke Marine, in Lowestoft, which had been privatised before VT. VT had been invited to quote for that contract too, but being in the run-up to privatisation at the time, all quotations were subject to strict scrutiny by British Shipbuilders and, being also something of a novelty and as such, a commercial risk, by the time the quote emerged it was laughably uncompetitive. This time a much more determined effort was made, particularly as Brooke Marine were bound to be bidding and Portchester badly needed the work.

The new challenger was designed by Peter Birkett, who had, together with Sonny Levi, designed the Branson boat. The owner was Tom Gentry, an American with many years experience of racing large power boats and considerable success in both that and his Hawaii-based business of property development. VT responded with enthusiasm and invited the designer, who was also to be the project manager in the UK, to visit Portchester.

It was clear from that first visit that the project would indeed be rather different from dealing with naval vessels. Instead of a group of uniformed or nattily suited customers, one young man in an open-necked shirt and jeans, wearing a single gold earring appeared carrying a brief case. Peter Birkett was not one for excessive formality! Neither could he see any necessity for producing the reams of detailed drawings to which VT was accustomed. His requirements were concisely stated on half a dozen typewritten sheets and a couple of sketches. After a couple of hours discussion, VT determined to bid.

In addition to Brooke Marine, one or two American Yards had expressed an interest, so competition would be fierce. Peter clearly favoured a British yard and seemed quite impressed with the Portchester facilities. However, he did have some reservations. British yards had a reputation, he said, for poor industrial relations. This boat simply had to be ready for the transatlantic attempt by the end of April 1988 and any delay would be absolutely unacceptable. The weather window would not wait.

The management took a deep breath, introduced Peter to two of the leading shop stewards, Tony Cridge and Ron Arrowsmith, explained the position and left them to discuss the problem. Whatever was said clearly satisfied Peter. It also demonstrated that, although the stewards could on occasions be difficult when defending their corner as they saw it, they could also rise responsibly to the occasion when required. Besides, they and the men they represented were now mostly shareholders in the company. Shortly after the management buy out, the plan to issue one hundred shares free to any employee who filled in the application form had been carried out and although the face value of the shares at the time was purely nominal, the gesture was appreciated more than we had anticipated. There were a few tales of shop floor workers chasing idlers back to the job with remarks like "*I'm a shareholder in this company! Get off yer arse!*". So much for the theory of public ownership!

Anyway, the Portchester estimators and works management put their heads together and made a concerted effort to determine exactly what it would really cost them to build Peter Birkett's design. The estimate was squeezed to the bone, as were many would be suppliers of materials and equipment and VT won the bid.

Since Branson had made two attempts, the first one sinking when almost in sight of the Scilly Isles, this Atlantic Challenger was the third and was instantly dubbed "AC3". Peter Birkett moved into Portchester to supervise the build, bringing with him two colleagues; Peter Downie who was responsible for all the mechanical engineering and Ian Starr who was in charge of the electronics. In

both these latter areas, virtually all the equipment was supplied 'free issue' to VT, who were contractually only responsible for supplying and building the boat.

There were some interesting and novel features of AC3. Firstly, the hull was all-welded aluminium alloy. Although used to working in this material, VT had not built an all-alloy hull of this size since the yacht, *Romantica*, had been built at Woolston in 1968. The superstructure of AC3 was made of very thin alloy sheet and stringers which were unsuitable for welding and were held together by epoxy adhesive. Peter Birkett had used the technique on his earlier projects and he soon overcame Portchester's suspicion of using 'glue' on aluminium. It worked well.

Propulsion was by two German MTU diesel engines, similar to many of those fitted by VT to patrol boats, but these were to drive two enormous water jet units, made by KaMeWa in Sweden.

The problem of economically and accurately cutting the aluminium sheet was neatly solved by subcontracting to a Dutch company, Centraal Staal, who had been soliciting VT for business for some time. Centraal Staal had been formed to supply the entire Dutch shipbuilding industry with accurately cut metal plate. They had invested considerable sums of money in computerised equipment which could draw and fair the lines of ships and their components at full size and in plasma cutting equipment which used this computer output to produce accurately cut parts. Use of this service saved VT many man hours in 'lofting', or drawing out components and jigs at full size on a loft floor, as well as solving the problem of how to cut the metal itself.

The hull of AC3 was built upside down in three sections, in No.4 shop. This allowed the units to be virtually self-jigging and in an easier attitude for the welding of joints and seams. When complete, the units were turned right way up and joined together. Deck and superstructure units which had meanwhile been assembled separately, could then be added.

Just before this stage was reached, the owner, Tom Gentry himself, visited Portchester for the first time and the press too began to take an interest. Tom turned out to be a relaxed and charming American in his mid fifties although he did not perhaps look like the popular image of a dashing speedboat ace. One of the reporters asked him all about his racing experience and his reasons for wanting to cross the Atlantic by boat faster than anyone else. Tom answered all the questions patiently and good humouredly. Eventually the reporter asked, *"Mr Gentry, don't you think you are a little old to go rushing across the Atlantic in a power boat?"*

Tom paused, looked the young man up and down and then said:

*"Well, I guess I can do more press-ups than you can!"*

Although the main structure of *Gentry Eagle*, as she was christened, was completed within budget, there were a few problems in fitting out which meant that, overall, the Company made no profit on the job. However, she was completed on time and Peter Birkett and his team commenced trials in the Solent in March 1988. Performance was well up to expectations, the boat clocking 55 knots light over the mile and still proved capable of 45 knots when loaded with the 45 tonnes of diesel fuel which would be needed if the Atlantic crossing was to be made with only one refuelling stop. On the day she was formally delivered, the American crew, including Tom's son Norman and his 'throttle man' from the racing circuits, John Connor, laid on a most spectacular demonstration for the Press, driving her up and down past the cameras at full throttle.

They then drove her to Rotterdam, where she was loaded aboard a container ship as deck cargo for the journey to Miami.

There had always been a plan to add a gas turbine on the centreline, driving a surface propeller, but this was not originally intended until after the Atlantic attempt. However, American enthusiasm overcame discretion and it was fitted on her arrival in the States. This boosted the top speed to an incredible 70 knots plus and she immediately took the Miami to Nassau and back record. She then attempted the Miami to New York record too, but the turbine broke down on the way and she only just succeeded, completing the course with minutes to spare on diesels alone.

There was then a long delay whilst the turbine was repaired, during which the capricious Atlantic weather turned nasty. The crew waited, day after day, until the weather men decided that the time was right.

They were wrong. *Gentry Eagle* encountered steadily worsening conditions and despite overcoming several problems caused by the appalling seas, gave up off Newfoundland when it became clear that it would be impossible to come alongside the refuelling ship with safety. *Gentry's* first attempt ended in failure, but Tom himself, despite having had no sleep for two days, immediately climbed on an aeroplane and flew to a press conference in London, where he gave a graphic account of their experiences.

Meanwhile, his crew were taking the boat back to New York. In poor visibility they ran aground on a rocky beach in Nova Scotia at around forty knots. Most of the bottom was torn out of *Gentry Eagle*, but they were unhurt, the rest of the boat and its equipment were in good shape and, fortunately, the accident had happened at the top of the spring tide, so she was left high and dry.

After being salvaged and transferred back to Miami for repair, a second attempt was made in the summer of 1989. This time weather conditions were perfect and with intermittent use of the gas turbine to conserve fuel, she crossed from New York to Bishops Rock in 62 hours and 7 minutes; an average of 48 knots and a massive 18 hours 23 minutes less than Branson's record.

On his arrival in the Scillies, Gentry was met by Branson, who generously presented him with a splendid trophy and then, assisted by Ecky Rastig, the German engineer from MTU who had crewed on both Branson's attempts as well as on *Gentry Eagle*, he threw Tom into the icy waters of the harbour at St Mary's. The victim submitted gracefully, but managed to drag Branson with him and the pair concluded the proceedings with a swim.

There had been plans to convert *Gentry Eagle* into what might have been the world's fastest yacht, but these never materialised and she returned to the USA unmodified under her own power in the late summer, after a triumphant visit to Woolston for some minor repairs.

The *Gentry* project made a loss for the Company

and caused long faces amongst the accountants whenever the contract assessment came up for discussion. However, things might have been a great deal worse at Portchester had it not been won and it caused a good deal of interest and enthusiasm in the works which contributed to the general improvement in atmosphere.

Further tentative efforts were made to enter the luxury yacht business and a Dutch expert Ernst Blomjous, who had considerable experience of this rather specialised market, was hired to advise. He succeeded in obtaining an order for Portchester to refit a yacht called *Harmony Bay*, which had originally been converted from a fishing boat and had experienced a disastrous fire whilst on charter in the West Indies. However, the yacht business proved difficult to penetrate and the differences of opinion on the Board as to its desirability continued. *Harmony Bay* was completed to the great satisfaction of her owner at the end of 1988 and many useful lessons were learned, but the market was not then pursued further.

At the same time the yard was busy building the fourth 56 metre strike craft for Oman. Not to be outdone by Woolston's dramatic increases in productivity whilst building GRP ships, the smaller yard also showed dramatic reductions in the number of man hours required to build these complex steel craft. Share ownership and the payment of basic wages more comparable with those of other local industries seemed to have transformed morale since privatisation.

As was now normal for Portchester, strike craft were launched from the ship lift which was excellent for everything except formal launching parties, since instead of a dramatic headlong rush into the water, the newly christened vessels descended at an almost imperceptible rate. The organisers of these launching parties were faced with the problem of how to entertain the guests during the long pause between the breaking of the bottle and the moment when the ship became water borne. There was time for the band to play even the longest National Anthem several times over and the release of coloured balloons or similar frivolities could only be spun out for so long. On one such occasion, Tony Dorey was officiating in the absence of Peter Usher and was suddenly faced with an embarrassing pause. Being a technical man, he immediately improvised with a lecture to the audience, in layman's terms, on the merits and mechanics of ship lifts, ending with the words, "... *as you can see, the ship will now sink*". The audience did not interpret this in quite the way that Tony had intended and there was a roar of laughter which filled in the pause admirably.

Meanwhile Woolston too was busy again. The crucial production order from the MOD(N) for a further four Single Role Mine Hunters, numbers 02 to 05, was won in July 1987, providing a real opportunity to exercise the new GRP production facilities. With this most important order secure, the future of the Company looked much healthier and thoughts began to turn to the prospect of floating the Company on the London Stock Exchange. However, before turning to that topic, it is high time to go back again in time to have a closer look at the history of those most important parts of the Company which have today become collectively known as the Products Division.

## Chapter Twelve

## THE PRODUCTS DIVISION

No history of Vosper Thornycroft would be complete without a record of what is now the Products Division. Although, like Support Services, this originally grew from the shipbuilding part of the company, dependence upon VT shipbuilding has generally been less, at least until recent years when Support Services activities too have become more independent of those of the parent organisation.

The origins of the Hydraulic Power and Controls Divisions go back to the prehistory of the company. The Vosper roll damping system was designed in the late 1940s by Peter Du Cane, who treated it almost as a hobby. The first trials at sea were conducted in the motor yacht *Sea Victory* in 1950.

The principle of the roll damping system is simple. As the ship rolls, the movement is sensed by a gyroscope, the output of which is used to control a number (usually two) of fins. These are similar to rudders, and project from each side of the hull below the water line. They are deflected in such a way as to counteract the rolling motion. Because they rely for their effect on the motion of the ship through the water, they are only effective when the ship is under way. They are sometimes referred to as stabilisers, although this is not strictly correct since ships must in any case be designed to be stable - that is, not to capsize under normal circumstances - without their influence.

The heart of this system, the gyro control panel, was designed with the help of a Mr. James Bell of Muirhead & Co. This company's present day equipment is incorporated in some of the Hydraulic Power Division's latest systems now being supplied to Japan. Nowadays however, most VT roll damping fins use a control system designed and built by VT's own Controls Division, which can also trace its ancestry to 1950, when the Electrical Division of Vosper Limited began to design and manufacture switchboards and other electrical items within the shipyard for Vosper built ships.

The first Vosper production roll damping equipment was fitted to the motor yacht *Calisto* in 1954, and two years later the first naval installation was fitted in the *Ton* class minesweeper HMS *Coniston*, built by J.I. Thornycroft at Woolston. The first front line warship was equipped in 1962, when an order was received to outfit the Leander frigate HMS *Sirius*, and within 10 years some 50 installations a year were being sold.

During the 60's, the Vosper Electrical Division was also expanding its market by building consoles and electrical distribution equipment for RN vessels being built elsewhere, notably submarines. Over the next 25 years orders were received for the *Valiant, Resolution, Swiftsure, Trafalgar, Upholder* and *Vanguard* class submarines.

In 1966 the Vosper Electrical department became the Industrial and Marine Controls Division and moved out of the Portchester shipyard to nearby premises at the Castle Trading estate, just in time to become part of the new Vosper Thornycroft company. As well as supplying the main switchgear and electrical distribution equipment for the Iranian Mk.5 frigates, which provided a substantial amount of work, the division also embarked on a new product line which was to provide a major part of its future business, the remote control and monitoring of propulsion and auxiliary machinery for those same frigates. In those days the systems were based on the then well-used and conventional electromechanical synchro technology.

The systems for the Mk.5s were of course soon followed by similar ones for the Libyan Mk.7 frigate, and for VT's own private venture strike craft, *Tenacity*. Soon afterwards, in 1968, came orders for the design and manufacture of new modular switch and distribution boards for the RN's Type 21 frigates. Vosper Electric also supplied the VCS - Versatile Console Systems- for these ships, VCS being a range of indicators, control boxes and the like which, fitted into standard sized consoles, is widely employed in the RN and other navies.

By way of contrast, and further diversification,

the division also won a contract in the same year for the manufacture of equipment for the detection of TV licence dodgers, and for fitting out a number of vans with this equipment!

Meanwhile, the roll damping activities were also expanding under the general managership of Peter Shepherd, and beginning to penetrate important overseas markets. In 1966 the Japanese Defence Association (JDA) had decided to evaluate the performance of Vosper roll damping fins, and Mitsubishi Heavy Industries (MHI) were contracted to conduct trials. The JDA ship *Ohtori* was retrofitted with a set which was wired up to a 24 channel data recorder. Trials at sea lasted for fourteen days and were followed by exhaustive analysis, during which all concerned learned a great deal. By chance, one of the Japanese naval officers concerned was the grandson of Dr. Shintoro Motora of MHI, who had invented a fin stabiliser in 1920.

As a result of the trials, the Hydraulic Power Division can boast that it has since stabilised the vast majority of Japanese naval ships. Although most of the mechanical equipment has been manufactured under licence in Japan, first by Tokyo Sangyo and later, since 1984, by MHI, the electronic control system is still being supplied from the UK. A small offset to the tons of Japanese electronics which have made the journey in the opposite direction!

Manufacture of equipment under licence naturally led to Vosper staff attending workshop trials in Japan, and it was here that they first observed a curious phenomenon which became known as the Vosper Fin Dance. During functional tests in the (static) workshop, signals were fed into the system to simulate ship rolling motion, resulting in the fins, mounted on their top plates on the shop floor, flapping up or down. To ensure that this movement was in the correct sense to stabilise the imaginary ship required the inspectors to simultaneously visualise the direction of roll and the required deflections of the fins. Inevitably, they would stand facing forwards, rolling gently from side to side whilst flapping their hands in sympathy with the test rig. The rhythm was obviously infectious, and the dance would soon be taken up by virtually all the other Japanese present!

Originally, roll damping installations were tailor-made for each ship, but in 1968 a standardised system called the Vosper Mini Fin was introduced. Mini Fin was designed for vessels between about 40 and 65 feet long, and was specifically aimed at the American yacht market. Two local agents were appointed; Merrill Stevens in Miami and Gaudin Products in California. These companies were so confident of the potential of Mini Fin that they placed orders for 100 and 50 sets respectively. Their confidence was not misplaced: success was such that for over a decade the yacht market referred to roll damping fins as "Vospers", rather as the word "Hoover" has become synonymous with vacuum cleaners! Later, VT introduced the Maxi Fin for vessels up to 100 feet long.

For three years, VT also ran its own marketing company in the USA. Vosper Incorporated operated from Hoboken, New Jersey, and also shared the very palatial "King of Prussia" New York offices of Aston Martin Lagonda, also subsidiaries of the David Brown organisation. Vosper Incorporated operated from 1969 to 1971, and was run by Peter Cope. Eventually, however, despite the success of the roll damping fins in the USA, it was felt that the overheads of Vosper Inc. could not be justified. Marketing was thereafter handled from the UK, or through the Agents.

By the late 1960s roll damping fin sales were still growing, and more space was required than was available in the shipyard at that time. The operation moved just along the road to Castle Trading estate, at the same time becoming an autonomous cost centre and officially becoming the 'Hydraulic Power Division'.

HPD of course continued to receive orders from the VT shipyards, and with the advent of the Brazilian Mk.10 frigate order, seized the opportunity to expand the product range by designing and manufacturing the steering gear for these ships. During the latter part of the 1970s and into the 1980s, expansion continued and more overseas manufacturing licences were issued, to India and the USA. Equipment was also built under subcontract in Brazil and Australia.

In the autumn of 1970, the lease of a factory building in Western Road, Cosham, a couple of miles from the Portchester Shipyard, was taken over and the Electrical Division moved in. In 1971, the Products Division was formed by the merging of the Electrical, and Hydraulic Power divisions, and the introduction of a new division; Controls.

There was also a fourth member of the organisation, the Oil Burner, or Combustion, division. Unlike Hydraulic Power and Controls, which were bred out of the Vosper stable, the Oil Burner division was originally part of Thornycroft. Thornycroft had built oil burners since well before the second world war in the days when shipbuilders manufactured virtually everything which found its way into the ship. This even included steam boilers and the associated oil firing equipment: Many Thornycroft boilers were installed in world war two destroyers.

In the late 1940s Thornycroft sold its last boiler, but the design and manufacture of oil burners continued. Installations were supplied to the Cunard liners *Queen Mary* and *Saxonia*, a number of Shell oil tankers and the RFAs *Tidespring* and *Tidepool*.

In the 1950s and 1960s, the marine market dwindled and attention turned to industrial outlets ashore. Glaxo laboratories, the BBC, Heathrow airport and several prisons still use heating equipment supplied by the Oil Burner division. Such diversity might have led into other forms of business. One lorry driver delivering parts to Wandsworth prison was even approached by a "guest" and asked if he would take out a load of lead which had somehow disappeared from the prison roof the night before!

The division prospered into the 1970s with the introduction of a new fully automated oil and gas burner known as the Variojet. Michelin Tyres, the Central Electricity Generating Board, East African Light and Power (for Mombasa power station) and the Bahamas Electricity Company were all numbered among VT's customers for oil burners.

On 9 January 1975, whether by over enthusiasm on the part of the development engineers, or by bad luck, there was an explosion at the test facility at the south end of the Woolston yard. The facility finished up egg shaped! This was perhaps the beginning of the end. Rapid increases in the price of oil began to reduce the division's potential order book to a level which was causing increasing

concern. In 1980 the division was transferred to Wallsend Engineering in Newcastle, a part of British Shipbuilders considered more appropriate, and better able to further the interests of oil burning.

Controls Division however went from strength to strength and also benefitted from the winning by the VT shipyards of the Brazilian order. They were awarded a contract to design the remote control and monitoring systems for all the main propulsion and auxiliary machinery systems aboard the Mk.10 frigates, whilst the Electrical Division supplied the modular switchboards and VCS consoles.

Based on this success, several more large orders for ship machinery control and monitoring systems were won during the next few years; for the Belgian Navy's E71 class frigates, the Spanish Navy's *Descubierta* class corvettes, the Nigerian Navy's Mk.9 corvettes (built by VT at Portsmouth) and the same Navy's *MEKO 360* frigate built by Blohm and Voss in Hamburg.

Seeing the desirability of expanding into different markets, considerable efforts were at the same time being put into the control and monitoring requirements of industry. Some success was achieved in such diverse areas as water and sewage treatment, processing plant, educational services, car manufacture, mains electricity failure equipment and engine test cells. During the late 1960s and early 1970s, semiconductors were rapidly replacing thermionic devices in all areas and new techniques were being developed to take advantage of solid state technology. One area was the encapsulation of devices such as timers, static switches and inverters, the idea being to make them rugged and maintenance free. The Division developed and sold a number of such devices but on the whole they were not a success. In 1974 the Controls Division won the contract to design and manufacture the ship control and monitoring systems for the new *Hunt* class MCMVs. These systems were based on the application of hybrid micro-technology.

When VT was nationalised the Products Division became loosely associated with the Engineering Group of British Shipbuilders. Fortunately, however, with the exception of the oil burner business, already mentioned, the division

A D77 control system.

The D86 computer.

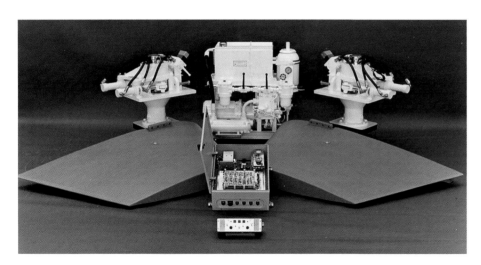

A set of roll damping fins
with their controls.

RN Type 23 machinery control system.

remained substantially intact and a part of VT.

In 1980 reorganisation within VT finally merged the activities of the Electrical and Controls divisions. At the time of nationalisation, the Controls Division were developing their first digital machinery control system based on the F100L microprocessor. The trials of the Mk.9 Corvettes provided an ideal opportunity to test the prototype system at sea and the success of this resulted in the development of a fully engineered computer known as D77.

The first application of D77 was in 1979, in the RN's HMS *Huntsman* training simulator interface and a similar machine was included in the Belgian Navy's E71 frigate training simulator the following year.

Over the next three years further development and engineering led to the replacement of the F100L processor by the Intel 8086 and the birth of the D86 system. VT's first D86 based machinery control and monitoring system successfully completed sea trials in 1982 in a high speed vessel built by Lurssen in West Germany. This marked the dawn of a new and highly successful era for the Controls division. Over the next seven years a large number of important orders were won by D86 systems, which were applied to machinery control and surveillance, or power generation and distribution systems in the RN's new Type 23 frigate; the Brazilian Navy's training frigate; the Type 2400 submarine; the Single Role Mine Hunter; the Trident submarine and control and monitoring systems aboard the ships of half a dozen or more overseas navies as well as several shore based training systems.

All of this was achieved by a considerable amount of sales effort, which was not without memorable incidents. One of these occurred during the factory trials of the first system, which presented a valuable but fleeting opportunity to demonstrate VT's new brain child to the MOD(N) before it was whisked off to Germany.

Two Very Important Men from the Ministry were duly invited to view the equipment, the programme having been arranged with great care and rehearsed in every detail until everybody was word perfect. The great day arrived and the visitors were ushered in. The demonstration began and was proceeding in accordance with the preordained split second timing when an unrehearsed extra decided to take a hand.

The maintenance engineer, a local 'character' whom everyone consulted on such important matters as how to repair old motor bikes or where to get the best deals on paint, was at work at the top of a ladder just out of sight of the vital performance. Suddenly there was a flash and a bang and all the power went off. The important guests were hastily whisked away for a rescheduled early lunch whilst behind the scenes various people rushed about restoring power, rearranging the demonstration and having words with the culprit. The latter, however, either had been rendered temporarily deaf by the incident, or was in no mood to have his schedule upset by mere visitors. No sooner had the demonstration recommenced after lunch than there came another loud bang followed by a total absence of electrical power. The important visitors departed without seeing the performance. Luckily, however, this disaster had no lasting adverse effect on the fortunes of D86.

On another occasion strenuous efforts were being made to become involved with the Spanish Navy in the building of a major training facility at El Ferrol. The Spanish Admiral in charge of logistics asked if VT could arrange a visit for him and his senior staff to RN training establishments in the Portsmouth area. A request was made via the Defence Export Sales Organisation and, as usual, MOD(N) co-operation was forthcoming. However, as this was to be an official Navy to Navy visit, strict protocol had to be followed, which meant formal visits and dinner parties.

The visit was a success, but the Spaniards apparently found the continual formalities somewhat trying. On the penultimate day, Peter Robinson, one of the VT team, was taken aside by the Admiral's aide and asked whether the Spanish party could perhaps spend an informal evening at an 'English Pub'. This was rapidly arranged for the same evening at a country pub, complete with plenty of oak beams, for a party of a dozen or so Spaniards and VT personnel. The evening started off well with a walk round Old Portsmouth and a few beers. In a relaxed and happy mood, the party then adjourned to the appointed hostelry for supper.

At this point, disaster struck. On arrival, Derek Macgregor of VT was taken aside by the landlord's distraught wife to be told that there were severe staff problems: she herself was fully occupied in the kitchen and there was only one waitress.

Undaunted, Derek took this little problem in his stride and became a waiter for the evening, taking orders and serving, complete with a napkin over his arm, all to the great amusement of the Spaniards, whom Peter's colleagues tried to convince that audience participation was part of the old English pub tradition! The evening was an enormous success and as the Admiral said good night, he asked VT representatives to meet him the following day to agree and sign a contract for a feasibility study.

This became the forerunner of a major training simulator contract which in due course the Spanish Navy placed with the Controls Division. For years afterwards, the Spanish Admiral would remind VT of "the evening which broke the ice".

Other export successes followed and, not to be outdone, the Hydraulic Power Division too continued to do business abroad. Orders were received for 16 sets of fins and steering gear for the US Coast Guard's *Island* class patrol boats which Bollinger were building under licence in Louisiana, to the VT 110ft design. Following this initial order, a further 33 sets of equipment were later ordered for the second batch of boats; the largest single production run for naval equipment in HPD's history.

Indeed, as the run-up to privatisation got under way in 1984, the Products Division was becoming responsible for an increasing share of the VT turnover and this was certainly a factor which helped the management buy-out team to win the necessary support in the City of London, which was generally unimpressed by the prospects of the shipbuilding industry of the time.

Successes continued after Privatisation: in 1988 HPD won a contract against stiff competition to supply the Korea Tacoma shipyard with seven sets of roll damping fins and steering gear for frigates being built for the Indian Navy. In 1989, another new market was successfully entered when the division won its largest ever order for 32 hydraulic ground support trolleys for the Tornado aircraft.

In addition to more orders for D86 systems, Controls scored further successes with a new single board controller based on the Intel 8088 processor. One of the first applications for this was the RN's Type 23 frigate propulsion order telegraph. In 1990, the controller was selected for the machinery control and surveillance systems of a further batch of *Island* class boats for the United States Coast Guard. Free from the constraints imposed by British Shipbuilders, VT continues to seek diversification of its talents into other new markets which will further reduce the dependence of the company on warship orders. Although a major part of this diversification will no doubt continue to be contributed by members of the Products Division, another route is by acquisition of other businesses. To achieve this of course requires access to capital and this was one of the reasons why VT turned to the London Stock Exchange in 1988.

## Chapter Thirteen

# FLOTATION AND AFTER

It had always been the intention to float the Company on the Stock exchange when the right conditions had been achieved. By the autumn of 1987 the bankers - County Bank and Gresham Trust - in consultation with various oracles in the City of London considered that the time was ripe. Although not all the modest sales projections made at the time of the management buy-out had been achieved, the Company did have a healthy order book, all the loans had been paid off ahead of time, and the cash flow situation looked very good. Given the intense competition for any warship building orders and the background of the shipbuilding industry in general, the Company had recovered quickly from the paralysis of Nationalisation, and the future looked promising.

At the time of the management buy-out, the volumes of paper full of barely intelligible legal jargon and the hints of the dire consequences of supplying misleading information, either wittingly or unwittingly, had seemed particularly daunting. However, the team soon discovered that all that had been as nothing compared to the documentation associated with floating a company on the Stock Exchange. The principle, of course, is that investors should be in possession of the truth, and nothing but the truth, before parting with their money, and in the event that it turns out not to be quite the whole truth, then anyone possessed of the rest of the story should not be allowed to take advantage of it. The system has been designed in the light of years of experience of clever, and occasionally unscrupulous, people and the spotlight plays equally upon the just and the unjust. That it is still not one hundred per cent effective in dissuading the latter continues to be demonstrated occasionally by various well publicised court cases, but it certainly worried some of the VT team, even though their consciences were spotless!

Of course, of all the times to choose to launch a new share issue, the autumn of 1987 was not exactly the best. Having burned a good deal of midnight oil, worried themselves almost sick with

reams of formidable paper, and over-frequently indulged again in the gastronomic delights of the Casey Jones hamburger stand on Waterloo station, the team had just keyed themselves up for the climax when Black Monday dawned. The world stock markets crashed overnight, and suddenly brokers could not even give away "blue chips". All the reams of paper were put back into drawers to await a more propitious time.

The opportunity came five months later, in March 1988. The markets were deemed to have recovered sufficiently, and the bankers and brokers went into a huddle again to prepare for the "placing". Despite all high technology computer links, much of the business of the Stock Exchange still seemed to rely on word of mouth and personal contact. (Who, after all, wants to trust a computer with their savings?) Several presentations on the Company were given in the City by the Directors to audiences of potential investors. Following that, various "parcels" of Vosper Thornycroft Holdings shares were "placed" with various institutional investors; early signs were that there was not going to be any trouble in selling them. In fact, when trading started on the 17 March, demand exceeded supply and the opening price of £1.60 rose sharply. Suddenly, the buy-out shareholders, instead of being mortgaged to the hilt, found that their financial worries were over.

There was, of course, a certain amount of envious comment. One could only contrast this with the attitudes prevalent at the time of the buy-out, when few showed interest in the Company, even fewer actually bid, and the Usher team were regarded as, at best, slightly eccentric by some observers and quite mad by others.

Not all of these critics had been outside the Company. Although at the time of the buy-out almost all of those employees eligible for the free gift of 100 shares had applied for them in the manner required by the rules, and many were pleased and proud to thus become shareholders, the possession of one hundred 10 pence shares

"HMS *Havoc*". Damage Repair Instructional Unit.

*Hawk* class patrol craft.

hardly seemed a financial bonanza; indeed, it was clearly regarded as a joke in some quarters. It was not until several days after flotation that all the shareholders began to realise that their original 100 shares had suddenly become 800, which were now changing hands at around £1.70 each! A few individuals who had scorned to apply for their free shares suddenly began to enquire why the Company Secretary had mislaid their applications! Unfortunately, it was by then too late!

All of this was of course very nice, but had not been the sole, or even the main, motive for flotation. With the intense contest for foreign orders, it had been felt that in dealing with Governments a private company would sooner or later be at a disadvantage when competing with rivals whose reputation could be publicly underwritten by a quotation on the international Stock Market. Moreover, VT had another sound business reason for seeking the accolade of the Stock Exchange, the need for development capital.

As has been explained, the pitfalls of shipbuilding had long been recognised. Orders for warships would always be received at irregular intervals, resulting even at the best of times in rapid fluctuations of labour loading. In order to help smooth out these 'bumps', as well as to reduce reliance on pure shipbuilding, the Company had already diversified via, for example, the Support Projects Division into the supply of various goods and services, which continued to derive business from shipbuilding projects long after the delivery of the ship itself. The Products Division - Controls and Hydraulic Power - also had become substantially independent of VT shipbuilding orders and in fact derived considerable business from shipbuilding projects won by rival shipbuilders.

Just as these 'non-shipbuilding' activities had successfully grown away from shipbuilding and become to a large extent self supporting, now there was scope for them too to develop further offshoots, as well as for the shipbuilding division itself to seek additional products. Diversification would give the Company greater stability, but it would also require access to further capital, either to expand the existing organisation or for new acquisitions. A sound track record would have to

be established on the Stock Market so that the new ideas for diversification could rely on the necessary financial backing.

Some of the new products which the shipbuilders were finding to produce were quite novel. The Damage Repair and Instruction Unit, DRIU, was an idea developed for RN use within the VT Shipbuilding Division, in close collaboration with MOD(N) and with substantial contributions from the Products Division. It comprised a large steel box fitted out inside to represent various compartments of a warship, and mounted on journals. Trainees inside could be subjected to various unpleasant experiences, such as clouds of smoke, fires, and jets of sea water which progressively flooded the compartment. With all this going on as well as the whole structure being rolled to simulate a rough sea, the unfortunate victims were trained to exercise damage control routines to extinguish fires, stop leaks, or rescue each other from impossible situations. Some of the ideas developed for "HMS *Havoc*", as the device was christened, were also applied to export training schemes.

The Company was also seeking other applications for its GRP expertise. The hulls of the Keith Nelson range of small patrol boats had always been moulded elsewhere, but now the question of whether to mould such items in house was reviewed again. In 1987 an enquiry was received from the Middle East for three 30m patrol craft, and there was intense competition for the order. Price was clearly going to be a major factor in deciding the winner, and obviously the cost of the hull moulding had a significant influence. The Portchester buyers set about getting the best deals they could from all the different equipment and material suppliers and a lot of agonising ensued as to whether the order for the GRP hulls should be placed with Woolston or an outside contractor. The decision was by no means straightforward, but eventually Woolston won the day. This meant that VT ideas could be incorporated in the hull design, which would then be available for other projects in the future.

The order was won, and production of the *Hawk* class, as it became known, commenced in 1988. Before Woolston could start laying up GRP they had to build a steel mould. While the hulls and decks were being moulded at Woolston, Portchester began work on the superstructures, which were of aluminium. Encouraged by the recent experience with *Gentry Eagle*, and spurred on by the powerful incentive of reducing costs, these superstructures were of all-welded construction, rather than the more usual, for Portchester, riveting. These boats represented a return to the production of relatively simple warships, the theme which had begun successfully over thirty years before with the 103 foot Vosper boats.

Another project which was in some ways a throwback to the fast torpedo boats of that same era was initiated as a private venture funded by the Company. The *Viper* was designed as a very fast interceptor, 18. 6 metres in length, with a crew of three, and the ability to carry ten troops, or a ton of supplies, and a couple of heavy machine guns or a small cannon. She was diesel powered and constructed entirely in reinforced plastic, using kevlar as well as glass fibre for lightness and strength. The prototype boat was launched in 1988 and began a programme of development which was to continue for some time, owing to the deliberately tight development budget and the growing commitment of available effort to other projects.

The *Hawk* class boats were subject to some delays, partly because of production problems due to new methods being introduced, but mainly on account of unexpected problems which the customer was experiencing with the finance for the project. Since money could not be made available at the rate which had been agreed in order to fund the project, the Company was effectively beginning to fund work with its own money, and production had eventually to be slowed down until the original problem was overcome.

Also in 1988, work began in the Bangkok shipyard of Italthai Marine on three ASW (Anti Submarine Warfare) corvettes for the Royal Thai Navy. VT supplied goods and services to enable these ships to be built, the design being based on the 56 metre strike craft. However, considerable modification was required to adapt the design for its new role, and an interesting exercise in long distance communication began. This was further complicated by the fact that one of the ships was built by the Royal Thai Navy Dockyard in Bangkok. VT's previous experience of assisting with local build projects came in very useful. The first ship was ready for trials in May 1991, and successfully achieved her design speed.

At Woolston, the first SRMH, HMS *Sandown*, was accepted by the Royal Navy on 17 March 1989. By then, construction of the first batch of her sister ships was under way, and agreement had been reached to supply three more *Sandown* class ships to the Royal Saudi Naval Forces, who also expressed the firm intent of acquiring a further three in due course. Woolston would be busy for at least another three years.

HMS *Sandown* did not see service in the Gulf war of 1991, but five VT built *Hunt* class MCMVs played a vital role in clearing paths through the huge numbers of Iraqi mines which were laid around the Kuwait coast. The training and professionalism of the RN crews, and the investment which the MOD(N) had made in minehunting over many years, paid off handsomely and the achievements of the British force surpassed that of all the other MCM forces in the area. In passing, it should be mentioned that another VT product, HMS *Gloucester*, also distinguished herself in the same conflict by shooting down the only Iraqi missile aimed at Allied warships. The Saudi press was generous in its praise of the RN.

Back home, Woolston had handed over the first of the Saudi *Sandown* class minehunters, and in the spring of 1991 yet further increases in GRP productivity were demonstrated when the second RN ship, HMS *Inverness*, was handed over, defect free, a month ahead of schedule.

Despite this further surge of activity for the shipbuilding division, its endeavours to diversify, as well as those of the other divisions, continued, and further successes were achieved on several fronts.

The Support Projects Division, of course, was heavily occupied in supplying a comprehensive training and support package for the new Saudi minehunters. Part of this exercise involved teaching English to Royal Saudi Naval personnel, and one of VT's instructors, Peter Dixon, also a keen amateur naturalist, found himself in Jubail faced

*Viper* fast interceptor.

ASW corvette for Royal Thai Navy. Designed by VT and built by Italthai Marine.

Some of the wide range of spares supplied by Support Project Division.

52 metre coastal patrol boat (PBC) for USN.

with the dreadful effects of the Gulf war on the local wildlife. Peter and his VT colleagues were soon spending most of their spare time helping to clean up oil-soaked cormorants and grebes. VT also assisted by supplying a video player to the RSPCA to help them show Saudi volunteers how to clean up the unfortunate birds.

Back at Portchester, Support Projects, under the management of Terry Turner, had long been diversifying in other unexpected directions. Amongst the more unusual items supplied in recent years were spares for a launch built by J.I. Thornycroft in 1920, and some musical instruments for the Yemen Navy band. Fortunately the drawings of the launch had been handed over to the Maritime Museum at Greenwich some years before, where they had been carefully preserved. More importantly, the Division, which had moved into Vosper House in 1984, also continued to provide an ever-widening range of more conventional services, including supplying spares to Royal Navy Type "A" (fighting) ships, as well as Type "B" (support) ships, and of course to all sorts of overseas customers.

With the completion of new GRP production facilities and the rapidly accumulating expertise with this high technology material, it had been clear for some time that there was considerable scope for other applications in addition to shipbuilding. In 1988 the Ministry of Defence produced a requirement for a device to magnetically treat submarines to reduce their magnetic signatures. This required a large number of electrical coils to be supported in a precise manner around the boat whilst it was still afloat. The support structure itself had to float, and had itself to be non-magnetic. GRP was an obvious candidate, but the structure would be massive, compared with anything previously built in that material. VT project engineers devised a very large toast-rack-like structure, and in conjunction with Dowty, won a contract from the MOD to produce a detailed design. However, having modified Portchester No.4 shop to allow the GRP sub-assemblies to be manufactured there, this project eventually fell victim to defence budget cuts.

Although the MOD(N) had long been convinced of the merits of this high quality GRP material, a lot of ingenuity and marketing effort was required in order to find other applications. VT themselves had to go out to find new problems in other industries with which they were unfamiliar, and then sell the merits of their form of GRP to potential customers, who at first might equate it with everyday fibreglass; a versatile but inferior relation!

One example of this was the offshore oil industry. The strength to weight ratio of the material, coupled with its proven fire resistance, made it ideal for the construction of fire and blast protection screens on oil rigs. Mervyn Roger Smith, who once led the Weapons team for the Mk.10 Frigate project, had subsequently joined Vosper Offshore under Alan Griffith and thus escaped being nationalised. Having accumulated some experience of the offshore oil world, he rejoined VT some years later after privatisation and as Offshore Marketing Manager spent some time promoting the application of GRP. In 1991, following various feasibility studies, success was achieved by landing a large contract with Shell for fire and blast protection walls to enclose emergency shutdown valves on rigs.

VT's Engineering and Manufacturing Division at Woolston also broke new ground in 1991 with a prestigious contract, in conjunction with the Hydraulic Power Division, for handling equipment used in the storage of nuclear waste at Harwell AEA Technology site. Several other manufacturing contracts were in hand at the same time for British Aerospace Space Systems.

In addition to internal diversification, VT has also acquired or set up several subsidiary companies in various areas. In order to gain a better foothold across the Atlantic VT, in partnership with the Bollinger Machine Shop in Lockport, Louisiana, set up a jointly owned company called the Chand Corporation. This venture began by providing a comprehensive support service to the *Island* class vessels which Bollinger had built for the US Coast Guard to VT's well tried design.

The shipbuilding partnership with Bollinger also scored another success in late 1990 when the US Navy ordered thirteen 52 metre patrol boats from the Louisiana shipyard. The boats were to be based on the 52 metre strike craft supplied by VT to Egypt and VT was awarded a contract to help

Bollinger to modify the design to the US Navy's requirements. VT was also awarded contracts for the roll damping system and steering gear, whilst Chand would supply further support. The achievement of this notable order owed much to the success of the US Coast Guard's experience with the *Island* class.

Another joint venture had been set up in the UK in 1987 in conjunction with Airwork Ltd. The task of A V Seawork Ltd is to recruit and supply skilled personnel on a contract basis to marine and engineering organisations throughout the world. Many navies have problems in recruiting, training and keeping skilled managers and maintainers for their support organisations, and the support of contract labour is a fast growing market. In 1991, A V Seawork became a wholly owned subsidiary of VT.

Back at home, systems engineering skills too were being marketed. The Systems Group, set up at Woolston, won, for example, a contract to study the future electrical power demands of both submarines and surface ships for the RN. Similar tasks are also undertaken by MSC Solent, an offshoot of the non-shipbuilding divisions of VT.

Yet another example of diversification is J B Microsystems Ltd. This small company in Leicester specialised in the application of microprocessors to industrial process control. It was formed by Jeff Court and his wife in 1978 and joined the VT Group in 1987. JBM's microprocessor expertise has been married to that of MSC Solent, developing more new products and moving into new markets.

In 1991 a contract was won to provide a weapons maintainer training simulator for the RN's HMS *Collingwood* shore establishment. The trainer replicates the weapon system of a *Sandown* class minehunter with a full mock-up of the Operations Room. The project is shared between VT's Support Projects and Controls Divisions, and MSC Solent.

As well as new ideas and new markets, moving into the nineties has also meant new faces. Whilst many of those who survived nationalisation and privatisation and the accompanying upheavals will, it is to be hoped, see the Company safely into the 21st century, recent years have seen yet another round of changes at the top. With the changing character of the Company, new blood was essential,

and organisational changes in any case take their toll. Peter Usher, after over twenty very active years in VT, virtually since its formation, made way for Martin Jay. Martin, formerly a member of the UK Board of Management of GEC, and Group Managing Director of GEC Electronic Components, joined VT in 1989 to take over as Managing Director and Chief Executive. Peter, who despite his passion for golf, has never been happy to be away from the office for very long, took over the Chairmanship from Roy Withers in 1990, after a short spell as Deputy Chairman. Roy, another workaholic, remained on the Board in a non-executive capacity.

Despite the fact that by 1992 the huge covered berth at Woolston had been almost empty since the launch of HMS *Gloucester* almost ten years before, and Portchester too was sorely missing a significant warship order, the fortunes of the Company continued to meet with the approval of that most capricious of judges, the London Stock Market, at a time when not only did the stock of many other concerns dwindle and the recession bite deeply into UK industry, but when, with the collapse of the Soviet Union, UK defence budget cuts appeared particularly ominous for the defence industry.

This confidence turned out to be well placed. With the last of the current batch of *Sandown* class minehunters due to be launched in July 1992, and the funding for the second batch of three Saudi *Sandowns* still not cleared, the future of shipbuilding was beginning to appear bleak again and redundancy for up to 350 people was unavoidably declared. But patient work by the design and sales teams on another project, which had been going on for several years already, bore fruit in the early summer of 1992 with the signature of a contract with the Government of Oman for the supply of two 83m corvettes.

These corvettes were the result of a prolonged and intensive design exercise incorporating much new technology and production engineering as well as VT's unique experience in bespoke warship design. The application of techniques such as advanced outfitting and modular construction, developed over the years, were essential to winning such an order against intense competition, and the Company also boldly invested in the latest laser

83 metre corvette for Oman. Artists impression.

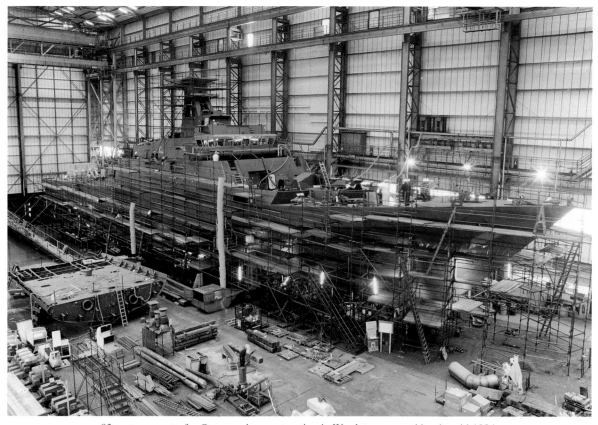

83 metre corvette for Oman under construction in Woolston covered berth, mid 1994.

56 metre strike craft for Qatar. Artists impression.

*Sentinel*. HM Customs and Excise cutter.

cutting equipment to enable the steel to be cut free of distortion and to an exceptionally high accuracy. As if to justify this bold step, as well as to emphasise the eternally perverse cyclic nature of the warship building market, this spectacular sale was almost immediately followed by another, a contract from the State of Qatar for four updated versions of the immensely successful 56 metre strike craft. Even this was not all, the UK Customs and Excise also placed an order for a 34 metre patrol boat, particularly significant as a success in the para-military market sector.

The significance of these orders for steel ships to VT as a shipbuilder is difficult to exaggerate. The four or five years preceding them had seen VT increasingly in danger of becoming thought of by the world at large as a builder in GRP only and this was unwelcome because, although the GRP work for the Royal Navy and the Royal Saudi Naval Forces had been of immense value, VT has always regarded itself as a general builder of warships and did not relish the thought of being typecast. However, in the last few years, the picture has changed completely and until July 1994 VT was in the postion of having no orders for GRP work but having these major contracts in hand for steel ships.These steel ships are exactly in the traditional line of VT's Family of Warships and having orders for ships the Company would call corvettes as well as for fast strike craft for export could hardly be better. To cap it, an order was received in July for a further seven *Sandown* class ships for the Royal Navy. This order doubled the number of ships on order from 7 to 14 with an excellent balance of 6 steel ships and 8 GRP (1 Saudi and 7 RN).

The Royal Navy ships are extremely close repeats of those built earlier, but the Oman and Qatar vessels are both new designs, although based heavily on past practices. The Oman ships are of the order of 1250 tonnes, thus bigger than any corvette previously built by VT but smaller than the Mk.5s; they therefore fill a gap in the "Family" rather than constitute a completely new departure. The future for surface ships seems likely to lie in hulls rather smaller than have been the norm in NATO navies up to now and these contracts therefore provide an extremely good basis for future years.

Although these substantial shipbuilding orders claimed the limelight, the steady progress by the rest of the Group in the same period should not be overlooked. PDL, manufacturers of aircraft maintenance facilities, and Van Dusen and Meyer, an American yacht stabiliser company, were both acquired, and the Controls Division won major contracts in Korea and USA for an Active Ride Control System for fast catamaran ferries. The Portchester facilities also scored a number of successes, including the refit of some large yachts.

In winding up this volume of the history of VT, the board changes which have recently taken place should be recorded. The executive board now consists of Martin Jay - Managing Director, Chris Girling - Financial Director, Alan Staff - Commercial Director, Dick Taylor - Shipbuilding Director and George Cameron - Managing Director, Systems Group. These executives are supported by Peter Usher as Chairman and Roy Withers, Norman Baldock and Tony Dorey as non-executives. This team, which combines long experience of company activities with the new and younger blood, always necessary to a successful business, looks forward to the future with confidence.

It is probable that Herbert Vosper and John I. Thornycroft could still recognise the features of the businesses which they founded over a hundred years ago, but success has largely been due to moving with the times; going out to find how customers' needs and wants are changing; introducing new technology and new products. Because these products have, by and large, been interesting as well as innovative, and because the Company is based in a pleasant and popular area of southern England, it has been possible, even during the darkest era of nationalisation, to attract and keep enough of the right sort of people; go-ahead managers and innovative engineers without whom all the achievements would have been impossible.

Looking ahead, what might the next twenty years hold in store for Vosper Thornycroft?

The changing world order, population growth and the increasing scarcity of natural resources, all suggest that the maintenance of law and order will remain a high priority of governments throughout the world. In particular, littoral states will need to pay increasing attention to the protection of the resources within their offshore waters, generating requirements for the types of naval and para-military vessels for which Vosper Thornycroft has become renowned. Together with continuing diversification with complementary industrial ventures, this suggests that VT will continue to flourish, thereby providing ample scope for a further update on the company history during the second decade of the 21st century.

## THE MANAGEMENT BUY-OUT TEAM

*From left to right*

Norman Baldock
Tony Dorey
Andrew Davison
Sidney Donald
Roy Withers
George Cameron
Peter Usher
Barry Stobart-Hook
Barry Jones
Keith Brown
Terry Grisley

## THE EXECUTIVE BOARD (CURRENT)

*From left to right*

Chris Girling
George Cameron
Alan Staff
Martin Jay
Dick Taylor

# DIAGRAMS TO SHOW MACHINERY ARRANGEMENTS OF SOME OF THE VT DESIGNS COVERED IN THE BOOK

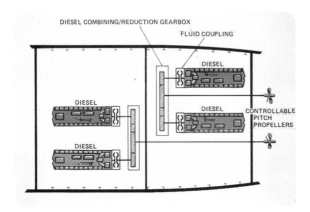

All diesel (Mk.9).

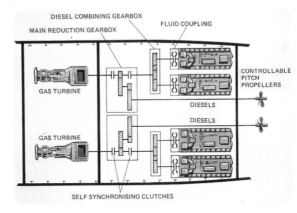

CODOG (Mk.10).

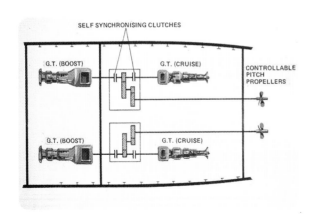

COGOG (Type 21, 42).

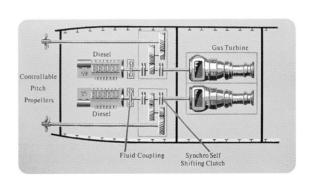

CODOG (Mk.5, 7).

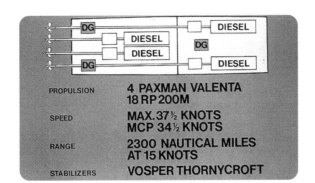

56 metre Machinery.

# VOSPER THORNYCROFT LIMITED

*(Registered in England No. 317293)*

*Directors:*
Sir David Brown (*Chairman*)
John Rix, M.B.E. (*Managing Director*)
Commander Christopher W. S. Dreyer, D.S.O., D.S.C., R.N.
Alan A. C. Griffith, O.B.E.
Alan D. Worton
The Hon. Sir Clive Bossom, Bt.

*Registered Office:*
Vosper House,
223 Southampton Road,
Paulsgrove,
Portsmouth, PO6 4QA.

*7th August, 1974.*

Dear Shareholder,

### NATIONALISATION—SHIPBUILDING AND SHIPREPAIRING

In his statement on July 31st, Mr. Wedgwood Benn made it clear that the Labour Government firmly intends to nationalise the Industry, including your Company. He bases his case on what he calls "the indifferent record" of the Industry.

Such an accusation is totally false so far as this Company is concerned and could be very damaging, particularly in relation to our exports. Accordingly your Directors are undertaking a campaign through the Members of Parliament, Press and other media to refute these allegations and to do everything possible to oppose nationalisation by every means available.

As this matter is of such importance to the future of your Company, I consider it only right to advise you of the action we are taking and to give you the essential elements of our case in refuting Mr. Wedgwood Benn's allegations. These are the facts we shall use in the next few weeks :—

1. Vosper took the initiative eight years ago to merge with Thornycroft to provide a specialist complex for surface warships from Patrol Boats to Destroyers. This was achieved entirely without Government financial assistance, except for a small contribution of £89,000 from the Shipbuilding Industry Board towards re-organisation costs.

2. Since the merger, Vosper Thornycroft has spent in excess of £6m. on re-organisation, re-equipment and development primarily from its own resources, including retained profits.

3. Apart from Government financial assistance available to Industry as a whole, for instance export rebates and investment grants, the only direct grants and loans received by the Company to date have been the Shipbuilding Construction Grant of £840,000 and grants and loans for Hovercraft development of £600,000.

4. Not being in a development area, the Company has never benefited from Regional Employment Premiums (now £3 per week per employee) which would amount to approximately £1m. per year in the case of your Company.

5. We have successfully taken the initiative in relation to shiprepairing in the Port of Southampton. The fragmentation mentioned by Mr. Wedgwood Benn has already been eliminated by merging, into a more effective unit, the two major shiprepairers in the Port—Vosper Thornycroft and Harland and Wolff.

6. Notwithstanding the limited Government assistance received, Vosper Thornycroft has an impressive record of achievement :—

   ★ In the last fifteen years contracts have been received from over thirty Navies of the world against world competition to a value approaching £250m.

   ★ In the last eight years turnover has increased from £6m. to £50m.

   ★ Exports represent at least 80% of the Company's shipbuilding turnover, recognised by three Queen's Awards.

   ★ Pre-tax profits have increased fourfold in the last eight years, and for the last half-year reached a record total of £957,000.

   ★ The numbers employed have increased by 20% since 1968.

   ★ In recent years we have raised £2m. by public issue, which would not have been possible if the Company had had an indifferent record.

I believe that your Company has a great future if it can remain outside State Control. If you agree with the attitude we are taking, please make your views known to your Member of Parliament and any other persons of influence to whom you may have access.

Yours sincerely,

DAVID BROWN,
*Chairman.*

Greenaways London HB 56209

# VO/PER THORNYCROFT LIMITED

PAULSGROVE · PORTSMOUTH · PO6 4QA

TELEPHONE: COSHAM 79481  TELEX: 86115  CABLES: REPSOV PORTSMOUTH

## STATEMENT BY THE CHAIRMAN
## SIR DAVID BROWN

## MADE AT THE ANNUAL GENERAL MEETING HELD
## THURSDAY, 17TH APRIL    1975

In my Annual Report I said I would keep you advised in regard to the Government's intention to Nationalise your Company. Mr. Benn has announced his proposed terms for compensation. Under his formula the total compensation for the entire Company is only £4·2 million. Roughly about one third of the net assets. I am sure you will agree that in the light of the Company's record of success the only interpretation one can place on such terms is confiscation, or to put it another way, daylight robbery. The Board will by every possible means endeavour to get these terms improved to a realistic level, and at the same time will continue to fight against Nationalisation. We still await the details of the Bill, but what is utterly clear is that there is no logic at all in the Nationalisation of this Company.

We do not meet any of the accepted criteria for Nationalisation. We are not a lame duck. We are not in receipt of large Government subsidies. We are not losing money. Mr. Benn is just not prepared to listen to any rational argument.

I say again that Nationalisation will be disastrous to our exports. Some of you may have seen Mr. Chapman Pincher's recent articles on the effect that Government intervention is having on military exports—intervention quite outside pure security. Political intervention, constant frustration and delay will become intolerable once the Government controls exporting businesses such as ours.

We shall continue the fight, but we need all the help we can get from you, the Shareholders and the Public.

REGISTERED OFFICE  223 SOUTHAMPTON ROAD  PAULSGROVE  PORTSMOUTH  PO6 4QA  REGISTERED NUMBER 317293 ENGLAND

 A SUBSIDIARY OF DAVID BROWN HOLDINGS LIMITED

## Appendix Two

# VESSELS BUILT BY VOSPER THORNYCROFT SINCE 1964

Note: Yard numbers between 2000 & 3000 built at Portchester or Broad Street Yards, numbers over 4000 built at Woolston.

| Yard No | Type | Length Overall | For Whom Built | Name | When Built |
|---------|------|----------------|----------------|------|------------|
| 2581 | Fast Patrol Craft | 96.0ft | Malaysia | KD PERKASA | 1965 |
| 2582 | Fast Patrol Craft | 96.0ft | Malaysia | KD HANDALAN | 1965 |
| 2583 | Fast Patrol Craft | 96.0ft | Malaysia | KD GEMPITA | 1965 |
| 2584 | Fast Patrol Craft | 96.0ft | Malaysia | KD PENDEKAR | 1965 |
| 2586 | Fast Patrol Craft | 103.0ft | Kenya | KNS SIMBA | 1965 |
| 2587 | Fast Patrol Craft | 103.0ft | Kenya | KNS CHUI | 1965 |
| 2588 | Fast Patrol Craft | 103.0ft | Kenya | KNS NDOVU | 1965 |
| 2589 | Fast Patrol Craft | 103.0ft | Malaysia | KD KRIS | 1965 |
| 2590 | Fast Patrol Craft | 103.0ft | Malaysia | KD SUNDANG | 1965 |
| 2591 | Fast Patrol Craft | 103.0ft | Malaysia | KD BADEK | 1966 |
| 2592 | Fast Patrol Craft | 103.0ft | Malaysia | KD RENCHONG | 1966 |
| 2593 | Fast Patrol Craft | 103.0ft | Malaysia | KD TOMBAK | 1966 |
| 2594 | Fast Patrol Craft | 103.0ft | Malaysia | KD LEMBING | 1966 |
| 2595 | Fast Patrol Craft | 103.0ft | Malaysia | KD SERAMPANG | 1966 |
| 2596 | Fast Patrol Craft | 103.0ft | Malaysia | KD PANAH | 1966 |
| 2597 | Fast Patrol Craft | 103.0ft | Malaysia | KD KERAMBIT | 1966 |
| 2598 | Fast Patrol Craft | 103.0ft | Malaysia | KD BELADAU | 1966 |
| 2599 | Fast Patrol Craft | 103.0ft | Malaysia | KD KELEWANG | 1967 |
| 2600 | Fast Patrol Craft | 103.0ft | Malaysia | KD RENTAKA | 1967 |
| 2601 | Fast Patrol Craft | 103.0ft | Malaysia | KD SRI JOHOR | 1967 |
| 2602 | Fast Patrol Craft | 103.0ft | Malaysia | KD SRI PERLIS | 1967 |
| 2603 | Fast Patrol Craft | 96.0ft | Brunei | PAHLAWAN | 1966/7 |
| 2604 | Race Boat | 38.0ft | UK | FLYING FISH | 1967 |
| 2605 | Fast Patrol Craft | 96.0ft | Libya | FPB SUSA | 1967 |
| 2606 | Fast Patrol Craft | 96.0ft | Libya | FPB SIRTE | 1967/8 |
| 2607 | Fast Patrol Craft | 96.0ft | Libya | FPB SEBHA | 1967/8 |
| 2608 | Patrol Craft | 78.0ft | Kuwait | PB MURSHED | 1967/8 |
| 2609 | Patrol Craft | 78.0ft | Kuwait | PB MARZOOK | 1967/8 |
| 2610 | Floating Bridge | 165.0ft | Southampton Corporation | WOOLSTON | 1967/8 |
| 2611 | Patrol Craft | 100.0ft | Libya | MISURATA | 1967/8 |
| 2612 | Patrol Craft | 100.0ft | Libya | BENINA | 1967/8 |
| 2613 | Patrol Craft | 78.0ft | Kuwait | MAYMOON | 1968 |

| Yard No | Type | Length Overall | For Whom Built | Name | When Built |
|---------|------|----------------|----------------|------|------------|
| 2614 | Patrol Craft | 78.0ft | Kuwait | AMAN | 1968 |
| 2615 | Patrol Craft | 100.0ft | Libya | HOMS | 1968 |
| 2616 | Patrol Craft | 100.0ft | Libya | AKRAMA | 1968 |
| 2617 | Hovercraft | 95.0ft | UK | 001 | 1969 |
| 2618 | Fast Patrol Craft | 142.0ft | UK - Vosper | TENACITY | 1969 |
| 2619 | GRP Patrol Craft | 56.0ft | Abu Dhabi | KAWKAS | 1968 |
| 2620 | GRP Patrol Craft | 56.0ft | Abu Dhabi | THOR BAN | 1968 |
| 2621 | Fast Patrol Craft | 110.0ft | Singapore, Type A | (Vosper built) | 1969 |
| 2622 | Fast Patrol Craft | 110.0ft | Singapore Type A | (Singapore built) | 1970 |
| 2623 | Fast Patrol Craft | 110.0ft | Singapore Type A | (Singapore built) | 1971 |
| 2624 | Fast Patrol Craft | 110.0ft | Singapore Type B | (Vosper built) | 1970 |
| 2625 | Fast Patrol Craft | 110.0ft | Singapore Type B | (Singapore built) | 1971 |
| 2626 | Fast Patrol Craft | 110.0ft | Singapore Type B | (Singapore built) | 1972 |
| 2627 | Patrol Craft | 78.0ft | Kuwait | WATHAH | 1968 |
| 2628 | Patrol Craft | 78.0ft | Kuwait | MASHHOOR | 1968 |
| 2629 | Pilot Launch (KN) | 40.0ft | Madeira | FUCHAL | 1968/9 |
| 2630 | Gen Purpose Launch | 40.0ft | Kuwait | | 1969 |
| 2631 | FPB Training Craft | 100.0ft | MOD(N) | HMS SCIMITAR | 1969 |
| 2632 | FPB Training Craft | 100.0ft | MOD(N) | HMS CUTLASS | 1970 |
| 2633 | FPB Training Craft | 100.0ft | MOD(N) | HMS SABRE | 1970 |
| 2634 | Mk3 Corvette | 203.0ft | Nigeria | NNS OTOBO | 1970 |
| 2635 | Mk3 Corvette | 203.0ft | Nigeria | NNS DORINA | 1970/1 |
| 2636 | Hovercraft | 95.0ft | UK (VT) | 002 | 1970 |
| 2637 | Hovercraft | 100.0ft | UK (VT) | 003 | 1971 |
| 2638/9 | Hovercraft | 100.0ft | UK (VT) | 004/5 (not built) | |
| 2640 | Patrol Launch | 56.0ft | Abu Dhabi | BANI YAS (P563) | 1969 |
| 2641 | Pilot Launch | 40.0ft | Holland | KOMER (lifeboat) | 1969 |
| 2642/3 | FG Hull (Survey) | 40.0ft | Sweden | Outfitted in Sweden | 1969 |
| 2644 | Patrol Craft | 78'6" | Kuwait | ANTISAR | 1969 |
| 2645 | Patrol Craft | 78'6" | Kuwait | ALSHURTI | 1969 |
| 2646 | Patrol Craft | 103.0ft | Panama | PANQUIACO | 1969/70 |
| 2647 | Patrol Craft | 103.0ft | Panama | LIGIA ELANA | 1969/70 |
| 2648 | Patrol Craft | 60.0ft | Bahamas PF | SAN SALVADOR | 1969 |
| 2649 | Patrol Craft | 60.0ft | Bahamas PF | ELEUTHERA | 1969 |
| 2650 | Patrol Craft | 60.0ft | Bahamas PF | ANDROS | 1969 |
| 2651 | Patrol Craft | 60.0ft | Bahamas PF | ACKLIN | 1969 |

| Yard No | Type | Length Overall | For Whom Built | Name | When Built |
|---------|------|----------------|----------------|------|------------|
| 2652 | Motor Yacht | 40.0ft | Nigeria | SUNFLOWER | 1968/9 |
| 2653 | Survey Launch | 34.0ft | Sierra Leone | RONA II | 1969 |
| 2654 | Pilot Launch | 40.0ft | Guyana | JAQUER | 1970 |
| 2655 | Pilot Launch | 40.0ft | Guyana | MARGAY | 1970 |
| 2656 | Pilot Launch | 40.0ft | Guyana | OCELOT | 1970 |
| 2657 | Pilot Launch | 40.0ft | Forth Pilots | GAZELLE | 1970 |
| 2658 | Not built | | | | |
| 2659 | Patrol Craft | 103.0ft | Trinidad & Tobago | HMTS CHAGUARAMS | 1970/1 |
| 2660 | Patrol Craft | 103.0ft | Trinidad & Tobago | HMTS BUCCO REEF | 1970/1 |
| 2661 | Patrol Boat | 40.0ft | Abu Dabi DF | P406 (MURRAYJIB) | 1970 |
| 2662/3 | Officers Transport Boat | 34.0ft | MOD(N) | for BRITANNIA | 1970 |
| 2664 | Patrol Boat | 40.0ft | Medway Patrol | | 1971 |
| 2665 | Patrol Boat | 40.0ft | Kuwait | FATEEN | 1970 |
| 2666 | Not built | | | | |
| 2667 | Patrol Launch | 34.0ft | Nigeria, Police | PL1 | 1970 |
| 2668 | Patrol Launch | 34.0ft | Nigeria, Police | PL2 | 1970 |
| 2669 | Patrol Launch | 34.0ft | Nigeria, Police | PL3 | 1970 |
| 2670 | Patrol Launch | 34.0ft | Nigeria, Police | PL4 | 1970 |
| 2671 | Patrol Launch | 34.0ft | Nigeria, Police | PL5 | 1970 |
| 2672 | Patrol Launch | 34.0ft | Nigeria, Police | PL6 | 1970 |
| 2673 | Patrol Launch | 34.0ft | Nigeria, Police | PL7 | 1970 |
| 2674 | Patrol Launch | 34.0ft | Nigeria, Police | PL8 | 1970 |
| 2675 | Pilot Launch | 40.0ft | Italy | CP 2001 | 1970/1 |
| 2676 | Pilot Launch | 40.0ft | Italy | CP 2002 | 1970/1 |
| 2677 | Pilot Launch | 40.0ft | Italy | CP 2003 | 1970/1 |
| 2678 | Pilot Launch | 40.0ft | Italy | CP 2004 | 1970/1 |
| 2679 | Pilot Launch | 40.0ft | Italy | CP 2005 | 1970/1 |
| 2680 | Patrol Craft | 75.0ft | Zanzibar | KM UNGUJA | 1973 |
| 2681 | Patrol Craft | 75.0ft | Zanzibar | KM PEMBA | 1973 |
| 2682 | Patrol Craft | 75.0ft | Zanzibar | KM MNEMBA | 1974 |
| 2683 | Patrol Craft | 75.0ft | Zanzibar | KM MIWI | 1974 |
| 2684 | Patrol Craft | 75.0ft | Oman (RO Police) | HARAS I | 1975 |
| 2685 | Patrol Craft | 75.0ft | Oman (RO Police) | HARAS II | 1975 |
| 2686 | Fast Patrol Craft | 120.0ft | Venezuela (A) | ARV CONSTITUCION | 1973 |
| 2687 | Fast Patrol Boat | 120.0ft | Venezuela (A) | ARV INDEPENDENCIA | 1973 |
| 2688 | Fast Patrol Boat | 120.0ft | Venezuela (A) | ARV PATRIA | 1973 |

| Yard No | Type | Length Overall | For Whom Built | Name | When Built |
|---------|------|----------------|----------------|------|------------|
| 2689 | Fast Patrol Boat | 120.0ft | Venezuela (B) | ARV FEDERACION | 1973 |
| 2690 | Fast Patrol Boat | 120.0ft | Venezuela (B) | ARV LIBERTAD | 1973 |
| 2691 | Fast Patrol Boat | 120.0ft | Venezuela (B) | ARV VICTORIA | 1973 |
| 2692 | Alum. Hydrofoil | 100.ft | Hong Kong | SUPRAMAR (ROSN) | 1973/4 |
| 2693 | Yard Boat | 34.0ft | VT (UK) Ltd | SWORDFISH | 1973 |
| 2694 | Patrol Craft | 103.0ft | Tunisia | TAZARKA (P205) | 1975/6 |
| 2695 | Patrol Craft | 103.0ft | Guyana | PECCARI (DF1010) | 1975/6 |
| 2696 | Patrol Craft | 110.0ft | Abu Dhabi | AL ADAID (P1101) | 1974 |
| 2697 | Patrol Craft | 110.0ft | Abu Dhabi | ZUHARA (P1102) | 1974 |
| 2698 | Patrol Craft | 110.0ft | Abu Dhabi | MURBAN (P1103) | 1974 |
| 2699 | Patrol Craft | 110.0ft | Abu Dhabi | AL GHULLAN (P1104) | 1974 |
| 2700 | Patrol Craft | 110.0ft | Abu Dhabi | RADIIN (P1105) | 1974 |
| 2701 | Patrol Craft | 110.0ft | Abu Dhabi | CHANADAN (P1106) | 1974 |
| 2702 | Patrol Craft | 110.0ft | Qatar | AL WUSAIL (Q14) | 1974 |
| 2703 | Patrol Craft | 110.0ft | Qatar | BAZRZAN (Q18) | 1974 |
| 2704 | Patrol Craft | 110.0ft | Qatar | HWAR (Q12) | 1974 |
| 2705 | Patrol Craft | 110.0ft | Qatar | THAT ASSUAN (Q13) | 1974 |
| 2706 | Patrol Craft | 110.0ft | Qatar | AL KHATAB (Q15) | 1975 |
| 2707 | Patrol Craft | 110.0ft | Qatar | TARIQ (Q16) | 1975 |
| 2708 | Personal Craft GRP | 45.0ft | British Virgin Is | BARAS STAR | 1974 |
| 2709 | Patrol Craft Mk2 | 75.0ft | Oman (RO Police) | HARAS III | 1975 |
| 2710 | Patrol Craft Mk3 | 75.0ft | (Hull only - shipped to Italy) | | 1975 |
| 2711 | Patrol Craft | 75.0ft | Oman (RO Police) | HARAS IV | 1975 |
| 2712 | Mk9 Corvette | 69.0m | Nigeria | NNS ERIN-OMI | 1975 |
| 2713 | Mk9 Corvette | 69.0m | Nigeria | NNS ENYIMIRI | 1975 |
| 2714 | Patrol Craft | 31.3m | Tunisia | MENZEL BOURGUIBA | 1976 |
| 2715 | Patrol Craft | 103.0ft | Bahamas | HMBS MARLIN (PO1) | 1976 |
| 2716 | Patrol Craft | 103.0ft | Bahamas | HMBS FLAMINGO (PO2) | 1976 |
| 2717 | Patrol Craft | 75.0ft | St Vincent (05) | GEORGE MCINTOSH | 1977/81 |
| 2718 | Patrol Craft | 75.0ft | Oman (RO Police) | HARAS V | 1977 |
| 2719 | Patrol Craft | 60.0ft | Bahamas | HMBS EXUMA | 1977 |
| 2720 | Patrol Craft | 60.0ft | Bahamas | HMBS ABACO | 1977 |
| 2721 | Patrol Craft | 60.0ft | Bahamas | HMBS INAGUA | 1977 |
| 2722 | Passenger Launch | 34.0ft | MOD(N) | Delivery - Plymouth | 1977 |
| 2723 | Passenger Launch | 34.0ft | MOD(N) | Delivery - Portland | 1977 |
| 2724 | Passenger Launch | 34.0ft | MOD(N) | Delivery - Portslade | 1978 |

| Yard No | Type | Length Overall | For Whom Built | Name | When Built |
|---|---|---|---|---|---|
| 2725 | Passenger Launch | 34.0ft | MOD(N) | Delivery - So'ton RNR | 1978 |
| 2726 | Passenger Launch | 34.0ft | MOD(N) | Delivery - Portsmouth | 1978 |
| 2727 | Passenger Launch | 34.0ft | MOD(N) | Delivery - Greenock | 1978 |
| 2728 | Passenger Launch | 34.0ft | MOD(N) | Delivery - HMS Eaglet | 1978 |
| 2729 | Passenger Launch | 34.0ft | MOD(N) | Delivery - Rosyth | 1978 |
| 2730 | Passenger Launch | 34.0ft | MOD(N) | Delivery - Bristol | 1978 |
| 2731 | Passenger Launch | 34.0ft | MOD(N) | Delivery - Govan | 1978 |
| 2732 | Passenger Launch | 34.0ft | MOD(N) | Delivery - Belfast | 1978 |
| 2733 | Fast Missile Craft | 52.0m | Egypt | RAMADAN | 1981 |
| 2734 | Fast Missile Craft | 52.0m | Egypt | KHYBER | 1981 |
| 2735 | Fast Missile Craft | 52.0m | Egypt | EL KADESSEYA | 1982 |
| 2736 | Fast Missile Craft | 52.0m | Egypt | EL YARMOUK | 1982 |
| 2737 | Fast Missile Craft | 52.0m | Egypt | BADR | 1982 |
| 2738 | Fast Missile Craft | 52.0m | Egypt | HETTEIN | 1982 |
| 2739 to 2750  Not built | | | | | |
| 2751 | GRP Whalers | 27.0ft | West Germany | Nigerian Ferries | 1978 |
| 2752 | GRP Whalers | 27.0ft | West Germany | Nigerian Ferries | 1978 |
| 2753 | GRP Whalers | 27.0ft | West Germany | Nigerian Ferries | 1978 |
| 2754 | GRP Whalers | 27.0ft | West Germany | Nigerian Ferries | 1978 |
| 2755 | GRP Whalers | 27.0ft | West Germany | Nigerian Ferries | 1978 |
| 2756 | GRP Whalers | 27.0ft | West Germany | Nigerian Ferries | 1978 |
| 2757 | GRP Whalers | 27.0ft | West Germany | Nigerian Ferries | 1978 |
| 2758 | Fast Missile Craft | 56.0m | Oman (SON) | SNV DHOFAR | 1980 |
| 2759 | Fast Missile Craft | 56.0m | Oman (SON) | SNV AL SHARQIYAH | 1981 |
| 2760 | Fast Missile Craft | 56.0m | Oman (SON) | SNV AL BATNAH | 1982 |
| 2761 & 2762  Not built | | | | | |
| 2763 | Fast Ferry | 63.0m | Hong Kong | JU KONG | 1985 |
| 2764 | Fast Ferry | 63.0m | Hong Kong | CHEUNG KONG | 1985 |
| 2765 | Fast Missile Craft | 56.0m | Kenya | KNS UMOJA | 1987 |
| 2766 | Fast Missile Craft | 56.0m | Kenya | KNS NYAYO | 1987 |
| 2767 | Fast Missile Craft | 56.0m | Oman | SNV MUSSANDAM | 1989 |
| 2768 | A/C III Race Boat | 100' | USA | GENTRY EAGLE | 1988 |
| 2769 | Patrol Craft | 30.0m | Jordan | AL HUSSEIN | 1989 |
| 2770 | Patrol Craft | 30.0m | Jordan | AL HASSAN | 1990 |
| 2771 | Patrol Craft | 30.0m | Jordan | ABDULLAH | 1990 |
| 2772 | Cutter | 34.0m | HM Customs & Excise | SENTINEL | 1993 |

| Yard No | Type | Length Overall | For Whom Built | Name | When Built |
|---------|------|----------------|----------------|------|------------|
| 2773 | Fast Planing Boat | 18.6m | VT | VIPER | 1993 |
| 4203 | Floating Ferry Bridge | 165'0" | So'ton Corporation | | 1964 |
| 4204 | TS Divers Launch | 55'0" | Aramco | MA'AGLA | 1964 |
| 4205 | GS Launch | 72'0" | War Office | TREVOSE | 1964 |
| 4206 | Catamaran Mooring Service | 39'0" | MOD (Air) | | 1964 |
| 4207 | Leander Class Frigate | 372'0" | Admiralty | JUNO | 1967 |
| 4208 | TS Tug | 110'0" | IOW Co. | CHALE | 1965 |
| 4209 | TS Passenger Vehicle Ferry | 188'3" | IOW Co. | COWES CASTLE | 1965 |
| 4210 | TS Exercise Minelayer | 265'0" | MOD(N) | ABDIEL | 1967 |
| 4211 | Passenger & Cycle Ferry | 100'0" | Portsmouth Harbour Ferry Company | PORTSMOUTH QUEEN | 1966 |
| 4212 | Passenger & Cycle Ferry | 100'0" | | GOSPORT QUEEN | 1966 |
| 4213 | TS Inshore Patrol Boat | 78'0" | Kuwait MOD | EL SALAMI | 1966 |
| 4214 | TS Inshore Patrol Boat | 78'0" | Kuwait MOD | EL MUBARAKI | 1966 |
| 4215 | Boiler Barge | 68'0" | MOD | | 1966 |
| 4216 | Nuclear Facilities Barge | 97'0" | MOD | | 1966 |
| 4217 | TS Customs Launch | 100'0" | Libyan Customs | ARRAKIB | 1966 |
| 4218 | TS Exercise Minelayer | 265'0" | Libyan Customs | FARWA | 1967 |
| 4219 | TS Yacht | 137'0" | Orange Yachts | ROMANTICA | 1968 |
| 4220 | Floating Bridge | 165'0" | Southampton Corp | | |
| 4221 | Mk.5 Fast Destroyer | 310'0" | Imp. Iranian Navy | SAAM | 1971 |
| 4222 | Mk.5 Fast Destroyer | 310'0" | Imp. Iranian Navy | FARAMARZ | 1972 |
| 4223 | TS Inshore Patrol Boat | 78'0" | Kuwait MOD | See 2627/8 - built at Broad Street Yard | |
| 4224 | TS Inshore Patrol Boat | 78'0" | Kuwait MOD | | |
| 4225 | TS Maintenance & Repair Ship | 324'0" | MOD Libya | ZELTIN | 1968 |
| 4226 | TS Passenger & Vehicle Ferry | 188'3" | IOW Co. | NORRIS CASTLE | 1968 |
| 4227 | Mk7 Fast Frigate | 329'0" | MOD Libya | DAT ASSAWARI | 1973 |
| 4228 | Type 21 Frigate | 383'11½" | MOD(N) | AMAZON | 1974 |
| 4229 | Mk3 Corvette | 202'9" | Nigeria | DORINA | 1972 |
| 4230 | Mk3 Corvette | 202'9" | Nigeria | OTOBO | 1972 |
| 4231 | Coastal Minehunter | 152'0" | MOD(N) | WILTON | 1973 |
| 4232 | Type 21 Frigate | 383'11½" | MOD(N) | ANTELOPE | 1975 |
| 4233 | Type 21 Frigate | 383'11½" | MOD(N) | ACTIVE | 1977 |
| 4234 | Mk10 A/S Frigate | 129.532m | Brazil | NITEROI | 1976 |
| 4235 | Mk10 A/S Frigate | 129.6m | Brazil | DEFENSORA | 1977 |
| 4236 | Mk10 GP Frigate | 129.6m | Brazil | CONSTITUICAO | 1978 |
| 4237 | Mk10 GP Frigate | 129.6m | Brazil | LIBERAL | 1978 |

| Yard No | Type | Length Overall | For Whom Built | Name | When Built |
|---------|------|----------------|----------------|------|------------|
| 4238 | Mk10 AS Frigate | 129.6m | Brazil | INDEPENDENCIA | 1978 |
| 4239 | Mk10 AS Frigate | 129.6m | Brazil | UNIAO | 1978 |
| 4240 | MCMV 01 | 60.0m | MOD(N) | BRECON | 1979 |
| 4241 | MCMV 02 | 60.0m | MOD(N) | LEDBURY | 1981 |
| 4242 | MCMV 03 | 60.0m | MOD(N) | CATTISTOCK | 1982 |
| 4243 | MCMV 05 | 60.0m | MOD(N) | BROCKLESBY | 1982 |
| 4244 | MCMV 07 | 60.0m | MOD(N) | DULVERTON | 1982 |
| 4245 | MCMV 09 | 60.0m | MOD(N) | CHIDDINGFOLD | 1982 |
| 4246 | MCMV 11 | 60.0m | MOD(N) | HURWORTH | 1982 |
| 4247 | Type 42 | 412'6" | MOD(N) | SOUTHAMPTON | 1981 |
| 4248 | Type 42 | 412'6" | MOD(N) | NOTTINGHAM | 1982 |
| 4249 | Type 42 | 463'0" | MOD(N) | GLOUCESTER | 1985 |
| 4250 and 4251 Re-allocated to Portchester | | | | | |
| 4252 | LSL | 93.0m | Algeria | KALAAT-BENI RACHED | 1984 |
| 4253 | Patrol Craft (Hull only) | 37.5m | Algeria | | 1983 |
| 4254 | MCMV 08 | 60.0m | MOD(N) | BICESTER | 1986 |
| 4255 | MCMV 10 | 60.0m | MOD(N) | ATHERSTONE | 1986 |
| 4256 | MCMV 12 | 60.0m | MOD(N) | BERKELEY | 1987 |
| 4257 | MCMV 13 | 60.0m | MOD(N) | QUORN | 1989 |
| 4258 | SRMH 01 | 52.5m | MOD(N) | SANDOWN | 1989 |
| 4259 | SRMH Saudi 01 | 52.5m | Saudi Arabia | AL JAWF | 1991 |
| 4260 | SRMH Saudi 02 | 52.5m | Saudi Arabia | SHAQRA | 1992 |
| 4261 | SRMH Saudi 03 | 52.5m | Saudi Arabia | AL KHARJ | 1994 |
| 4262 - 4264 Not allocated | | | | | |
| 4265 | SRMH 02 | 52.5m | MOD(N) | INVERNESS | 1991 |
| 4266 | SRMH 03 | 52.5m | MOD(N) | CROMER | 1991 |
| 4267 | SRMH 04 | 52.5m | MOD(N) | WALNEY | 1992 |
| 4268 | SRMH 05 | 52.5m | MOD(N) | BRIDPORT | 1993 |
| 4269 | Not allocated | | | | |
| 4270 | Corvette | 83.0m | Oman | 01 | |
| 4271 | Corvette | 83.0m | Oman | 02 | |
| 4272 | Not allocated | | | | |
| 4273 | Fast Strike Craft | 56.0m | Qatar | 01 | |
| 4274 | Fast Strike Craft | 56.0m | Qatar | 02 | |
| 4275 | Fast Strike Craft | 56.0m | Qatar | 03 | |
| 4276 | Fast Strike Craft | 56.0m | Qatar | 04 | |

| Yard No | Type | Length Overall | For Whom Built | Name | When Built |
|---------|------|----------------|----------------|------|------------|
| 4277 | SRMH | 52.5m | MOD(N) | 06 | |
| 4277 | SRMH | 52.5m | MOD(N) | 07 | |
| 4277 | SRMH | 52.5m | MOD(N) | 08 | |
| 4277 | SRMH | 52.5m | MOD(N) | 09 | |
| 4277 | SRMH | 52.5m | MOD(N) | 10 | |
| 4277 | SRMH | 52.5m | MOD(N) | 11 | |
| 4277 | SRMH | 52.5m | MOD(N) | 12 | |
| | | | | | |
| | | | | | |
| | | | | | |
| | | | | | |
| | | | | | |
| | | | | | |

*Appendix Three*

## CONTENTS OF DATA SHEETS

As listed in the following table

### BUILT AT PORTCHESTER

| | |
|---|---|
| 2617 | Hovercraft VT1 |
| 2617 (C) | Hovercraft VT2 |
| 2618 | Tenacity Patrol Boat |
| 2634 | Mk.3 Corvette |
| 2686 | 37m Fast Patrol Craft |
| 2695 | 103ft Patrol Craft |
| 2702 | 110ft Patrol Craft |
| 2712 | Mk.9 Corvette |
| 2717 | 75ft Patrol Craft |
| 2733 | 56m Fast Patrol Craft |
| 2758 | 56m Fast Patrol Craft |
| 2763 | Fast Ferry |
| 2765 | 56m Fast Patrol Craft |
| 2769 | Patrol Craft |
| 2772 | 34m Cutter |

### BUILT AT WOOLSTON

| | |
|---|---|
| 4207 | Leander Class Frigate |
| 4210 | Exercise Minelayer |
| 4213 | Patrol Craft |
| 4217 | Patrol Craft |
| 4219 | Yacht |
| 4221 | Mk.5 Destroyer |
| 4225 | Maintenance/Repair Ship |
| 4226 | Passenger/Vehicle Ferry |
| 4227 | Mk.7 Frigate |
| 4228 | T.21 Frigate |
| 4231 | Coastal Minehunter |
| 4234 | Mk.10 A/S Frigate |
| 4236 | Mk.10 GP Frigate |
| 4240 | MCMV |
| 4247 | T.42 Destroyer |
| 4249 | Stretched T.42 Destroyer |
| 4258 | SRMH |
| 4270 | 83m Corvette |
| 4273 | 56m Fast Strike Craft |

## GLOSSARY OF TERMS USED IN DATA SHEETS

| | |
|---|---|
| Dimensions | Length overall x Breadth x Depth |
| WL | Waterline |
| GT | Gas Turbine |
| SR | Senior Rating |
| JR | Junior Rating |
| RR | Rolls Royce |
| MTU | Machinen und Turbinen Union (German diesel engine manufacturer) |
| A/S | Anti-submarine |
| nm | Nautical Miles |
| SHP | Shaft Horse Power |
| BHP | Brake Horse Power |
| DC | Depth charge |
| Displacement | In imperial tons or tonnes depending on year of build |

# DATA SHEETS

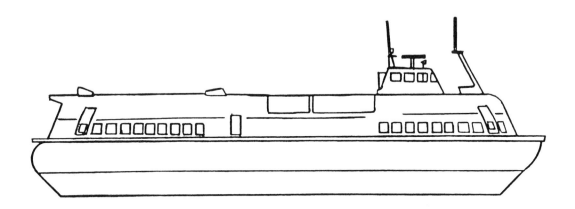

| SHIP NO. | 2617,2636-7 | FIRST OF CLASS NAME | VT1 |
|---|---|---|---|
| **CLASS DESIGNATION** | HOVERCRAFT | | |
| **DIMENSIONS (M)** | 31.5m WL | 33.75 x 7.2 x 4.16 | |
| **DISPLACEMENT (DEEP)** | 178 Tonnes | | |
| **SPEED (MAXIMUM)** | 25 knots | | |
| **ACCOMMODATION** | 17 | | |
| **MACHINERY** | **Type** | Diesels - Paxman Valenta | |
| | **Details** | 2 x 1900kW | |
| **PROPELLERS** | 2 x Fixed Pitch | | |

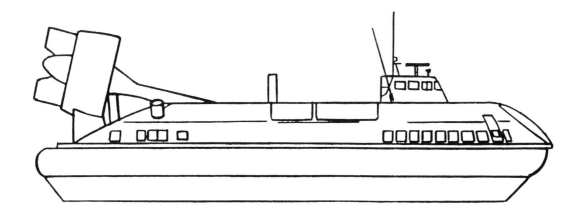

| SHIP NO. | 2617 (converted) | **FIRST OF CLASS NAME** | | VT2 |
|---|---|---|---|---|
| **CLASS DESIGNATION** | | HOVERCRAFT | | |
| **DIMENSIONS (M)** | | 30.2m x 13.3m (Structure) | | |
| **DISPLACEMENT (DEEP)** | | 111 Tonnes | | |
| **SPEED (MAXIMUM)** | | 62 knots | | |
| **ACCOMMODATION** | | Living accommodation for 9 men plus payload - 32 tonnes: either troops, vehicles or palletised freight. | | |
| **MACHINERY** | **Type** | | Rolls Royce Proteus Marine Gas Turbines | |
| | **Details** | | 2 x 3104kW | |
| **PROPULSORS** | | 2 x 4.1m ducted fans | | |

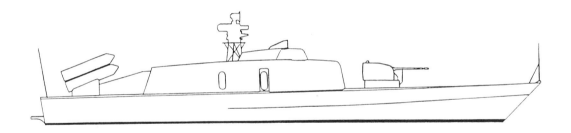

| SHIP NO. | 2618 | FIRST OF CLASS NAME | TENACITY | |
|---|---|---|---|---|

| CLASS DESIGNATION | Patrol Craft | | | |
|---|---|---|---|---|
| DIMENSIONS (M) | 39.6 (WL); | 44 X 8.1 X 4.1 | | |
| DISPLACEMENT (DEEP) | 220 tonnes | | | |
| SPEED (MAXIMUM) | 39 knots | | | |
| ENDURANCE (N. MILES) | 2500 nm at 15 knots on diesels | | | |
| ACCOMMODATION | 4 Officers, 4 SR, 20 JR | | | |

| MACHINERY CODOG | Type | | Diesels | Gas Turbines |
|---|---|---|---|---|
| | | | Paxman 6YJCM | RR Proteus |
| | Details | | 2 x 700 bhp | 3 x 4250 bhp |

| PROPELLERS | 3 x Fixed Pitch | |
|---|---|---|
| GENERATORS | 2 x 100 KVA GT sets | |

| ARMAMENT | Guns | 1 x Oerlikon GPM-A35mm |
|---|---|---|
| | Missiles | 4 x Contraves Sea Killer |
| | Fire Control | Contraves Sea Hunter Mk.4 |

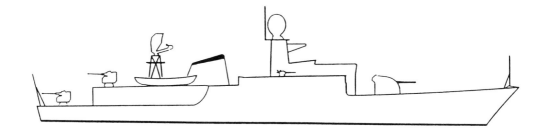

| SHIP NO. | 2634/5 | FIRST OF CLASS NAME | NS DORINA |
|---|---|---|---|
| **CLASS DESIGNATION** | | CORVETTE | |
| **DIMENSIONS (M)** | | 56.4 (WL); | 61.8 x 9.5 x 5.6 |
| **DISPLACEMENT (DEEP)** | | 660 | |
| **SPEED (MAXIMUM)** | | 22 knots | |
| **ENDURANCE (N. MILES)** | | 3000 nm at 14 knots | |
| **COMPLEMENT** | | 6 Officers, 54 crew | |
| **MACHINERY** | **Type** | Diesels - MAN V8V24/30B | |
| | **Details** | 2 x 3940 | |
| **PROPELLERS** | | 2 x Fixed Pitch | |
| **GENERATORS** | | 3 x 176 kW | |
| **ARMAMENT** | **Guns** | 1 x 4" Mk.19 twin mounting<br>2 x 40mm Bofors<br>2 x 20mm Oerlikon | |
| | **Radar** | Plessey AWS1 | |
| | **Fire Control** | HSA M22 | |

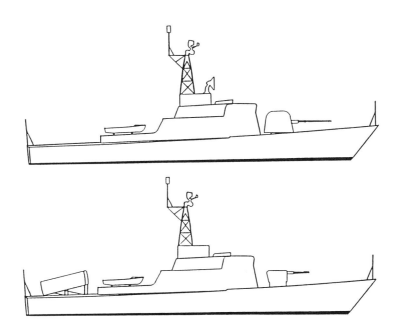

| SHIP NO. | 2686-91 | FIRST OF CLASS NAME | CONSTITUCION |
|---|---|---|---|
| **CLASS DESIGNATION** | | 37m Fast Patrol Craft | |
| **DIMENSIONS (M)** | | 33.5 (WL);      36.9 x 7.2 x 3.8 | |
| **DISPLACEMENT (DEEP)** | | 150 tons | |
| **SPEED (MAXIMUM)** | | 30 knots | |
| **ENDURANCE (N.MILES)** | | 1350 nm at 16 knots | |
| **ACCOMMODATION** | | 3 Officers, 2 SR, 10 JR | |

| **MACHINERY** | **Type** | Diesels - MTU 16V 538 TB90 | |
|---|---|---|---|
| | **Details** | 4 x 3180 bhp | |
| **PROPELLERS** | | 2 x Fixed Pitch | |
| **GENERATORS** | | 3 x 125 kW | |
| **ARMAMENT** | **Guns** | **Missile Version** | **Gun Version** |
| | | 1 x Bofors 40mm SAK L/70 | 1 x Oto 76mm |
| | **Missile System** | 2 x Otomat | - |
| | **Radar** | RQN1A | SPQ 2D Elsag NA10 Tracker |
| | **Fire Control** | Elsag for missiles | Elsag |

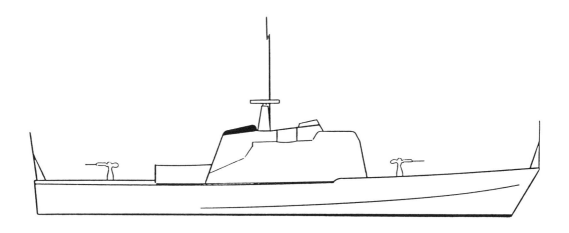

| SHIP NO. | 2695 | FIRST OF CLASS NAME | PECCARI |
|---|---|---|---|
| **CLASS DESIGNATION** | | 103ft Patrol Craft | |
| **DIMENSIONS (M)** | | 28.9 (WL); | 31.2 z 5.9 x 3.3 |
| **SPEED (MAXIMUM)** | | 24 knots | |
| **ENDURANCE (N. MILES)** | | 1800 nm at 14 knots | |
| **ACCOMMODATION** | | 5 Officers, 4 SR, 18 JR | |
| **MACHINERY** | **Type** | Diesels - Paxman Ventura 12YJCM | |
| | **Details** | 2 x 1800 bhp | |
| **PROPELLERS** | | 2 x Fixed Pitch | |
| **GENERATORS** | | 2 x 32 kW | |
| **ARMAMENT** | **Guns** | 2 x 20mm | |

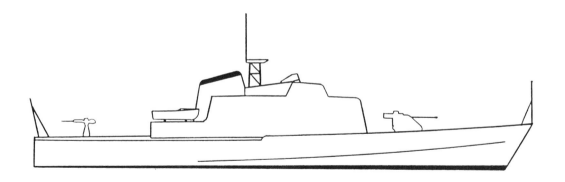

| SHIP NO. | 2702/7 | FIRST OF CLASS NAME | AL-WUSAIL |
|---|---|---|---|
| **CLASS DESIGNATION** | 110ft Patrol Craft | | |
| **DIMENSIONS (M)** | 31.6 (WL); | 33.5 x 6.4 x 3.4 | |
| **DISPLACEMENT (DEEP)** | 120 tons | | |
| **SPEED (MAXIMUM)** | 30 knots | | |
| **ENDURANCE (N. MILES)** | 1400 nm at 14 knots | | |
| **ACCOMMODATION** | 5 Officers, 8 SR, 12 JR | | |
| **MACHINERY** | **Type** | Diesels - Paxman Valenta 16RP200 | |
| | **Details** | 2 x 3300 bhp | |
| **PROPELLERS** | 2 x Fixed Pitch | | |
| **GENERATORS** | 2 x 49 kW | | |
| **ARMAMENT** | **Guns** | 2 x 30mm Hispano Suiza A32 | |

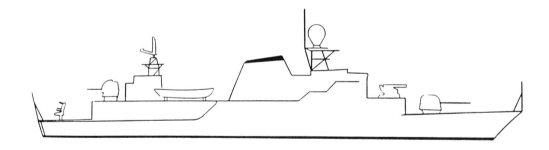

| SHIP NO. | 2712/3 | FIRST OF CLASS NAME | NS ERIN-OMI |
|---|---|---|---|
| **CLASS DESIGNATION** | Mk.9 CORVETTE | | |
| **DIMENSIONS (M)** | 64.0 (WL); | 69.0 x 9.6 x 5.7 | |
| **DISPLACEMENT (DEEP)** | 780 | | |
| **SPEED (MAXIMUM)** | 27 knots | | |
| **ENDURANCE (N. MILES)** | 2200 nm at 14 knots | | |
| **COMPLEMENT** | 13 Officers, 19 SRs, 57 JRs | | |
| **MACHINERY** | **Type** | Diesels - MTU 20V 965 TB92 | |
| | **Details** | 4 x 6044 bhp | |
| **PROPELLERS** | 2 x Controllable Pitch | | |
| **GENERATORS** | 3 x 260 kW | | |
| **ARMAMENT** | **Guns** | 1 x Oto Melara 76mm<br>1 x 40mm Bofors<br>2 x 20mm Oerlikon | |
| | **Missile System** | 1 x Seacat triple launcher<br>1 x Bofors twin 375mm rocket | |
| | **Sonar** | Plessey PMS 26 | |
| | **Radar** | Plessey AWS2 | |
| | **AIO and Fire Control** | HSA WM 24 | |

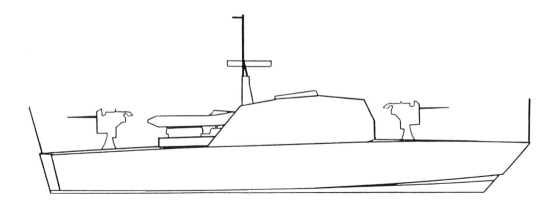

| SHIP NO. | 2717 | FIRST OF CLASS NAME | GEORGE McINTOSH |
|---|---|---|---|
| **CLASS DESIGNATION** | | 75ft Keith Nelson Patrol Craft | |
| **DIMENSIONS (M)** | | 22.9 x 5.95 x 1.7 | |
| **SPEED (MAXIMUM)** | | 24 knots | |
| **ENDURANCE (N. MILES)** | | 1000 nm at 11 knots | |
| **ACCOMMODATION** | | 3 Officers, 2 SR, 6 JR | |
| **MACHINERY** | **Type** | Diesels | |
| | **Details** | Caterpillar 12 cylinder | |
| **PROPELLERS** | | 2 x Fixed Pitch | |
| **GENERATORS** | | 2 x 12 kW | |
| **ARMAMENT** | **Guns** | 1 x 20mm | |

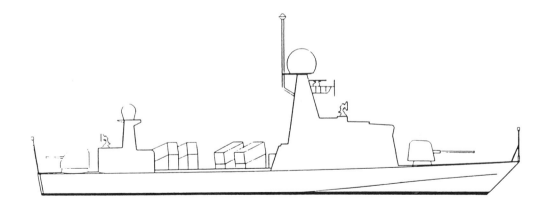

| SHIP NO. | 2733/8 | FIRST OF CLASS NAME | RAMADAN |
|---|---|---|---|

| CLASS DESIGNATION | 52m Fast Patrol Craft | | |
|---|---|---|---|
| DIMENSIONS (M) | 48.0 (WL); | 52.0 x 7.60 x 4.1 | |
| DISPLACEMENT (DEEP) | 324 | | |
| SPEED (MAXIMUM) | 40 knots | | |
| ENDURANCE (N. MILES) | 1600 nm at 16 knots | | |
| COMPLEMENT | 4 Officers, 6 SR, 20 JR | | |
| MACHINERY | Type | Diesels - MTU 20V 538 TB91 | |
| | Details | 4 x 4400 bhp | |
| PROPELLERS | 4 x Fixed Pitch | | |
| GENERATORS | 3 x 120 kW | | |
| ARMAMENT | Guns | 1 x Oto Melara 76mm<br>1 x Breda 40 L70 twin | |
| | Missile System | 4 x Otomat | |
| | Radar | Surveillance - Marconi S820<br>Tracker - Marconi ST 802 | |
| | Fire Control/AIO | Ferranti CAAIS, (FM1600B computers) | |

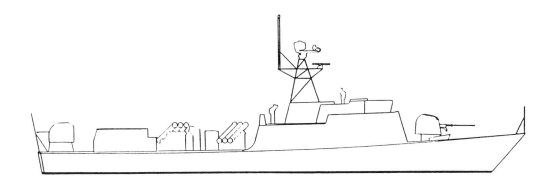

| SHIP NO. | 2758-60 & 2767 | FIRST OF CLASS NAME | | DHOFAR |
|---|---|---|---|---|
| **CLASS DESIGNATION** | | 56m Fast Patrol Craft | | |
| **DIMENSIONS (M)** | | 52.0 (WL); | | 56.7 x 8.20 x 4.2 |
| **DISPLACEMENT (DEEP)** | | 400 tonnes | | |
| **SPEED (MAXIMUM)** | | 36 knots | | |
| **ENDURANCE (N.MILES)** | | 2000 nm at 14 knots | | |
| **ACCOMMODATION** | | 5 Officers, 10 SR, 30 JR, 14 training | | |
| **MACHINERY** | | **Type** | Diesels - Paxman 18RP 200 | |
| | | **Details** | 4 x 4550 bhp | |
| | | Electrical slow speed drive also fitted. | | |
| **PROPELLERS** | | 4 x Fixed Pitch | | |
| **GENERATORS** | | 3 x 140 kW | | |
| **ARMAMENT** | | **Guns** | 1 x Oto Melara 76mm<br>1 x Breda Bofors 40mm twin | |
| | | **Missile System** | 6 x Exocet MM40 - 2758 only<br>8 x Exocet MM40 - 2769/60 and 2767 | |
| | | **Radar** | Plessey AWS4 - 2758<br>PEAB 9GR600 - 2759/60/67<br>plus Plessey AWS6 on 2767 only | |
| | | **Fire Control and AIO** | British Aerospace Sea Archer - 2758<br>PEAB 9LV200 - 2759/60 and 2767 | |

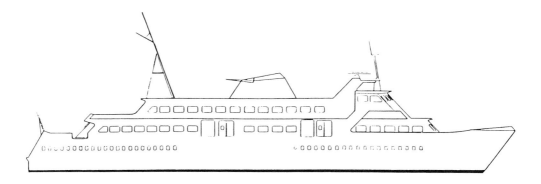

| SHIP NO. | 2763/4 | FIRST OF CLASS NAME | JU KONG |
|---|---|---|---|
| **CLASS DESIGNATION** | | FAST FERRY | |
| **DIMENSIONS (M)** | | 58.3 (WL); | 62.5 x 10.2 x 4.3/6.6 |
| **DISPLACEMENT (DEEP)** | | 500 tonnes | |
| **SPEED (MAXIMUM)** | | 27.5 knots | |
| **ACCOMMODATION** | | Passengers: 683; Crew: 8 | |
| **MACHINERY** | **Type** | 4 x Diesels | |
| | **Details** | Paxman Valenta 16cm | |
| **PROPELLERS** | | 2 x controllable pitch | |

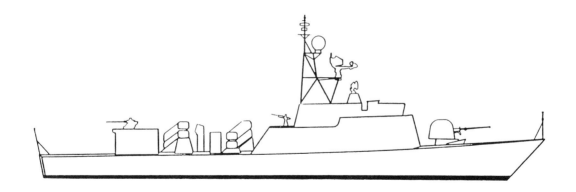

| SHIP NO. | 2765/6 | FIRST OF CLASS NAME | KNS UMOJA |
|---|---|---|---|
| CLASS DESIGNATION | 56m Fast Patrol Craft | | |
| DIMENSIONS (M) | 52.0 (WL); | 56.7 x 8.2 x 4.4 | |
| DISPLACEMENT (DEEP) | 396 tonnes | | |
| SPEED (MAXIMUM) | 38 knots | | |
| ENDURANCE (N. MILES) | 2900 nm at 17 knots | | |
| ACCOMMODATION | 7 Officers, 6 SR, 22 JR | | |
| MACHINERY | Type | Diesels | |
| | Details | Paxman 18 RP200 | |
| PROPELLERS | 4 x Fixed Pitch | | |
| GENERATORS | 3 x  kW | | |
| ARMAMENT | Guns | 1 x 30mm Oerlikon GCM-AO3-2 twin<br>1 x Otomelara 76mm | |
| | Missile System | 4 x Otomat Mk.2 | |
| | Radar | Plessey AWS4 | |

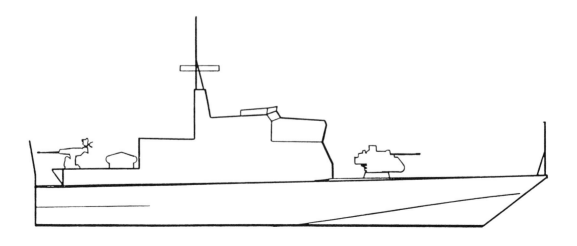

| SHIP NO. | 2769/71 | FIRST OF CLASS NAME | AL HUSSEIN |
|---|---|---|---|
| **CLASS DESIGNATION** | | Patrol Craft | |
| **DIMENSIONS (M)** | | 26.6 (WL); | 30.5 x 6.9 x 4.1 |
| **DISPLACEMENT (DEEP)** | | 126 tonnes | |
| **SPEED (MAXIMUM)** | | 30 knots | |
| **ENDURANCE (N. MILES)** | | 750 nm at 15 knots | |
| **ACCOMMODATION** | | 3 Officers, 2 SR, 11 JR | |
| **MACHINERY** | **Type** | Diesels - MTU 16V396 TB94 | |
| | **Details** | 2 x 3180 bhp | |
| **PROPELLERS** | | 2 x Fixed Pitch | |
| **GENERATORS** | | 2 x 90 kW | |
| **ARMAMENT** | **Guns** | 1 x 30mm Oerlikon GCM-AO3-2 twin<br>1 x 20mm Oerlikon GAM-BO1 | |

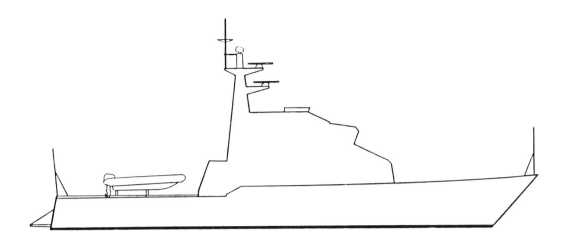

| SHIP NO. | 2772 | FIRST OF CLASS NAME | | SENTINEL |
|---|---|---|---|---|
| **CLASS DESIGNATION** | | 34M CUTTER | | |
| **DIMENSIONS (M)** | | 31.5m WL | 33.75 x 7.2 x 4.16 | |
| **DISPLACEMENT (DEEP)** | | 178 Tonnes | | |
| **SPEED (MAXIMUM)** | | 25 knots | | |
| **ACCOMMODATION** | | 17 | | |
| **MACHINERY** | **Type** | Diesels - Paxman Valenta | | |
| | **Details** | 2 x 1900kW | | |
| **PROPELLERS** | | 2 x Fixed Pitch | | |

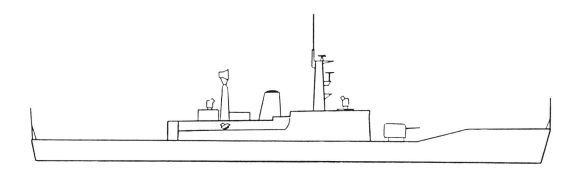

| SHIP NO. | 4207 | FIRST OF CLASS NAME | HMS JUNO |
|---|---|---|---|
| **CLASS DESIGNATION** | FRIGATE | | |
| **DIMENSIONS (M)** | 109.7 (WL); 113.4 x 12.5 x 8.6 | | |
| **DISPLACEMENT (DEEP)** | 3200 | | |
| **SPEED (MAXIMUM)** | 28 knots | | |
| **ENDURANCE (N. MILES)** | 4000 nm at 15 knots | | |
| **ACCOMMODATION** | 251 | | |
| **MACHINERY** | **Type** | Steam Turbines | |
| | **Details** | 2 x 15,000 shp | |
| **PROPELLERS** | 2 x Fixed Pitch | | |
| **GENERATORS** | 1900 kW | | |
| **ARMAMENT** | **Guns** | 1 x 4.5" twin mounting<br>2 x 20mm single<br>1 Limbo DC mortar | |
| | **Missile System** | 1 x Seacat quadruple launcher | |
| | **Helicopter** | 1 x Wasp | |

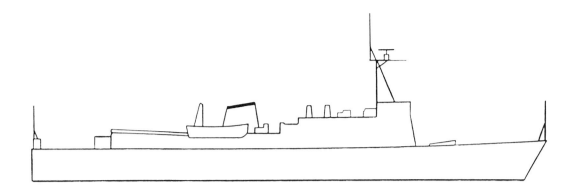

| SHIP NO. | 4210 | FIRST OF CLASS NAME | HMS ABDIEL |
|---|---|---|---|
| **CLASS DESIGNATION** | | EXERCISE MINELAYER | |
| **DIMENSIONS (M)** | | 76.8 (WL); | 80.8 x 11.8 x 5.2 |
| **DISPLACEMENT (DEEP)** | | 1430 | |
| **SPEED (MAXIMUM)** | | 16 knots | |
| **ACCOMMODATION** | | 77 | |
| **MACHINERY** | **Type** | Diesels - Paxman Ventura | |
| | **Details** | 2 x 1345 bhp | |
| **PROPELLERS** | | 2 x Fixed Pitch | |
| **ARMAMENT** | | 44 Mines | |

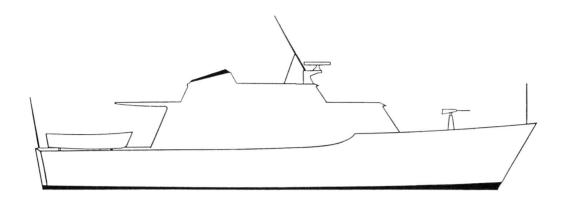

| SHIP NO. | 4213/4 | FIRST OF CLASS NAME | EL SALAMI |
|---|---|---|---|
| **CLASS DESIGNATION** | PATROL CRAFT | | |
| **DIMENSIONS (M)** | 21.3 (WL); | | 23.8 X 4.7 X 2.9 |
| **DISPLACEMENT (DEEP)** | 59 Tons | | |
| **SPEED (MAXIMUM)** | 20.5 knots | | |
| **ENDURANCE (N. MILES)** | 700 at 15 knots | | |
| **COMPLEMENT** | 2 x officers, 6 x crew | | |
| **MACHINERY** | **Type** | Diesels - Rolls Royce DV8 | |
| | **Details** | 2 x 670 bhp | |
| **PROPELLERS** | 2 x fixed pitch | | |
| **ARMAMENT** | 1 x 12.7mm Machine Gun | | |

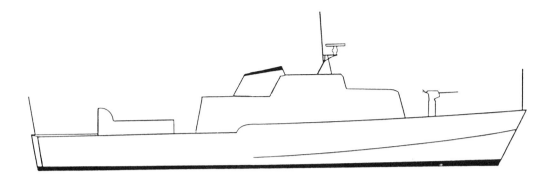

| SHIP NO. | 4217/8 | FIRST OF CLASS NAME | ARRAKIB |
|----------|--------|---------------------|---------|
| **CLASS DESIGNATION** | | PATROL CRAFT | |
| **DIMENSIONS (M)** | | 28.0 (WL); | 30.5 x 6.4 x 3.3 |
| **DISPLACEMENT (DEEP)** | | 122 Tons | |
| **SPEED (MAXIMUM)** | | 18 knots | |
| **ENDURANCE (N. MILES)** | | 1800nm at 14 knots | |
| **COMPLEMENT** | | 18 | |
| **MACHINERY** | **Type** | Diesels - Rolls Royce DV8 | |
| | **Details** | 3 x 600 bhp | |
| **PROPELLERS** | | 3 x fixed pitch | |
| **ARMAMENT** | | 1 x 20mm Oerlikon Gun | |

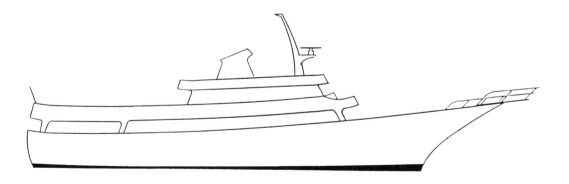

| SHIP NO. | 4219 | FIRST OF CLASS NAME | ROMANTICA |
|----------|------|---------------------|-----------|
| **CLASS DESIGNATION** | | TS Aluminium Yacht for J C Bamforth | |
| **DIMENSIONS (M)** | | 34.0 (WL); | 41.9 x 7.9 x 4.8 |
| **DISPLACEMENT (DEEP)** | | 288 Tons | |
| **SPEED (MAXIMUM)** | | 15.5 knots | |
| **ACCOMMODATION** | | Owners & Guests - 10<br>Crew - 8 | |
| **MACHINERY** | **Type** | Diesels - Caterpillar D398 | |
| | **Details** | 3 x 1050 bhp | |
| **PROPELLERS** | | 2 x fixed pitch | |

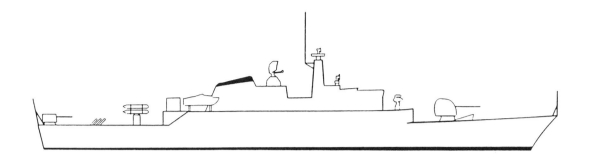

| SHIP NO. | 4221/2 | FIRST OF CLASS NAME | | IIS SAAM |
|---|---|---|---|---|
| **CLASS DESIGNATION** | | MK.5 DESTROYER (FAST FRIGATE) | | |
| **DIMENSIONS (M)** | | 88.4 (WL);        94.5 x 11.1 x 7.6 | | |
| **DISPLACEMENT (DEEP)** | | 1540 | | |
| **SPEED (MAXIMUM)** | | 39 knots | | |
| **ENDURANCE (N. MILES)** | | 3650 nm at 18 knots | | |
| **COMPLEMENT** | | 146 (8 Officers, 25 SR, 79 JR) | | |
| **MACHINERY**<br><br>CODOG | **Type** | | Diesels | Gas Turbines |
| | **Details** | | Paxman Ventura 2 x 1900 hp | RR Olympus 2 x 23000 hp |
| **PROPELLERS** | | 2 x Controllable Pitch | | |
| **ARMAMENT** | **Guns** | | 1 x 4.5" Mk.8<br>1 x 35mm twin Oerlikon<br>1 x triple A/S Mk.10 mortar | |
| | **Missile System** | | 1 x Sea Killer 2 quintuple launcher surface to surface<br>1 x Seacat triple launcher | |
| | **Sonar** | | 1 x Graseby 174 hull mounted<br>1 x Graseby 170 hull mounted | |
| | **Radar** | | Plessey AWS1 | |
| | **Fire Control** | | Contraves Sea Hunter | |

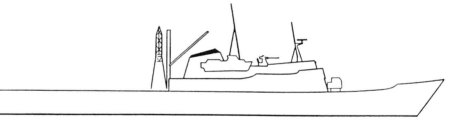

| SHIP NO. | 4225 | FIRST OF CLASS NAME | ZELTIN |
|---|---|---|---|
| **CLASS DESIGNATION** | | MAINTENANCE AND REPAIR SHIP | |
| **DIMENSIONS (M)** | | 91.5 (WL);     30.5 x 6.4 x 3.3 | |
| **DISPLACEMENT (DEEP)** | | 2470 Tons | |
| **SPEED (MAXIMUM)** | | 14.5 knots | |
| **ENDURANCE (N. MILES)** | | 3000 nm at 14 knots | |
| **COMPLEMENT** | | 15 Officers, 86 crew | |
| **MACHINERY** | **Type** | Diesels - Paxman Ventura | |
| | **Details** | 2 x 1832 bhp | |
| **PROPELLERS** | | 2 x fixed pitch | |
| **ARMAMENT** | | 2 x 40mm Bofors Gun | |

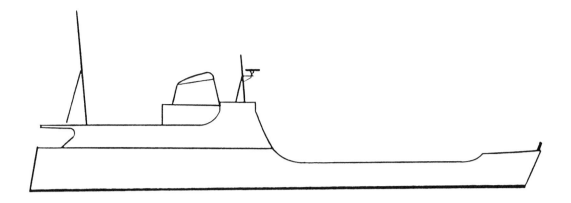

| SHIP NO. | 4226 | FIRST OF CLASS NAME | NORRIS CASTLE |
|---|---|---|---|
| CLASS DESIGNATION | | Passenger & Vehicle Ferry for Red Funnel Steamers | |
| DIMENSIONS (M) | | 54.9 (WL); | 57.4 x 12.2 x 3.5 |
| DISPLACEMENT (DEEP) | | 762 Tons | |
| SPEED (MAXIMUM) | | 14.5 knots | |
| MACHINERY | Type | Diesels - Crossley | |
| | Details | 2 x 860 bhp | |
| PROPELLERS | | 2 x fixed pitch | |

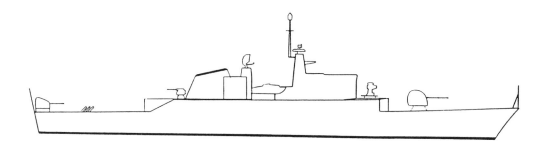

| SHIP NO. | 4227 | FIRST OF CLASS NAME | DAT ASSAWARI |
|---|---|---|---|
| **CLASS DESIGNATION** | FRIGATE | | |
| **DIMENSIONS (M)** | 94.5 (WL); | 100.3 x 11.7 x 7.8 | |
| **DISPLACEMENT (DEEP)** | 1650 | | |
| **SPEED (MAXIMUM)** | 35 knots | | |
| **ENDURANCE (N. MILES)** | 5700 nm at 17 knots | | |
| **COMPLEMENT** | 132 | | |

| MACHINERY | **Type** | Diesels | Gas Turbines |
|---|---|---|---|
| CODOG | **Details** | 2 x Paxman Ventura | 2 x RR Olympus 19400 shp (mcp) |

| **PROPELLERS** | 2 x Controllable Pitch | |
|---|---|---|
| **ARMAMENT** | **Guns** | 1 each: 4.5 Mk.8 Vickers, twin 35mm Oerlikon, A/S Mortar Mk.10 |
| | **Missile System** | 1 x Seacat triple launcher |
| | **Sonar** | 1 x Graseby 174, 1 x Graseby 170 |
| | **Radar** | Plessey AWS1 |
| | **Fire Control** | Contraves Sea Hunter |

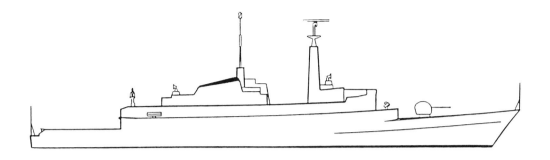

| SHIP NO. | 4228 4232/3 | FIRST OF CLASS NAME | HMS AMAZON |
|---|---|---|---|
| **CLASS DESIGNATION** | | TYPE 21 FRIGATE | |
| **DIMENSIONS (M)** | | 109.8 (WL);   117.1 x 12.7 x 8.4 | |
| **DISPLACEMENT (DEEP)** | | 3053 | |
| **SPEED (MAXIMUM)** | | 33 knots | |
| **ENDURANCE (N. MILES)** | | 4000 nm at 17 knots | |
| **COMPLEMENT** | | 13 Officers, 162 Crew   (Accommodation - 192) | |
| **MACHINERY** COGOG | **Type** | Gas Turbines | |
| | **Details** | 2 x Rolls Royce Olympus TM3B 2 x Rolls Royce Tyne RM1C | |
| **PROPELLERS** | | 2 x Controllable Pitch | |
| **ARMAMENT** | **Guns** | 1 x 4.5 Mk.8 Vickers | |
| | **Missile System** | 1 x Seacat quad launcher FBNW Exocet MM38 (fitted later) | |
| | **Sonar** | 1 x Graseby 184 | |
| | **Radar** | Marconi 992 | |
| | **Fire Control** | Ferranti WSA4 with Selenia trackers | |
| | **AIO** | Ferranti CAAIS | |
| | **Torpedoes** | Plessey A/S Torpedo Tubes | |
| | **Helicopter** | Lynx | |

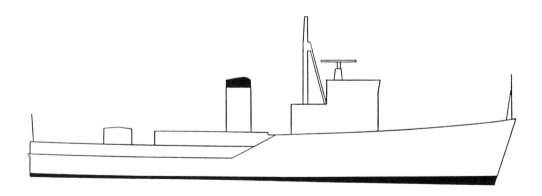

| SHIP NO. | 4231 | FIRST OF CLASS NAME | | HMS WILTON |
|---|---|---|---|---|
| **CLASS DESIGNATION** | | COASTAL MINEHUNTER | | |
| **DIMENSIONS (M)** | | 42.7 (WL); | 46.3 x 8.5 x 4.5 | |
| **DISPLACEMENT (DEEP)** | | 484 | | |
| **SPEED (MAXIMUM)** | | 15.5 knots | | |
| **ENDURANCE (N. MILES)** | | 2300nm at 13 knots | | |
| **COMPLEMENT** | | 5 officers, 32 crew | | |
| **MACHINERY** | **Type** | Diesels | | |
| | **Details** | 2 x 1500 bhp Napier Deltic 18 cylinder | | |
| **PROPELLERS** | | 2 x Fixed Pitch, 2 x Active Rudders | | |
| **GENERATORS** | | 4 x 60 kW | | |
| **ARMAMENT** | **Guns** | 1 x 40mm Bofors | | |
| | **Minehunting Sonar** | 1 x Plessey 193m | | |

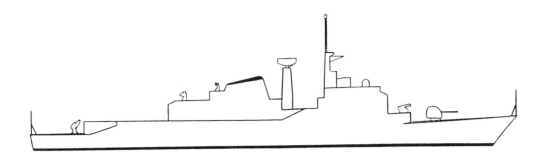

| SHIP NO. | 4234-5 | **FIRST OF CLASS NAME** | BNS NITEROI | |
|---|---|---|---|---|
| **CLASS DESIGNATION** | | MARK 10 FRIGATE | | |
| **DIMENSIONS (M)** | | 122.2 (WL); | 129.6 x 13.5 x 9.1 | |
| **DISPLACEMENT (DEEP)** | | 3600 | | |
| **SPEED (MAXIMUM)** | | 30 knots GT, 22 knots Diesels | | |
| **ENDURANCE (N.MILES)** | | 5300 nm at 17 knots | | |
| **COMPLEMENT** | | 22 Officers, 49 SRs, 132 JRs | | |
| **MACHINERY**<br><br>CODOG | **Type** | Gas Turbines | Diesels | |
| | **Details** | 2 x 28,000 shp RR Olympus TM3B | 4 x 4900 MTU 16V956 | |
| **PROPELLERS** | | 2 x Controllable Pitch | | |
| **ARMAMENT**<br><br>ANTI-SUBMARINE | **Guns** | 1 x 4.5 Mk.8 Vickers, 2 x Bofors 40mm | | |
| | **Missile Systems** | 2 x Seacat triple launcher<br>1 x Ikara A/S;  4 x Exocet MM38<br>1 x Bofors SR375 A/S Rocket System | | |
| | **Sonar** | 1 x EDO 610E hull mounted<br>1 x EDO 700E variable depth | | |
| | **Radar** | Plessey AWS2 | | |
| | **Fire Control** | 2 x Ferranti WSA4 using FM1600B computer and Selenia RTN10X trackers | | |
| | **AIO** | Ferranti CAAIS | | |
| | **Torpedoes** | 2 x Triple  A/S Torpedo Tubes | | |
| | **Helicopter** | Lynx | | |

NB:  4238-9 built in Brazil

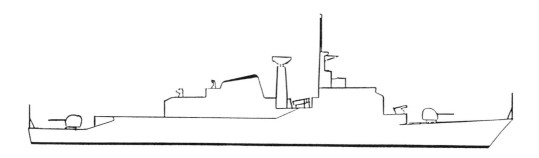

| SHIP NO. | 4236-7 | FIRST OF CLASS NAME | | BNS CONSTITUICAO |
|---|---|---|---|---|
| **CLASS DESIGNATION** | | MARK 10 FRIGATE | | |
| **DIMENSIONS (M)** | | 122.2 (WL);     129.6 x 13.5 x 9.1 | | |
| **DISPLACEMENT (DEEP)** | | 3600 | | |
| **SPEED (MAXIMUM)** | | 30 knots GT, 22 knots Diesels | | |
| **ENDURANCE (N. MILES)** | | 5300 nm at 17 knots | | |
| **COMPLEMENT** | | 22 Officers, 49 SRs, 132 JRs | | |
| **MACHINERY** | **Type** | Gas Turbines | | Diesels |
| CODOG | **Details** | 2 x 28,000 shp RR Olympus TM3B | | 4 x 4900 MTU 16V956 |
| **PROPELLERS** | 2 x Controllable Pitch | | | |
| **ARMAMENT** | **Guns** | 2 x 4.5 Mk.8 Vickers, 2 x Bofors 40mm | | |
| GENERAL PURPOSE | **Missile Systems** | 2 x Seacat triple launcher<br>4 x Exocet MM38<br>1 x Bofors SR375 A/S Rocket System | | |
| | **Sonar** | 1 x EDO 610E hull mounted | | |
| | **Radar** | Plessey AWS2 | | |
| | **Fire Control** | 2 x Ferranti WSA4 using FM1600B computer and Selenia RTN10X trackers | | |
| | **AIO** | Ferranti CAAIS | | |
| | **Torpedoes** | 2 x Triple  A/S Torpedo Tubes | | |
| | **Helicopter** | Lynx | | |

NB:  4238-9 built in Brazil

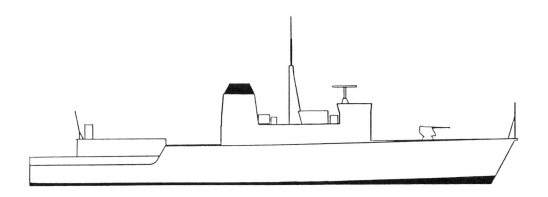

| SHIP NO. | 4240 | FIRST OF CLASS NAME | HMS BRECON |
|---|---|---|---|

| CLASS DESIGNATION | MINE COUNTERMEASURE VESSEL | |
|---|---|---|
| DIMENSIONS (M) | 57 (WL); | 60 x 10 x 7.1 |
| DISPLACEMENT (DEEP) | 700 tonnes | |
| SPEED (MAXIMUM) | 15 knots | |
| ENDURANCE (N. MILES) | 1500 nm at 12 knots | |
| COMPLEMENT | 6 officers, 39 crew | |
| MACHINERY | Type | Diesels |
| | Details | 2 x 950 bhp Napier Deltic 9-59K |
| | Plus Slow Speed Hydraulic Drive | |
| PROPELLERS | 2 x Fixed Pitch | |
| ARMAMENT | Guns | 1 x 40mm Bofors |
| | Minehunting Sonar | 1 x Plessey 193M |
| | AIO | Ferranti CAAIS |

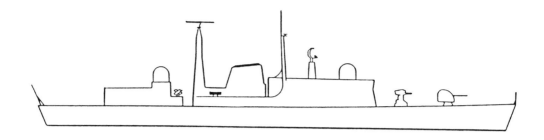

| SHIP NO. | 4247/8 | FIRST OF CLASS NAME | HMS SOUTHAMPTON |
|---|---|---|---|
| **CLASS DESIGNATION** | | TYPE 42 DESTROYER (Batch 2) | |
| **DIMENSIONS (M)** | | 119.5 (WL);    125 x 14.3 x 9.1 | |
| **DISPLACEMENT (DEEP)** | | 4100 | |
| **SPEED (MAXIMUM)** | | 29 knots | |
| **ENDURANCE (N. MILES)** | | 4000 nm at 18 knots | |
| **COMPLEMENT** | | 24 Officers, 229 Crew | |
| **MACHINERY**<br><br>COGOG | **Type** | Gas Turbines | |
| | **Details** | 2 x 25000 HP RR Olympus TM3B<br>2 x 4850 HP RR Tyne RM1C | |
| **PROPELLERS** | | 2 x Controllable Pitch | |
| **GENERATORS** | | 4 x 1000 kW | |
| **ARMAMENT** | **Guns** | 1 x 4.5 Mk.8 Vickers<br>2 x 20mm Oerlikon | |
| | **Missile System** | 1 x Sea Dart | |
| | **Sonar** | 1 x Graseby Type 184P hull mounted | |
| | **Radar** | Marconi/Signaal Type 1022<br>Marconi Type 992Q/R | |
| | **Fire Control** | Marconi Type 909 trackers | |
| | **AIO** | ADAWS 4 | |
| | **Torpedoes** | 2 x triple Plessey STWS Mk.2 A/S<br>Torpedo Tubes | |
| | **Helicopter** | Lynx | |

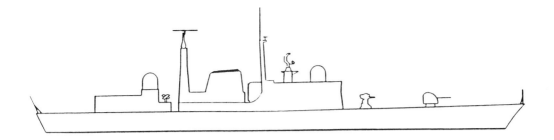

| SHIP NO. | 4249 | FIRST OF CLASS NAME | HMS GLOUCESTER |
|---|---|---|---|
| CLASS DESIGNATION | | TYPE 42 DESTROYER (Batch 3) | |
| DIMENSIONS (M) | | 132.3 (WL);          141.1 x 14.9 x 9.1 | |
| DISPLACEMENT (DEEP) | | 4775 | |
| SPEED (MAXIMUM) | | 29.5 knots | |
| ENDURANCE (N. MILES) | | 4000 nm at 18 knots | |
| COMPLEMENT | | 26 Officers, 275 Crew | |
| MACHINERY  COGOG | Type | Gas Turbines | |
| | Details | 2 x 25000 hp RR Olympus TM3B  2 x 4850 hp RR Tyne RM1C | |
| PROPELLERS | | 2 x Controllable Pitch | |
| GENERATORS | | 4 x 1000 kW | |
| ARMAMENT | Guns | 1 x 4.5 Mk.8 Vickers  4 x 20mm Oerlikon | |
| | Missile System | 1 x Sea Dart GWS30 | |
| | Sonar | 1 x Plessey Type 2016 hull mounted | |
| | Radar | Marconi/Signaal Type 1022  Marconi Type 992Q/R | |
| | Fire Control | Marconi Type 909 trackers | |
| | AIO | ADAWS 7 | |
| | Torpedoes | 2 x triple Plessey STWS Mk.2 A/S  Torpedo Tubes | |
| | Helicopter | Lynx | |

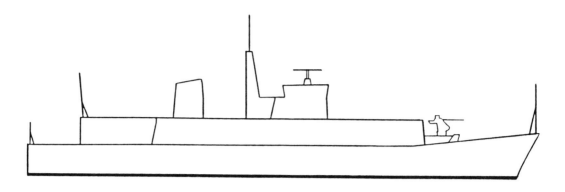

| SHIP NO. | 4258 | FIRST OF CLASS NAME | HMS SANDOWN |
|---|---|---|---|
| **CLASS DESIGNATION** | | SINGLE ROLE MINEHUNTER | |
| **DIMENSIONS (M)** | | 50.0 (WL); | 52.5 x 10.5 x 5.45 |
| **DISPLACEMENT (DEEP)** | | 500 tonnes | |
| **SPEED (MAXIMUM)** | | 13.5 knots | |
| **ENDURANCE (N. MILES)** | | 1500 nm at 10 knots | |
| **COMPLEMENT** | | 7 officers, 9 SRs, 24 JRs | |
| **MACHINERY** | **Type** | Diesels | |
| | **Details** | 2 x Paxman 6RPA 200M | |
| | Plus Slow Speed Electric Drive | | |
| **PROPELLERS** | | 2 x Voith Schneider | |
| **GENERATORS** | | 3 x 250 kW | |
| **ARMAMENT** | **Guns** | 1 x MSI DS30B 30mm | |
| | **Minehunting Sonar** | Variable depth 2093 | |
| | **AIO** | Nautis M | |

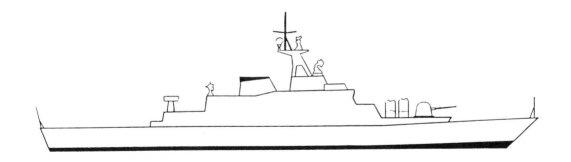

| SHIP NO. | 4270/4271 | FIRST OF CLASS NAME | CONQUEROR OF THE WAVES |
|---|---|---|---|
| **CLASS DESIGNATION** | | MUHEET Class Corvette | |
| **DIMENSIONS (M)** | | 76m WL | 83.7 x 11.5 x 7.2 |
| **DISPLACEMENT (DEEP)** | | 1450 Tonnes | |
| **SPEED (MAXIMUM)** | | 27½ knots | |
| **ENDURANCE (N. MILES)** | | 1500 nm at 22 knots | |
| **ACCOMMODATION** | | 15 Officers, 30 SR, 36 JR | |
| **MACHINERY** | **Type** | Diesels | |
| | **Details** | Crossley Pielstick 16PA6V | |
| **PROPELLERS** | | 2 x Controllable Pitch | |
| **GENERATORS** | | 3 x 350kW, 1 z 70kW | |
| **ARMAMENT** | **Guns** | 1 x Oto Melara 76mm<br>2 x Oerlikon 20mm | |
| | **Missile System** | 8 x Crotale Naval NG<br>8 x Exocet MM40 | |
| | **Radar** | HSA MW 08<br>HSA Sting | |
| | **Fire Control** | Thomson CSF Tacticos | |
| **HELICOPTERS** | | Flight Deck for Super Puma | |

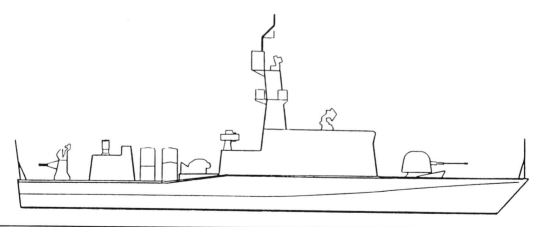

| SHIP NO. | 4273 - 6 | FIRST OF CLASS NAME | BARZAN |
|---|---|---|---|
| **CLASS DESIGNATION** | | 56M FAST STRIKE CRAFT | |
| **DIMENSIONS (M)** | | 52m WL | 56.0 x 9.0 x 6.0 |
| **DISPLACEMENT (DEEP)** | | 465 Tonnes | |
| **SPEED (MAXIMUM)** | | 34.5 knots | |
| **ENDURANCE (N. MILES)** | | 1800 nm at 12 knots | |
| **ACCOMMODATION** | | 7 Officers, 12 SR, 12 JR, 4 training | |
| **MACHINERY** | Type | Diesels | |
| | Details | MTU 20V 538 TB 93 | |
| **PROPELLERS** | | 4 x Fixed Pitch | |
| **GENERATORS** | | 3 x 260kW, 1 x 140kW | |
| **ARMAMENT** | Guns | 1 x Oto Melara 76mm<br>1 x Goalkeeper CIWS | |
| | Missile System | 8 x Exocet MM40<br>1 x Sadral | |
| | Radar | Thomson MRR<br>HSA Sting | |
| | Fire Control | Thomson CSF Tacticos | |